ON NATURE

The Library of Liberal Arts
OSKAR PIEST, FOUNDER

ON NATURE

LUCRETIUS

Translated, with an Introduction and Notes, by

RUSSEL M. GEER

Professor Emeritus of Classical Languages,

Tulane University

The Library of Liberal Arts

published by

THE BOBBS-MERRILL COMPANY, INC.
A Subsidiary of Howard W. Sams & Co., Inc.
Publishers • Indianapolis • New York • Kansas City

Lucretius: *c.* 96–55 B.C.

. . . .

Printed in the United States of America
Library of Congress Catalog Card Number 63–12204
First Printing

PREFACE

The purpose of this translation is to express as clearly as possible the ancient atomic system as it was set forth in the first century before Christ by the Roman poet, Lucretius. Since clarity is its purpose, it is in prose. The purpose of the introduction and commentary that accompany the translation is to make available to the reader with no command of Latin or Greek the material that has long been available to classical scholars in annotated editions of the Latin text, together with such light from more modern physical theory as I can add.

The work had its beginning during the Second World War. At that time the Physics Department at Tulane, flooded with students from the various naval programs then in effect at the University, had to seek aid from unlikely quarters; for several years I taught more physics than Greek and Latin. During one semester I had a course in Lucretius sandwiched between two sections of general physics, and I found that each subject aided the other. Lucretius' flock of milling sheep which looks, to a distant observer, like a single white cloud is a more vivid illustration of molecular motion in a solid than anything I have seen in a physics textbook. On the other hand, I at least learned the difference between weight and mass, a point which seems to have escaped some of Lucretius' editors and was not altogether clear to the poet himself.

The first draft of the translation and of part of the commentary was made some fifteen years ago using Bailey's OCT text and the commentaries in the editions of Munro and of Leonard and Smith. Because of the press of other work it was laid aside for ten years or more. The translation and the commentary have both been revised since then, and the introduction added. In this revision I have used Bailey's 1947 text and have made constant use of his commentary. Most of the material that I have taken from the commentary, however, is the common property of several generations, since Bailey's own contributions are for the most part too specialized for an edition such as this. Where I have departed from Bailey's text, I have noted the fact in the commentary. The introduction owes much to *The Presocratic Philosophers* by Kirk and Raven (Cambridge, 1957).

Permission has been granted by the Oxford University Press to quote a few passages from Bailey's commentary, and by Professor Frank E. Robeson to quote from his *Physics* (Macmillan, 1943). For both these favors I owe thanks. I also acknowledge my debt to the Library of Bowdoin College for the unfailing generosity shown to a summer visitor.

RUSSEL M. GEER

CONTENTS

INTRODUCTION

I. Greek Physical Philosophy Before Epicurus

In his poem *On Nature* Lucretius' purpose is to teach men to accept that explanation of the natural world which forms the foundation of the whole Epicurean philosophical system, and thus to free them from superstitious fears of death and of the gods, which seemed to him to be the root of all human ills. He constantly reiterates his debt to Epicurus; since nearly all the writings of Epicurus have been lost, Lucretius' work is the chief source for our knowledge of the Epicurean physical theories. Since Epicurus himself had taken his physics with little change from Leucippus and Democritus, the first of the atomists, and since these were in many ways dependent upon their predecessors, a brief survey of this early phase of Greek philosophy is in order.[a]

FROM THALES TO PARMENIDES

This first group of Greek philosophers is perhaps more important for the questions they asked than for the answers they gave. Before them men had, in general, been content with mythological explanations of the origin of the world and of the life upon it. Now an effort was made to give an answer to the riddle of creation and existence in terms of a single basic substance, from which everything is formed and to which everything returns. When Thales of Miletus[1] (*fl. c.* 585 B.C.) said that the basic substance was water, he may have meant no more than that water is essential for the growth of all forms of living

[a] For this and all subsequent references indicated by superior letters, see Appendix, pp. 249–85.

[1] For Thales, see Cyril Bailey, *The Greek Atomists and Epicurus* (Oxford, 1928), pp. 12–13; John Burnet, *Early Greek Philosophy* (4th edn.; London, 1930), pp. 39–50; G. S. Kirk and J. E. Raven, *The Presocratic Philosophers* (Cambridge, England, 1957) pp. 74–98.

things. However, when his fellow townsman, Anaximander[2] (*fl. c.* 570 B.C.), said that the basic substance was the "undefined," he clearly meant that from this—itself lacking all the qualities we associate with material things, and infinite in extent—are formed all the things of the world that we know. Moreover, he undertook to explain how the world (that is, the earth and the heavenly bodies that appear to revolve about it) was formed from the "undefined," and how, after the world was formed, the first life came into being from the slime along the edge of the sea. Anaximander had stripped his basic substance of all qualities so that there might be nothing to interfere with the formation of things with differing qualities. Another Milesian, Anaximenes,[3] a few years younger than Anaximander, believed that he had found a way in which quantitative changes in a single substance could account for the qualitative differences in the things of sense. His basic substance was air, infinite in extent as was the "undefined," but having, in its basic state, the qualities that we associate with air. When this was compressed and condensed, it first became mist, then, in order, water, earth, and the hardest substances. By rarefaction it returned through the series from rock to air, and if the process went a step further, to fire.

Of the writings of Heraclitus of Ephesus[4] (*c.* 540–*c.* 480 B.C.) over a hundred brief fragments (i.e., passages quoted by later writers whose works we have) remain, as well as a large number of statements about his beliefs. Unfortunately Zeno (355–263 B.C.), the founder of the Stoic school, took as the foundation of his own system the physical theories of Heraclitus, altering them as he saw fit, and many of our statements about Heraclitus appear to have been more or less influenced by this Stoic adaptation. Thus Lucretius' criticism of Heraclitus (I. 635–704) is

[2] For Anaximander, see Bailey, 14–16; Burnet, 50–71; Kirk and Raven, 99–142.

[3] For Anaximenes, see Bailey, 16–18; Burnet, 72–79; Kirk and Raven, 143–62.

[4] For Heraclitus, see Bailey, 18–23; Burnet, 130–68; Kirk and Raven, 182–215.

aimed at the Stoics of Lucretius' own day rather than at Heraclitus himself. Heraclitus' universe is one of constant, harmonious, balanced change. A flame burning in still air served him as an example. In a sense such a flame is a continuous thing with its own clearly visible properties, but in another sense it is constantly changing, receiving particles from the oil on the wick, which become incandescent as they pass up through the flame and vanish as they are consumed at the flame's edge. But fire is more to Heraclitus than an illustration. Fire, in the form of the aether[5] that surrounds the world, is the ultimate matter, which changes into water and then into earth, and then back from earth to water and to fire. Plato, perhaps with intentional exaggeration, credits Heraclitus with the belief that all things are like the flowing river, never the same in two consecutive moments, but it seems more probable that the process of change was slow and intermittent—that a rock might remain a rock for a long time. One thing seems certain: these changes were always in balance, and fire, water, and earth have always been and will always be in the same proportions as they now are.

Parmenides,[6] who was born about 515 B.C. in Elea in southern Italy, was the last of the monists, that group of thinkers beginning with Thales who sought to explain the world in terms of a single ultimate unity. Those before him had started with the evidence of the senses and had tried to construct theories that explained the manifold variety of the world without too greatly violating what the senses tell us. To Parmenides sensation was not a valid source of knowledge. The foundation of his system was an assertion, which he assumed as self-evident: "What is, is; what is not, is not since it cannot be thought." Thought, or visualization, is the touchstone of existence. Only what we can visualize can be real. Since we cannot form a mental

[5] The aether (or ether, but for the word with this meaning the Latin spelling may well be retained) is the pure upper air in the region of the stars, sometimes thought of as fire.

[6] For Parmenides, see Bailey, 24–27; Burnet, 169–96; Kirk and Raven, 263–306. We possess quite substantial parts of his writings, which were in hexameter verse.

picture of "nothing," "nothing" cannot exist. There is, therefore, no empty space. What exists, then, can have no empty space within it or outside it, and therefore it cannot move. It cannot have been created, since there is nothing other than itself from which it can have been formed; it cannot be destroyed, since there is nothing else into which it can pass. Since existence is all that can be predicated of it, it must be the same in all its parts and extend equally in all directions. That which exists is therefore a solid, undifferentiated, unchanging sphere, uncreated and indestructible, with nothing, not even empty space, about it.

By pushing monism to its logical limit, Parmenides killed it; but the total effect of his teaching was by no means negative. He raised several questions that no later thinker could ignore. For one thing, he forced serious consideration of the nature and source of knowledge. When the senses, reason, and intuition are in conflict, what can be accepted as true? Again, those before him had taken motion for granted; henceforth, it had to be explained or accounted for in some way. Finally, although his theory of the one unchanging whole seems utterly opposed to atomism with its ceaseless motion, it actually pointed the way to the latter system. One of his followers, Melissus, defending the Parmenidean universe, argued: "But if the many exist, they must each be such as the one of Parmenides." In the atomic systems we shall find that each atom is indeed like "the one of Parmenides," solid, unchanging, uncreated, and eternal; but the atoms are infinite in number and instead of being at rest they move in ever-changing patterns through an infinite void, the existence of which is as essential as is that of the atoms themselves. However, before we come to the atomists, there are others who tried to solve the dilemma created by Parmenides.

EMPEDOCLES

Empedocles[7] (*fl. c.* 450 B.C.), from Acragas in Sicily, agreed with Parmenides that the world was a sphere and was eternal,

[7] For Empedocles, see Bailey, 27–34; Burnet, 197–250; Kirk and Raven, 320–61.

and that there was no empty space. Parmenides' sphere, however, had been single and homogeneous, and he had insisted that out of the one the many could not be formed. Empedocles met this by teaching that the sphere was composed of four elements—earth, air, fire, and water—and that from their changing combinations all the things of the sensible world can be made. He explained motion by two forces, Love and Strife, which cause the changing combinations of the four. Since incorporeal existence was still beyond the compass of Greek thinking, Love and Strife are thought of as corporeal—really two more elements. The sphere is eternal, but it is constantly passing through a cycle of four changing states. In one state, Love is victorious and has driven Strife to the outer periphery, while within the sphere the four elements have been brought into a uniform mixture, with Love in the center. In the course of the next state, Strife, forcing its way in, gradually drives Love out, at the same time separating the elements, each after its own kind. In the state that follows, victorious Strife is at the center, the elements are completely separated, and Love is on the outside. During the fourth state, Love slowly overcomes Strife, and at its end the sphere is once more in the condition first described. This cycle is eternal, without beginning or end. It is clear that a world such as ours could exist only in one of the transitional periods, and there is some evidence that Empedocles placed it in the period in which Strife is gaining mastery.

From the three hundred fifty scattered lines that remain from Empedocles' poem *On Nature,* we can see that he worked out these cycles with ingenious detail. We can also learn a little of his astronomy and his psychology. The earth is surrounded by two hemispheres, one of fire, which causes day, and one of darkness mixed with a little fire, which causes night. Both the sun and the moon shine by reflected light. It is not day because the sun shines; rather, the sun shines because the bright hemisphere causes the day. Sensation is explained as the recognition of like by like; for example, the fire in us somehow responds to the fire in other things. Sight is due to effluences from the object seen, which come to the eye and cause vision. Thought is located in the blood near the heart, since the blood has equal portions of all the elements. Consciousness thus depends on the combination of the elements, which ought to mean that the soul is mortal. However, in another poem, *The Purifications,* of which little survives, Empedocles speaks of reincarnation, transmigration, and the final escape of the soul to a state of bliss. How these two views were reconciled, if they were, is unknown.

ANAXAGORAS

Anaxagoras[8] (*c.* 500–*c.* 428 B.C.) is the most enigmatic of the figures with whom we shall deal. His life is fairly well known. Born at Clyzomenae in Asia Minor, he came to Athens, where he taught for many years and won the friendship of Euripides and of Pericles. Foes of the latter, not strong enough to move against the statesman but able to assail his friends, secured the exile of Anaxagoras on a charge of "impiety," perhaps around the year 430 B.C., and he died in Lampsacus not long thereafter. But though his life is better known than that of any of the other physicists, no one today can speak with certainty of his beliefs, and our confusion seems to have been shared by the ancients. To take the example most closely at hand, it is inconceivable that a man of Anaxagoras' intellectual stature (and there seems never to have been a question of his importance in the history of thought) could have maintained the views ascribed to him by Lucretius (I. 830–920). If we neglect what is said about Anaxagoras by others and limit ourselves to what appear to be actual fragments of his one book, the following statements emerge: (1) Matter can be neither created nor destroyed. (2) A thing cannot be formed from what is unlike itself. (3) Matter is infinitely divisible. (4) Each thing contains a share of every kind of thing. (5) Each thing appears to be that of which it contains the most. The first of these statements agrees with the monism of Parmenides, and the second does not contradict it, but the third emphatically denies the Parmenidean idea of the one sole, eternal existence, and the last two are developed from

[8] For Anaxagoras, see Bailey, 34–45, 537–58; Burnet, 251–75; Kirk and Raven, 362–94.

the third. We shall find that the atomists supposed the existence of an infinite number of invisible particles, differing from each other in shape and size but all of the same substance and not subject to division. The matter of Anaxagoras is infinitely divisible, and each particle, however small, contains within itself portions of all sensible objects and may share in their composition. Anaxagoras was applying to physical matter what is true in geometry. A line, no matter how short, contains an infinite number of points. If this is assumed to be true of matter, then however finely matter is divided, each particle will still contain infinite parts, and so each may contain portions of all things. One essential point has been thus far omitted. After Parmenides it was necessary to give some account of motion. For Anaxagoras the cause of motion was *nous,* a word ordinarily translated "mind," but here having a special meaning and best left untranslated. *Nous,* like Empedocles' Love and Strife, is described in physical terms, but it differs from other physical things in that it always remains pure, never containing a portion of anything else. Before the formation of our world there was simply a mass of undifferentiated matter. *Nous,* being outside this mass, set a portion of it revolving, and as the revolution became ever greater the parts separated, with the earth in the center and the heavenly bodies revolving about it. *Nous* entered into some things, but not into all. The presence of *nous,* which we may here call "mind," quite certainly distinguishes animate things from inanimate ones; but beyond this we know little of the psychology of Anaxagoras. Since *nous* always remains pure, we may assume that on the death of a man his mind returned to the main body of *nous*; but this is far from a belief in individual immortality such as seems to have been envisaged by Empedocles in his *Purifications.*

LEUCIPPUS AND DEMOCRITUS

With Leucippus (*fl. c.* 440 B.C.) and his greater pupil, Democritus of Abdera[9] (*fl. c.* 420 B.C.), we finally come to the atomic

[9] For Leucippus and Democritus, see Bailey, 64–214; Burnet, 330–49; Kirk and Raven, 400–26.

system. Leucippus may have written one book, *The Greater World System,* although this is also ascribed to Democritus, one of the most voluminous writers of antiquity. Some seventy works by Democritus are known by name, their titles running the whole gamut from *On Harmony* to *On Fighting in Armor.* Twenty-one of these belong to the field of physics in its broadest sense, but unfortunately for our present purpose nearly all of the almost three hundred fragments that survive come from his unimportant ethical works. For our information on his physical theories, as on those of Leucippus, we have to depend on what was said of them by others, usually in adverse criticism. Epicurus—who took over their system of physics with very minor changes, and from whom we might expect a sympathetic and understanding account—claims everything as his own and ignores his predecessors. Lucretius, who does not mention Leucippus at all, refers to Democritus three times (III. 371, 1039, V. 622) with great respect, but tells us almost nothing of his life or his theories. Usually ancient writers group Leucippus and Democritus together, and today it is rarely possible for us to discover specific points on which Democritus advanced beyond his senior. We can assume that the theory in its broad outlines was developed by Leucippus and then elaborated by Democritus.

The atomists start with the law of the permanence of matter, which, as we have seen, was already accepted by their predecessors; for them, however, this matter existed in the form of atoms —indivisible particles, all composed of the same substance, each of them possessing as its sole properties shape, size, mass varying directly with size, and ceaseless motion. These atoms are indestructible, either because they possess no parts (Leucippus) or because they have no void within them (Democritus). They are infinite in number, and they are infinitely varied in form. Leucippus believes that they are all so small that they are beyond the reach of the human senses, but Democritus admits the possibility that if the shapes are of infinite variety, some of the atoms will be large enough to be visible. In addition to the atoms, there is the empty space in which they move. Empedocles, although he denied the reality of the void, seems to have tacitly assumed its presence in order to make motion possible. Leucippus and Democritus are the first who frankly proclaim empty space as an immaterial existence, perhaps not real in the same sense as matter but certainly as essential. The void makes possible the motion of the atoms; however tightly the atoms may be united, there is always space between them, and hence there is still the possibility of the individual atoms' continued motion within the complex. With homogeneous matter and no void, only the changeless Parmenidean sphere could exist. Even if exchange between parts within the sphere were possible, nothing would really be changed, since all the parts are identical. With void and with the homogeneous matter existing as eternal, ever-moving particles of various shapes and sizes, the infinite variety of the world of sense is possible while the basic substance of all things remains one, and matter is neither created nor destroyed.

Aristotle complains that neither Leucippus nor Democritus gives any cause for the motion of the atoms. Both would certainly have replied that the atoms, which have always existed and will always exist, have always been in motion and will always remain in motion, and that their motion no more requires explanation than does their very existence. We may suppose that the original motion of the atoms was random (if we may say "original" when dealing with what never had an origin), but the actual motion of the atoms is conditioned by their collisions with each other. After colliding, the atoms rebound, and may resume their free flight in an altered direction; but sometimes they become entangled with each other and remain close together although each still retains its motion in some fashion, perhaps in the form of vibration.[10]

Leucippus and Democritus give an account of the origin of our world (which is one of many) out of a portion of the infi-

[10] It is possible, but not very probable, that Democritus believed that when the atoms formed a solid their motion ceased, or that it was in some way changed into the motion of the solid as a whole. See Lucretius, II. 80–82, and note.

nite number of eternal atoms. These atoms, happening to come together in space and to impart to each other a rotary motion, assumed the form of a great vortex. Because the larger atoms (or more probably the larger complexes of atoms), because of their greater mass, offered more resistance to the rotary motion than did the smaller, they gathered in the center as do pebbles or grains of sand in the center of an eddy of water. (This tendency to the center in the vortex, and so in our world, can be identified with weight, which, in this earlier form of the atomic system, is not a property of the atom but results from its mass and the motion of the whirl.) These larger and heavier bodies formed the earth, while the lesser and lighter ones were thrust out and up, forming the air and the heavenly bodies.

The sensations are explained in terms of changes brought about by external contacts. The spirit, consisting of spherical atoms and scattered throughout the body, is moved by a touch from without; it, in turn, moves the mind, which consists of similar atoms concentrated in the breast. Of all the sensations, touch, in the ordinary sense, is the easiest to explain, and it was probably regarded by Democritus as the truest—not only because it is the most direct, but also because it gives information only about size, shape, mass, and motion, the properties that are present in the atoms and therefore the only ones that are actually possessed by material things in general. In taste we have an actual contact as we do in touch; however, a thing's taste is not a real property of the thing tasted, but only an interpretation given by the tongue to the real properties. It is therefore subjective and depends upon the one who tastes as well as upon the thing tasted. With smell the subjective element is the same, and since the particles causing smell have to pass through the air from their source to our nostrils, another possibility of uncertainty is introduced. Hearing and sight are also subjective, since they interpret the real properties of the object in terms of sound and of color—which, Democritus says, are "by convention"—and they require a more elaborate and less trustworthy mechanism to bring about the contact. Sound is material, a bundle of atoms emitted by the source, passing through the air, and striking the ear. Sight is more complicated. Leucippus seems to have been content to borrow from Empedocles the theory of effluences or "idols" given off by the object in unending succession and impinging upon the eye, an explanation that Epicurus later adopted. Democritus, however, combined this with the belief that what we see is not the object itself or its idol, but the image that is actually visible in the pupil of the eye. The object and the eye both give off effluences. These meet, and the image of the object is formed in the air and returns into the eye, which then sees it. The chances of distortion are considerable, and while the shape, size, and motion of the object are real, its color can be only the eye's interpretation of the real atomic properties. It may appear that Democritus had little trust in the validity of sensation, and since he says that thought and sensation are the same, we might expect his skepticism to be complete. Yet he clearly did believe that the truth about nature—that is, about the atoms and the void—could be known, and that this knowledge depended ultimately upon the evidence of the senses. We do not know how he reconciled these two positions; it is quite probable, in fact, that he did not recognize their incompatibility or make any effort to reconcile them. Neither do we know what effort, if any, he made to explain the great difficulty in any materialistic system, the step from the physical motion of the soul atoms, caused by contact from outside, to the conscious interpretation of that motion in terms of sensation and thought; or, to state the problem in other terms, the difference beween the inanimate and the animate, between matter and spirit.

SUMMARY

With Leucippus and Democritus we have come to the end of the great formative period in the Greek effort to give a rational explanation of the world in purely material terms. Starting with an instinctive feeling that there must be one basic substance that somehow underlies the manifold, changing world of sense, the monists had presented their various theories. Thales had seen water as the basis of all existence, but he probably did not go beyond the bare assertion. Anaximander, feeling with surprisingly true insight that the basic substance must be something different from any of the things of sense, had posited the "undefined." Anaximenes, taking air as his basic matter, had sought to explain its changes by rarefaction and condensation, and Heraclitus had formed all things from fire as it moved along the way up or the way down. All these explanations were open to the criticism that we shall find several times repeated by Lucretius: "If ever a thing is changed and departs from its proper limits, that is at once the end of that which was before" (I. 670–71, 792–93, II. 753–54, III. 519–20).

Next Parmenides stated the monistic theory in its most absolute and unambiguous form. The basic substance can never submit to change of any sort. It has always been and will always be such as it is now, the same, one and immovable; aside from it, nothing exists. There were three answers to this. Empedocles agreed that matter was eternal and that its sum never changed, but for him matter existed in the form of the four elements—earth, air, water, and fire—which, alternately combining and separating under the compulsion of Strife and Love, formed our world, and after its passing will form others in an endless series. This preserved the totality and eternity of the universe, but it substituted four basic substances for one, and was still open to the objection that when the elements became parts of other things they ceased to exist, and the new thing took their place, formed from something different from itself. Anaxagoras, on the other hand, supposed that matter was infinitely divisible and that the most infinitesimal particles each contained portions of all things and might therefore share in the creation of any one of those things without changing its nature. He thus hoped to avoid any change in the character of matter as the various things were formed, but in place of a basic unity, multiplicity was carried down to the smallest part.

Finally, in the atomism of Leucippus and Democritus, the basic matter is one and the same, and is indestructible; but it exists in minute particles of many shapes and sizes, infinite in number, in constant motion through the infinite void, whose existence is now clearly asserted for the first time. These particles have always existed and will always exist, each one unchanging in itself; but by their many constantly changing combinations they make up the multiform, changing world. Matter is still of one sort, but the void makes possible its division and motion; these, in turn, make possible this world and many others, like or unlike it, through infinite space and time. This system, ignored by Plato and rejected by Aristotle, was further refined by Epicurus and made the basis of his ethics; it is best known to us in the poem *On Nature* by his Roman disciple, Lucretius.

II. Epicurus

FROM DEMOCRITUS TO EPICURUS

In the years between Democritus and Epicurus there seems to have been only one change in the atomic theory, and we do not know to whom this should be ascribed. As we have seen, the atoms of Democritus had no weight, and no tendency downward or to the center, until their self-caused, random motions had chanced to result in a vortex such as that from which the world was formed. Outside a vortex the actual motion of an atom would be the end result of the normal random motion and the series of collisions with other atoms. Within a vortex, and so within our world, there would also be a tendency toward the center. Apparently someone after Democritus made this tendency to the center, now stated simply as a tendency downwards (i.e., weight), the primary cause of atomic motion, and explained the collisions as due to the more rapid fall of the heavier atoms. In any case Epicurus, followed by Lucretius, assumes that the atoms have weight and that their normal motion is downward; and both are at pains to point out that the velocity of bodies falling through the void would not be affected by their varying weights and that therefore this unnamed predecessor is wrong in explaining the collisions as caused by the varying rates of fall. Although direct evidence of Epicurus' solution of the problem is lacking, Lucretius (II. 216–50) is quite certainly following his master when he introduces as the cause of the collisions the uncaused swerve of the atoms, at uncertain times and places.

LIFE OF EPICURUS

Our chief source for the life of Epicurus[b] is Diogenes Laertius, whose account forms the first part of Book Ten of his *Lives of Eminent Philosophers.* Epicurus was born either in Athens or on the island of Samos, where he certainly spent his early years. He was about eighteen when Alexander the Great died in 322 B.C., and he spent part of the subsequent troubled period in Athens and part in several Asia Minor towns, where he doubtless heard the discussions of the various philosophers of the time and read the works of their predecessors. In 311 B.C., at the age of about thirty, he gathered a few disciples about himself, and a few years later moved to Athens, where he purchased the home in which he lived until his death at the age of about seventy, and also the "Garden" which formed the site of his school and gave it its name. As far as we can tell, he did not teach in a formal way; he and his followers lived quietly and without luxury, seeking the happiness that comes from the simple life. Many details, true and false, can be found in Laertius, including Epicurus' last testament with its thoughtful care for the welfare of his friends.

WORKS

Like Democritus, Epicurus was a voluminous writer; Laertius has preserved a list of forty-one titles. Most of these works[c] seem to have been short—with the exception of the *Physics,* in whose thirty-seven books Epicurus must have given a full statement of his physical system, which furnished the foundation for his ethics. The *Greater Epitome,* in which he appears to have presented his physical doctrines in briefer form, was probably the chief immediate source for Lucretius. All of Epicurus' major works are lost except for a few passages quoted by later writers and a considerable number of tantalizing papyrus fragments from Herculáneum. These last are all that remain from the library of an Epicurean, covered by the eruption of Vesuvius in A.D. 79. Of Epicurus' whole literary output we have, aside from the fragments, only the three *Letters* and the forty *Principal Doctrines* that Laertius included in his *Life,* and a collection of brief *Sayings* in a manuscript now in the Vatican Library. Of the three *Letters,* the second, *To Pythocles,* deals with astronomy and meteorology, fields in which the Epicureans were very weak, as we shall abundantly see in Lucretius. The third, *To Menoeceus,* is a very brief statement of some of the ethical doctrines. The first, *To Herodotus,* is concerned with the basic physical principles, and because of its close relationship to Lucretius' subject matter, it deserves a rather full summary.

SUMMARY OF "LETTER TO HERODOTUS"

This letter presents a brief compendium of the physics to refresh the memories of those already familiar with the theories; it is intended for the beginner, and also as an easily remembered outline for the more proficient.

Matter can neither be created nor destroyed. The universe as a whole is unchanging; like each of its elements, it is also infinite, for there is nothing to bound it. It consists of matter, recognized by the senses, and space in which matter moves; anything else that we can conceive is an "accident" or a "property" of these. Sensible objects are composed of atoms which themselves are indestructible. To account for the differences in these objects, the atoms must exist in many forms, the number of different forms being inconceivably great but not infinite, although the number of atoms of each form is infinite. The atoms move continuously, both freely in space and with more limited motion, as when they form gases, liquids, and solids—both sorts of motion had no beginning. Atoms and space are infinite; consequently the number of worlds, whether like or unlike ours, is infinite also.

Thin films called "idols"—which, because their unsurpassed fineness frees them from internal and external collisions, move with almost atomic speed—are constantly given off by objects, retaining the original object's form and color. These films, replaced by new matter as soon as they leave the surfaces of bodies, usually retain their forms; but sometimes an idol may be formed in mid-air. The idols coming to us from objects cause both thought and sight, and the mental picture from the intent look or the concentrated thought is true; only when opinion adds something does error result. Hearing is caused by an effluence from a source of sound; this splits up into particles, each of which is like the whole, and which come in sequence to the ear. Likewise, the sense of smell is roused by effluences.

The unchanging atoms possess no qualities of their own save size, mass, and shape; other qualities result from atomic position or motion. The atoms vary in size, yet they cannot be of every size, or else some of them would be visible. We cannot assume matter to be infinitely divisible, for a thing containing infinite material parts, no matter how small they were, would itself be infinitely large. As in a visible thing there is a smallest part recognizable by the eye, yet not to be seen by itself—the total of these smallest parts comprising the whole—so in the atom there is also a least part which, although it is recognizable by the mind, cannot exist by itself, and the total of these parts comprises the atom. Although in infinite space there can be neither up nor down, the terms "up" and "down" have meaning with respect to ourselves. The atoms are always moving in the void, and whether their motion be caused by collision or by weight, they always possess the same velocity; if unchecked, an atom will cross any conceivable distance in an inconceivably short time. At any point of time the atoms of a compound body are moving with atomic speed in all directions, but because of their constant collisions and changes of direction, the motion of the body as a whole during any appreciable time may be brought within the reach of our senses.

The soul is material, composed of finely divided particles; some are like breath and some like fire, while some are of a third, unnamed kind. The soul experiences sensation only when enclosed in the body, which, in turn, receives from the soul a share in this sensation. Sensation may survive the loss of parts of the body, but it ceases with the destruction either of the soul or of the whole body. The term "incorporeal" is properly applied only to the void, which can neither act nor be acted upon; since the soul can both act and be acted upon, it is not incorporeal.

Shape, mass, etc., are properties of things. They cannot exist by themselves, and are not separable from the things to which they belong; these things could not be perceived without them. Like properties, accidents can be recognized only in connection with bodies; but accidents, unlike properties, are not permanent attributes. Time presents a special problem: we cannot visualize it, and can recognize it only as an accident of an event, which is itself an accident.

Each world was formed by being separated from its own whirling mass, and each will be dissolved again. We may assume that animal and vegetable life on the other worlds is similar to ours.

Instinct led men to the first developments of civilization; reason subsequently improved upon these early developments. Language developed naturally, differing from one tribe to another, and later speech was clarified by deliberate selection.

The heavenly bodies are not themselves divine, nor—for this would be inconsistent with divine happiness—does any divinity direct them. While knowledge of the general principles governing the heavenly bodies is essential to our happiness, the study of the details is vain, and we must accept the possibility of multiple causes. Imagining that the celestial bodies are divine, men nonetheless ascribe to them purposes inconsistent with divinity, and anticipate eternal suffering after death. But if we trust to our immediate feelings and sensations, we will gain the peace of mind that follows freedom from such fears.

ETHICS

The ethical theory[11] of Epicurus rests squarely on the physical one. Since like everything else the soul is a temporary combination of atoms, death, which is merely the dissolution of that

[11] For Epicurus' own statements on ethics, see the entire *Letter to Menoeceus*. Most of the *Principal Doctrines* and of the *Vatican Sayings* deal with ethical matters.

combination, brings a complete and final end to consciousness. The atoms continue to exist, of course, but the soul as an individual existence is no more. From this Epicurus reasons that death, being nothingness, is not to be feared, and that happiness in this life is to be sought as the highest good, the only thing that men actually do seek as an end in itself and not as a means to something else. Just as the sensations are the criteria of knowledge, so the feelings are the criteria of happiness. We cannot go beyond this fact, but the wise man will weigh various forms of happiness and will avoid those that involve pain. Indeed, happiness can be defined as freedom from pain, and in particular, freedom from the pain caused by unfulfilled desires. Desires are divided into three classes: desires for things that are both natural and necessary (e.g., food enough to satisfy, clothing enough to keep us warm), desires for things that are natural but not necessary (e.g., food that is pleasing as well as satisfying, clothing that is beautiful as well as warm), and desires for things that are neither natural nor necessary (e.g., food that pleases the taste but harms the body, clothing whose chief purpose is to arouse the envy of those who see it). If we limit our desires to the first class and satisfy these, we shall be happy. Gaining things in the second class will not increase the amount of our happiness but will vary its quality; desiring these things and not gaining them, however, will bring unhappiness. Desires of the third class, whether fulfilled or not, always bring unhappiness. The one certain road to happiness, then, lies through the limitation of desires, rather than through their satisfaction. Lucretius nowhere develops the Epicurean ethical theory at length, but he everywhere assumes that it is not only understood by his reader but is also accepted by him (e.g., II. 16–54).

RELIGION

Like his ethical teachings, Epicurus' religious doctrines[12] rest on his physics. The existence of the gods is proven by our dreams

[12] For Epicurus' religious beliefs, see *Letter to Menoeceus* 123–24a; *Principal Doctrines* I, XIII; *Vatican Sayings,* LXV. Compare also Lucretius, I. 44–49, 62–135, V. 1161–93.

and visions, since these are caused by idols that must have some material origin. But all that happens in the world is explained by the atoms and their laws, leaving no place for the activities of the gods. The latter live lives of perfect happiness, and men may worship them as models but should not expect prayers to them to be answered, nor should they interpret signs from heaven as marks of the anger or good will of the gods. Lucretius is more interested in this than in the ethics, and we shall find a number of passages where he turns from the subject at hand to emphasize one of the religious teachings of the school (e.g., II. 167–81, 1090–1104, V. 156–234, VI. 379–422).

SCIENTIFIC METHOD

Epicurus rejected formal logic but set up certain rules (*The Canon*) to be followed in the search for truth, and Diogenes Laertius represents him as giving three criteria of truth.[13] Of these sensation is the most important, for it gives us true information about phenomena, although we may misinterpret what it tells us.[14] In the second place, from a series of similar sensations the reason may extract what is common, and establish a true concept by which it can test and clarify further sensations. After seeing many individual men, no two of whom are identical, we can establish the general concept "man," and thereafter can recognize individual men as belonging to that class. But the concept depends ultimately on experience and cannot exist before experience. The gods could not have created the world because, before it was created by the chance motions of the atoms, they could not have had the concept "world," and thus would have had no model to follow.[15] The first two criteria are concerned with what is true; the third,

[13] Diogenes Laertius, *Life of Epicurus* 31a: "They [i.e., the Epicureans] reject theoretical logic on the ground that it draws the seeker for truth aside from his purpose. It is enough for the student of the natural world to make progress in accordance with the direct evidence of the phenomena themselves. Thus in the *Canon* Epicurus says that the bases on which the truth is to be judged are the sensations, the concepts, and the feelings. To these the Epicureans add mental apprehension of appearances."

[14] *Letter to Herodotus* 50b–52a; see Lucretius, IV. 353–63, 469–521.

[15] See Lucretius, V. 181–86.

namely the feelings, distinguishes between what is good and what is bad, what is to be chosen and what avoided.

These three are simple. But there are certain things that are beyond the reach of sensation, in particular the atoms and the void on which the whole Epicurean system rests. The atoms are so small that our senses cannot reach them, and the void is, by definition, that which can neither touch nor be touched. Yet about both of these Epicurus felt that he had sure knowledge. Nowhere in the extant works does he make it clear how this may be, but in the passage from Laertius cited above we are told that the "Epicureans" added to the other criteria the "mental apprehension of appearances." The words so translated mean literally "the mind's forward cast in the matter of images (or appearances)." Lucretius (II. 1047) seems to be translating this expression by *animi iactus liber,* "the free projection of the mind." The probable meaning is that the mind has the power to concentrate upon concepts, which it has based upon phenomena directly perceived by the senses, and from these to form, by analogy, new concepts (as of the atoms or the void), which are to be accepted if (1) they furnish a satisfactory explanation of the phenomenon under investigation, and (2) they are not contradicted by any of the phenomena which can be observed directly. This problem is discussed at length by Bailey (*Atomists,* 559–76) and, with somewhat different results, by DeWitt (*Epicurus,* 133–54).

III. Lucretius

FROM EPICURUS TO LUCRETIUS

As far as physics is concerned, there seems to have been no progress in Epicurean theory after the master's death. This may have resulted from Epicurus' own attitude, for he claimed that his system was complete and perfect and that he alone had discovered it, acknowledging no debt to any who had gone before him and holding out no hope for any future improvements. At all events, his followers were content to take the physics for granted as the foundation for the ethical system, in which they were more interested, and to make no particular effort to explain or even to understand the theories. Lucretius seems to have been the first to set forth the whole physical system anew, and he constantly claims that he is merely presenting the teachings as Epicurus left them. He seems to have worked with one of the lost treatises, probably the *Greater Epitome,* constantly before him; therefore it is reasonably safe to accept the *De Rerum Natura* as our fullest and most accurate statement of Epicurus' own teachings in the field of physics.

LIFE OF LUCRETIUS

Lucretius tells us almost nothing about himself.[16] From his poem we may learn a good deal about his character, but little about his life. Our chief knowledge of the latter comes from two very brief statements, both of which may go back to Suetonius. In the additions that Saint Jerome made to the *Chronology* of Eusebius we find under the year 94 B.C. (or in certain of the manuscripts, 93 or 96) the following:

> Titus Lucretius the poet is born. Afterwards, having been driven mad by a love potion, when he had composed a number of books in the intervals of insanity, which Cicero afterwards edited, he killed himself with his own hand in the forty-fourth year of his life.

In the *Life of Virgil* ascribed to Donatus we have the following:

> Virgil passed his life at Cremona up to the time when he assumed the toga of manhood, which he did on his birthday in his seventeenth year under the same consuls in whose earlier term he had been born; and it happened that on that very day the poet Lucretius died.

The first statement, which puts the birth in 94 (or 93 or 96), would place the death in 51 (or 50 or 53). The second, which puts the death in the second consulship of Pompey and Crassus, i.e., in 55, might seem more reliable, insofar as consulships are

[16] The General Introduction of the edition of Lucretius by Leonard and Smith (Madison, Wis., 1942) is by Professor Leonard. Out of his lifelong study of the poem, he has constructed a rather detailed and quite convincing picture of the kind of man the poet must have been.

less likely to be confused than numbers in the manuscript tradition; but this notice is inconsistent with itself since, if Virgil was born in the first consulship in 70, he would have been seventeen in 53, not in 55. We can at least be sure that Lucretius' life fell in the first half of the first century before Christ, and that is really enough.

Not only are the dates given in Jerome's notice uncertain, but every other statement has been questioned. Could a love philter cause madness? Can the words "a number of books" describe a single great poem? Could such a poem, a single work of art, be composed in brief periods of sanity? What, if anything, does the poem owe to the "editing" of Cicero? Little light is shed on the last point by a letter of Cicero to his brother in February, 54 B.C., in which he writes: "The poetry of Lucretius is, as you say, marked by many flashes of genius, yet is of much art. But more of this when you come." We cannot be sure whether or not these words are complimentary, but at least they show that both brothers had seen the poem, or some part of it, early in 54, which may suggest that the poet had died in 55. One more unanswered question is why Lucretius entrusted his poem to Cicero, who, as is clear from his own works, was no friend of Epicureanism—at least of the ordinary type—and who would be expected to have little sympathy for or understanding of the physical theories of the school.

The question of madness and suicide cannot be settled from the evidence that we possess. It is certain that the Romans believed that madness might be induced by a love potion. The bitter attack on love which closes Book Four of *On Nature* may reflect some unhappy love experience of the poet which might have led to suicide, but it is equally possible that the presence of that passage in the poem suggested the love philter and its consequences to some biographer working with scanty information. There are certain passages in the poem filled with a brooding over death that may indicate a mind not at peace with itself. Perhaps when the poet speaks (III. 79–83) of those who, fearing death, have slain themselves, he is voicing his own dread. It is true that the poem shows many signs that it was never completed; but this argues at most an early death, not a self-inflicted one.

THE POEM

As far as we know, Lucretius wrote only a single poem, the *De Rerum Natura,* or *On Nature.*[d] This is the oldest extant Latin poem written in dactylic hexameter, a Greek meter that the Roman poet, Ennius (d. 169 B.C.), was the first to use in Latin, and which from that time to the end of Latin literature remained the commonest meter for all poems except short lyrics. It reached its greatest perfection in the works of the Augustan poet, Virgil (70–19 B.C.). With Lucretius it is still a little rough at times, although far more polished than it is in the few fragments of Ennius' *Annales* that remain.

Lucretius' poem is a little less than 7,500 lines in length. It is divided into six books, and these fall into three groups of two books each. The first pair of books deals with the basic principles of the atomic system; these are then applied to mankind in the second pair, and to the world in the third. In more detail, Book One deals with the existence of matter and void and with the nature of the atom, then considers rival theories and disposes of them, and finally presents proofs of the infinity of the universe. Book Two discusses the motion of the atoms, various atomic shapes and the effect of the shapes on the compounds formed from them, and the total lack in the atoms of such secondary qualities as color. The last one hundred and fifty lines of this book, which take up the formation and decay of worlds, may represent a period in the construction of the poem in which Book Five immediately followed Book Two; its presence here may be regarded as one of the signs that the poet's sudden death prevented a final revision of the poem. Book Three treats of the material nature of the soul and presents a series of arguments to prove its mortality. Here we come to one of Lucretius' dearest themes—if the soul is mortal, if death is a complete and absolute end to consciousness, then death is no more to be feared than a dreamless sleep. The book ends with a triumph song over the fear of death. The mind or soul is further treated in

Book Four, which first explains the nature of sensation (with sight treated at length and the other senses briefly), and then turns to thought, which is regarded as closely akin to sight. After this some of the functions of the body are considered, and the book ends with a violent attack on the passion of love. As indicated above, the last two books are an effort to explain our world (i.e., our earth and the heavenly bodies that appear to move about it) and its place in the universe. At the end of Book One Lucretius showed that the universe is infinite, and at the end of Book Two, that our world had a beginning and will have an end. Now in Book Five he tells how the world came into existence out of atoms moving in the infinite void, and then presents his views in regard to the sun, the moon, and the stars (by all odds the weakest part of the Epicurean system) . After this he returns to the earth and to the beginning of life upon it, and traces the development of living creatures, of men, and of human civilization. Book Six considers, in a rather unorganized way, both the phenomena of the region between the earth and the heavenly bodies, such as lightning and rain, and also strange phenomena of many kinds on the earth itself, such as earthquakes, the summer floods of the Nile, and plagues. The last leads to a description of the pestilence that devastated Athens in the early years of the Peloponnesian War, and with this the poem ends. It is in this last book that we see the clearest marks that the poem lacked the poet's last revision. There is little connection between the parts, and some of the subjects discussed might well have been treated earlier.

The poem gives us our best statement of the ancient atomic system as developed by Leucippus and Democritus and adopted by Epicurus; but the poet's purpose is not merely to set forth this materialistic explanation of the natural world. Lucretius was profoundly convinced that the source of all human ills could be traced to two things—man's fear of death and of what followed it, and his fear of the arbitrary power of the gods. It is to rid man of the first of these fears that in Book Three he argues eloquently that the soul of a man—a mere ever-changing complex of atoms—does not exist as an entity after the man's death, and that therefore death can bring no evil to the soul. To rid man of the fear of the arbitrary power of the gods, he shows that the world, all that is in it, and the universe of which it is a small part can be explained by atoms moving in the void subject only to their own laws, with neither any purpose nor any divine power to direct them. He believes that the gods exist—in his material explanation of thought the mere fact that we can think of gods proves their existence—but they live lives of perfect happiness, free from all labor and care, in their homes in the *intermundia,* the peaceful regions between the many worlds that exist in the universe. That the superstitious fear of the gods and of their arbitrary power over human affairs was a very real thing is clearly evidenced by the literature. The historian Livy, for every year from 218 B.C. to the end of the extant books, seriously recounts the prodigies of that year and the means taken to expiate them. An illustration that, thanks to Shakespeare's borrowings from Plutarch's *Life of Caesar,* is more familiar is furnished by the portents that preceded the murder of the Dictator. The old Roman religion, long overlaid by Greek myths of questionable morality and Etruscan teachings about the horrors that befell the dead, did little to assuage men's fears. The new mystery religions that were coming in from the east, with their highly emotional rituals, may have brought comfort to some with their promises of a happy immortality for the initiated, but for many they served only to increase the burden of superstition. Cicero and his group may have been able to make light of these fears, and to have said, in effect, that no sane man would be frightened by what the Epicureans said they would have feared but for the teachings of their master; but Lucretius may well have been closer to the feelings of the common man.[17] At all events, he believed that the one way to secure freedom from these fears was through acceptance of the atomic explana-

[17] Farrington (*Science and Politics in the Ancient World,* Oxford, 1940, pp. 160–212) argues with some plausibility that the *religio* that Lucretius is attacking is not the superstition of the common people but the official cult and, in particular, the machinery of augury, through which the senatorial oligarchy controlled the state.

tion of man and nature. If death is the end of all, then it need not be feared, since it can bring no evil to those who no longer exist. If all that happens in nature is the result of atoms moving according to their own laws, then the gods have no control over phenomena. We therefore need neither fear the gods nor pray to them, although we should revere them as examples of the perfect happiness which we seek but never attain. This side of Epicureanism had been implicit in the system from the beginning, but, as far as our knowledge goes, it had never before been so put in the forefront as it was by Lucretius. What had been prominent, the happy life secured by limiting desires rather than by satisfying them, is barely mentioned in the poem; still less is there anything of so-called Epicureanism of the "eat, drink, and be merry" type.

The poem belongs to the type known as didactic. In the early days of literature, when the poet himself could probably write but the ability to read was still rare, didactic poetry had a real purpose. Hesiod, the poet of the old Greek didactic poem, *On Works and Days,* gives in hexameter verse his moral precepts, his weather signs, and his practical instructions on farming, because those for whom he wrote could remember what was in metrical form more easily than what was in prose. This literary form occurred throughout Greek literature, although little didactic poetry is extant. We have seen that several of the early philosophers expressed their teachings in this way. Lucretius' praise of Empedocles (I. 705–33) suggests that he took his poem as a model and a warrant for his own use of verse. In extant Roman literature the *De Rerum Natura* stands by itself. Later Virgil wrote his *Georgics,* didactic in form, and in form perhaps the most perfect example of didactic poetry in any language; his aim, however, was less to teach than to charm. He gave some instruction for the farmer, but his main purpose was to praise the rustic life as that best fitted for the Roman character. If at any point his material proved intractable, he tended to drop it and pass on to something else. Lucretius' real purpose, on the other hand, was to instruct. If a matter was difficult he did not abandon it but repeated it again—and, if necessary, again, changing the form each time—in order to make sure that his point was clear. As he himself says (I. 927–50), his poetry is the honey on the rim of the cup, tempting the reader to drain the draught within. He clearly failed to attain Virgil's perfection, but the goal he sought was higher, and he may well have left us the greater work.

EPICUREAN PHYSICS AFTER LUCRETIUS

Although the atomic explanation of the universe remained the basis for Epicureanism, it was of little interest to most of the later Epicureans and was practically forgotten. Because it was stained with the brush of hedonism, it was thrust into the background by the Christian Church. Interest in it was revived by the French philosopher and scientist, Pierre Gassendi (1592–1655), and the system was restated on the basis of experimental science by Dalton (1766–1844). Gassendi was certainly influenced by his acquaintance with Epicurus and Lucretius, but the atomic system of modern times owes little except this initial impulse to the system of the Greeks. However, the modern reader familiar with what are now accepted as facts will find striking anticipations of some of these in the ancient writers, anticipations based not on evidence from controlled experiment but upon imaginative deduction from uncontrolled observations of the natural world.

NOTE ON THE TRANSLATION: The chapter headings and the summaries in italic type have been inserted by the translator. Lucretius probably did not divide the books into smaller units; chapter headings are found in some of the manuscripts, but they are certainly the work of some later hand.

SELECTED BIBLIOGRAPHY

(Limited, except for Greek and Latin texts, to works in English)

I. Pre-Socratic Philosophy

TEXTS AND TRANSLATIONS

DIELS, HERMANN. *Die Fragmente der Vorsokratiker, griechisch und deutsch.* 10th edition by Walther Kranz. 3 vols. Berlin, 1961. This is a complete collection of the surviving fragments (i.e., quotations by later writers preserving more or less exactly the actual words) and *testimonia* (less direct citations and discussions) of all the pre-Socratic philosophers. The fragments and the *testimonia* are given in the original language (Greek for the most part), and the actual fragments are translated into German.

FREEMAN, KATHLEEN. *Ancilla to the Pre-Socratic Philosophers, A Complete Translation of the Fragments in Diels'* Fragmente der Vorsokratiker. Oxford, 1949.

MODERN WORKS

BAILEY, CYRIL. *The Greek Atomists and Epicurus.* Oxford, 1928. The main emphasis is on Epicurus, but there are very full discussions of Leucippus and Democritus, with much briefer treatment of their predecessors.

BURNET, JOHN. *Early Greek Philosophy.* 4th edition. London, 1930. This is probably still the most useful work in its field. It is now available as a Meridian paperback.

KIRK, G. S., and RAVEN, J. E. *The Presocratic Philosophers.* Cambridge, England, 1957. The preface states: "This book is designed primarily for those who have more than a casual interest in the history of early thought; but by translating all the Greek passages . . . we have aimed to make the book useful for those students of the history of philosophy or science who have no previous acquaintance with this important and fascinating field." Unfortunately the format is unnecessarily confusing. The book is available in a paperback reprint.

II. Epicurus and Epicureanism

TEXTS AND TRANSLATIONS

ARRIGHETTI, GRAZIANO. *Epicuro, Opere, Introduzione, testo critico, traduzione e note*. Torino, 1960. This is the only complete edition of all the extant remains, including all the papyri from Herculaneum, even bits so fragmentary that translation is hopeless. All that can be translated is translated into Italian, and there is an Italian commentary.

BAILEY, CYRIL. *Epicurus, the Extant Remains.* Oxford, 1926. Contains the extant remains except for the papyrus fragments. There is an excellent introduction, an English translation, and a very full commentary. The commentary would be very difficult for a person without a good knowledge of both Greek and Latin.

GEER, RUSSEL M. *Epicurus: Letters, Principal Doctrines, and Vatican Sayings.* "Library of Liberal Arts," No. 141. New York, 1964. A translation with introduction and commentary intended primarily for the student without knowledge of Greek or Latin.

HICKS, R. D. *Diogenes Laertius, Lives of Eminent Philosophers, with an English Translation.* "Loeb Classical Library." 2 vols. Cambridge, Mass., 1925. Book X of Laertius' *History of Philosophy,* found in Vol. II, consists of the *Life of Epicurus,* including the *Letter to Herodotus, Letter to Pythocles, Letter to Menoeceus,* and the *Principal Doctrines.*

USENER, H. *Epicurus.* Lipsiae, 1887. Until Arrighetti's edition appeared, this was the most complete collection of the works, the fragments, and the ancient references to Epicurus. It is still essential, since it contains much more in the way of indirect testimony than does the more recent work. The actual fragments (as distinct from the *testimonia*) are translated into German. References to the fragments of Epicurus are regularly made by Usener's numbers.

MODERN WORKS

BAILEY, CYRIL. *The Greek Atomists and Epicurus.* See Part I of this Bibliography.

HICKS, R. D. *Stoic and Epicurean.* New York, 1910.

DEWITT, NORMAN W. *Epicurus and His Philosophy.* Minneapolis, 1954.

FARRINGTON, B. *Science and Politics in the Ancient World.* Oxford, 1940.

There is no completely satisfactory work on Epicureanism in English. There has been much work in the field by Italian scholars during the past two generations, but this is not reflected in any collected form in English. Of the books listed, Bailey's two works (his *Greek Atomists* and his *Epicurus*), which are sane and conservative, are certainly the best, even if rather dated. DeWitt and Farrington are more controversial. DeWitt writes with missionary zeal, intent on showing that Epicurus was not a mere hedonist, and that he placed intuition alongside of sensation as a source of knowledge (which would certainly have surprised Lucretius, who had access to many works of Epicurus that are lost to us). Farrington's thesis is that Epicurus and Lucretius represent enlightened science struggling against the enthroned power of priesthoods and oligarchies which were using religion as a prop to political power. There is much truth to what he says, but he presents a rather one-sided view.

III. Lucretius

TEXTS AND TRANSLATIONS

BAILEY, CYRIL. *Lucreti De reum natura libri sex.* 2nd edition. Oxford, 1922. This text, in the Oxford Classical Text series, has been the standard text edition for English students since 1900. It has been many times reprinted.

BAILEY, CYRIL. *Titi Lucreti Cari De rerum natura libri sex: Edited with prologomena, critical apparatus, translation, and commentary.* 3 vols. Oxford, 1947. The most complete annotated edition in English, probably the best in any language. One without a working knowledge of Latin would have difficulty with some of the commentary although he would find the summaries and discussions of each section of much use. Bailey's translation has been published separately.

ERNOUT, A., and ROBIN, L. *Lucrèce de rerum natura: Commentaire exégétique et critique.* 3 vols. Paris, 1925. This is designed to accompany Ernout's edition and French translation in the Budé series. The philosophical portions of the commentary, which are the work of Robin, are particularly good.

LEONARD, W. E. *Lucretius: Of the Nature of Things.* "Everyman's Library." London, 1921. A metrical translation.

LEONARD, W. E., and SMITH, S. B. *T. Lucreti Cari De Rerum Natura, libri sex.* Madison, Wis., 1942. The commentary by Smith is primarily intended as an aid to translation. The very full introduction, which is by Leonard, would be of great value even to a student with no Latin.

ROUSE, W. H. D. *Lucretius, with an English Translation.* "Loeb Classical Library." Cambridge, Mass., 1924.

MODERN WORKS

FARRINGTON, B. *Science and Politics in the Ancient World.* See Part II of this Bibliography.

HADZITS, G. D. *Lucretius and His Influence.* New York, 1935.

ON NATURE

BOOK ONE

I. Introduction

1–145

The poet invokes the aid of Venus in composing his poem, and asks that Memmius attend closely to his words; he praises Epicurus, whose philosophy frees men from the religious superstition which, making them live in fear of death, enslaves them and leads them to evil. Difficult as is the task of putting Greek thought into Latin verse, it is rewarded by its goal: the initiation of Memmius into the hidden nature of the universe.

Mother of the race of Aeneas, delight of men and of gods, fostering Venus,[1] it is you who fill with life the ship-bearing sea and the fruitful lands beneath the gliding constellations of heaven. For because of you, the whole race of breathing creatures is conceived, and when born beholds the sunlight; before you, O Goddess, the winds flee; at your approach the clouds of heaven disperse; for you the wonder-working earth sends up its sweet flowers; for you the expanses of the sea smile, the heaven becomes tranquil and shines with diffused light. As soon as the 10 beauty of a day of spring has been revealed, and the life-giving breath of the west wind has been set free and blows with all its strength, then the birds of the air, their hearts seized by your force, are the first to hail you and your coming. Next the beasts of the farm, roused to madness, leap through the pleasant pas-

[1] An invocation to one of the gods presented with full mythological background (lines 31–40) is a strange introduction to a poem one of whose chief purposes is to show that the gods have no power over men and cannot heed their prayers. If, however, Lucretius felt it necessary to yield to convention and begin in this way, Venus was a natural choice, since she could be presented, as she is in the first thirty lines, as the source of the life-giving powers of the natural world.

tures and swim the swift streams; thus each creature, enslaved by your charm, eagerly follows wherever you urgently command. Yea, throughout the seas and mountains, the greedy rivers, the leafy homes of birds, and the verdant fields, you
20 pierce the hearts of all with winsome love, making each hot to reproduce its own kind. Since you alone govern the universe, and since without you nothing comes forth into the bright regions of light nor is anything created that is pleasing and worthy of love, I am eager that you be my ally in writing these verses on the nature of the universe, which I am undertaking to compose for our Memmius.[2] It has been your will, O Goddess, that he be honored, and that he excel at all times and in every way; grant all the more then, Divine One, eternal charm to my words.

30 Meanwhile cause the fierce labors of war to cease, lulled to sleep throughout all lands and seas. I make this prayer to you because you alone are able to bless mortals with the gift of quiet peace; for Mars, powerful in arms and ruler of war's fierce labors, often throws himself into your bosom, overpowered by the eternal wound of love; then bending back his shapely neck and looking upward, he gazes on you and feeds his greedy eyes with love; and as he lies there his breath hangs on your lips. Bend down your sacred body above the reclining god, O glorious
40 Goddess, and pour forth sweet words from your mouth, winning quiet and peace for the Romans; for when danger threatens our homeland, we cannot carry out our task with calm mind, nor can the famous son of Memmius be careless of the common welfare during such a crisis. It is necessary that the gods in their whole beings and from their own power enjoy unending life in

[2] The Memmius to whom Lucretius dedicates his poem is quite certainly the Gaius Memmius who was praetor in 58 B.C., although no reason can be given why he was selected for this honor. He was a literary dilettante (Cicero, *Brutus* 247), the author of love poems (Ovid, *Tristia* II. 433, Aulus Gellius, XIX. 9. 7), and the not very generous patron of Catullus (Catullus, 10, 28). He may have been an Epicurean of the eat-drink-and-be-merry type (Cicero, *Letters to Friends* XIII. 1), but he seems to have had no interest in the scientific Epicureanism represented by Lucretius. Since the name "Memmius" is difficult to work into the dactylic verse, the poet is here driven to the use of the patronymic "Memmiades," or "son of Memmius."

perfect peace, far removed and separated from our experience. Free from every grief and from all dangers, powerful in their own might, and with no need of us, they are neither won nor angered by our services.[3]

. . . Finally, turn to the true teaching attentive ears and a keen mind freed from anxiety, so as not to despise and reject, before understanding them, the gifts I have drawn up for you with faithful zeal. For I shall proceed to set forth to you the highest law of the heavens and of the gods.[4] I shall explain to you those first beginnings from which Nature creates, increases, and nourishes all things, and into which she resolves these same things when they are destroyed. In discussing these first beginnings, we shall usually use the term "matter," or "life-giving bodies of things," or name them "seeds of things," or else—since from them, as first elements, all things are formed—we shall term them "first bodies."[5] 50 60

When human life lay basely on the ground before our eyes, crushed by brutish Religion, whose dreadful face peered down from the regions of the sky to menace mortal beings, a man of the Greeks[6] was the first who dared raise his human eyes to meet her glance, and the first who stood against her. Neither the repute of the gods, nor the lightning, nor the threatening murmurs of heaven daunted him; instead they roused, all the more, his mind's keen courage to desire to be the first to break through the tightly fixed bars of Nature's gate. Thus the living force of 70

[3] Lines 44–49 give a picture of the gods in the usual Epicurean terms. Lucretius repeats the passage at II. 646–51, where it better fits the context. Many editors omit it here in Book I. In any case a lacuna of unknown length precedes line 50, since the poet there is addressing Memmius. In the lost line or lines he may have urged his patron to give up politics, war, and society.

[4] There is much incidental discussion of the gods in the poem, but nowhere is there a detailed treatment such as seems to be promised here.

[5] In this translation the word "atom" will frequently be used to represent any one of these terms. The Latin noun *atomus,* from a Greek adjective *atomos* meaning "not to be cut," is not found in Lucretius, although it is often used by Cicero.

[6] Epicurus. See Introduction, pp. xxi–xxviii.

his soul prevailed; and his mind and spirit went far beyond the flaming walls of our world, traversing all of unmeasured space. Returning in triumph, he reported to us what can come into being and what cannot, and by what law there is for each thing a power that is limited, and a boundary that is firmly fixed. Therefore Religion in her turn has been hurled down, and is trodden beneath our feet; and his victory has raised us to the sky.

80 In these matters I fear this: that you perhaps may think you are beginning an impious study and entering upon an evil path. But on the contrary:[7] Religion herself has more often been the cause of evil and impious acts. For example, at Aulis the chosen leaders of the Greeks—the foremost of men—foully defiled the altar of virgin Diana with the blood of Iphianassa.[8] When the fillet was bound about her maiden locks and hung down equally over each cheek; when she saw her wretched father standing 90 close to her before the altar, the priests beside him hiding the knife, and his subjects pouring forth tears as they looked at her —then her knees failed her and, silent in her fear, she sought the ground. At such a time it could be of little aid to the poor girl that she had been first to call the king by the name of father. For, lifted by men's hands, she was led trembling to the altar— not that when the ritual was over she might be escorted by the clear-sounding marriage hymn, but that, at the very time of marriage, this pure girl might foully fall, an unhappy victim offered 100 by the hand of her father to gain for the fleet a well-omened and propitious departure. So great are the evils to which Religion has been able to persuade.

But the time will come when you yourself, overcome by the priests' terrifying words, will seek to free yourself from us; and naturally, for how many empty tales can they fashion for you, able to overthrow your reasoned plans for life and to confuse in fear all your fortunes! They act with reason, for if men were to

[7] See Epicurus, *Letter to Menoeceus* 123–27a, and *Principal Doctrines* I, II, XII.

[8] More commonly called Iphigenia.

see that there is a fixed end to their troubles, they would be able to find some way of resisting the threats that the priests base upon man's religious scruples; but now men have neither means nor opportunity for resisting, since they must fear eternal punishment in death. For men do not know the nature of the soul, whether it is born with us or is added to us from without at birth; nor do they know whether it perishes along with us, destroyed by death, or goes to visit the vast and gloomy deeps of Orcus, or else, by divine power, finds its way into creatures of another sort as our Ennius sang, who was first to bring from charming Helicon a wreath of undying foliage, to shine brightly among the Italian races of men. Yet Ennius in his immortal verses also taught that the Acherusian regions do exist, the abode neither of our souls nor of our bodies, but of ghosts wondrously pale. He said, too, that the spirit of ever-famous Homer rose up to him from this place, and, pouring forth salt tears, began to explain the composition of the universe.[9] Therefore we must not only consider the bodies above us, explaining on what principle the sun and the moon follow their courses and by what force each thing on earth takes place; but also, and especially, we must discover by acute reasoning whence the spirit and the mind come into being and what those things are that meet us—both when we are awake but weakened by disease and when we are buried in sleep—and so terrify our minds that we seem to see and hear, face to face, those who have died and whose bones the earth embraces.[10]

110

120

130

It does not escape my mind that it is difficult to set forth clearly in Latin verse the obscure discoveries of the Greeks,

[9] If we suppose Ennius to have presented a consistent view of man's fate after death, it would appear to have been that the soul of a man passed into another living creature, either man or beast, that his body perished, and that a third something, a wondrously pale ghost, passed to the lower world. It is more probable, however, that the poet sometimes assumed transmigration as the normal fate, and at other times pictured a colorless and empty post-existence like that which Homer describes, or like the Sheol of the early Hebrews.

[10] The spirit and mind are discussed, and the arguments for their mor-

especially since in discussing many of these I must make use of strange terms because of the poverty of our language and the
140 novelty of my subject. Yet your worth and the hoped-for pleasure of sweet friendship[11] persuade me to endure any hardship, and encourage me to spend the quiet nights without sleep as I seek the words and the poetry with which, at length, I may be able to spread before your mind clear lights by which you may see deeply into hidden matters.

II. The Atomic Theory: General Principles

146–482

No thing can be created from nothing, nor can matter be destroyed; Nature wastes nothing, and the formation of the new depends on the destruction of the old. Particles of matter exist that we cannot see, and there is void in objects that seem to be solid. The existence of matter is proved by sensation; void is necessary to the existence and motion of matter; all other things are accidents or properties of these two.

This terror, this darkness of the soul, must be dispelled neither by the rays of the sun nor by the bright weapons of the day, but by an understanding of Nature's outer form and inner
150 laws. Our study will begin with this principle: matter is never brought into existence by divine aid out of nothing.[12] Indeed, such dread as we described above grips all mortals because, see-

---

tality presented, in Book III. In Book IV sensation is explained as due to thin films, which are given off in rapid succession from the surfaces of objects, pass through the air, and impinge on the sense organs. Some such films survive long after the objects from which they came have perished. These solitary films wandering at random are too weak to stir our senses, but they may act directly on the mind. When we are awake and in normal health, our reason rejects such films; but when we are asleep or ill, we may accept them and believe that we "see and hear, face to face, those who have died."

[11] For the value placed on friendship by Epicurus, see *Principal Doctrines* XXVII and XXVIII.

[12] See Epicurus, *Letter to Herodotus* 38c; the antitheological turn is not found in Epicurus' *Letter*, but it is characteristic of Lucretius.

ing many phenomena of earth and sky whose causes they can in no wise understand, they believe that these occur by divine power. Therefore, when we have seen that no thing can be created from nothing, we shall see our way more clearly to that which we are seeking: the source out of which each thing can be created, and the manner in which each comes into existence without the aid of the gods.

If things were made from nothing, any kind could spring from any source, and none would need a seed.[13] In the first place, men would come from the sea, and the scaly fish from the land; birds would be hatched from the open sky; cattle and other domestic animals, and wild beasts of every kind, would occupy farmland and wilderness alike if birth were bound by no rule. The fruits upon the trees would not remain the same but would be changed, and any tree might bear any fruit. Indeed, if each thing had not its specific life-giving bodies, in what way could the source from which each comes be limited? But since each kind is in fact produced from specific seeds, each is born and comes forth into the shores of light from that place where its own matter and its own first seeds are present. Therefore all things cannot be born from all, for the reason that separate and distinct powers exist in particular things. 160 170

Next, why do we see the rose produced in the spring and the grain in the heat of the summer; why does the vine bear fruit when autumn invites? Is it not because, when the prescribed seeds of things have come together at their proper time, then whatever is being created comes forth while the favorable season is at hand, and it is safe for the life-giving earth to send out its tender offspring into the shores of light? But if they were produced from nothing, they would appear suddenly, at irregular times and in seasons of the year not proper to them; for in that 180

[13] Although Lucretius is undertaking to prove that in nature no thing is ever created from nothing, his examples go a step beyond this. A rose blooms only on the proper bush at the proper season. It must therefore be formed of particles of a certain kind under conditions that favor the union of these particles. *A fortiori*, the rose cannot have come into existence without the previous existence of matter of some kind.

case there would be no first seeds whose life-giving combinations an unfavorable season could prevent.

Then too, the growth of things would not require a period of time for the gathering together of matter, if growth could take place from nothing. Young men would be formed suddenly from small infants; and groves of trees would spring from the earth and grow up in a moment. It is clear that none of these things occur, since all things actually grow little by little, preserving their nature as they grow, as is proper if each grows from
190 seed of a prescribed kind. From this you may know that each takes its growth and nourishment from matter peculiar to itself.

Furthermore, the earth cannot send forth its welcome fruits without the regular showers of the year, nor can animals if kept from food propagate their kind and maintain life. You may therefore rather believe that there are many seeds common to many things (as we see many letters common to many words) than that anything can exist without first bodies.

200 Next, why is it that Nature cannot produce men so great that they can wade on foot across the sea, uproot mighty mountains with their hands, and outlive many mortal generations, unless it be because there is a definite type of matter assigned each thing for its growth, which controls what can come into being? Thus each thing needs a seed from which it can be formed and sent out into the gentle breath of the air; one must confess, then, that no thing can be made from nothing.

Lastly, since we see that cultivated land is superior to un-
210 cultivated and returns better fruits for our labor, it is clear that there are first beginnings of things in the earth, which we rouse to birth as we turn the fertile clods with the plowshare, cultivating the surface of the land. If there were no such seeds, you would see much better things grow of their own accord, without our labor.

Our next principle is this:[14] Nature dissolves each thing into its own seeds, and she does not reduce any thing to nothing. If a

[14] See Epicurus, *Letter to Herodotus* 39a. The two principles are obviously two sides of one of the contemporary bases of conventional physics: the law of the indestructibility of matter.

thing were wholly mortal, it might be snatched away from our eyes and perish in an instant. There would be no need for a force capable of causing the breaking up of the parts and of dissolving 220 their bonds. But as it is, since each thing consists of eternal matter, Nature does not permit us to see the destruction of a thing until it meets a force great enough to shatter it by a blow or to dissolve it by penetrating its empty spaces.[15]

And if, when time removes things because of their age, she destroys them completely and consumes all their matter, whence does Venus restore the various living creatures, each after its kind, to the light of life? And after they have been restored, from what does the wonder-working earth furnish each with its proper food, nourishing it and causing it to grow? From 230 what do the springs within or the rivers far outside supply the sea? Whence does the aether feed the stars? For the limitless period of time that is past must have consumed all things of mortal body; but if throughout that time, throughout all the ages that are gone, there has been something from which this world has been renewed and maintained, surely that something is endowed with an ageless body. It is therefore impossible that any thing can be changed into nothing.

Next, the same force and the same cause would destroy all things together unless eternal matter, more or less closely inter- 240 woven, preserved them; a touch would certainly be sufficient cause for destruction, for there would be no seeds of eternal body whose interweaving only an appropriate force could dissolve.[16] But as it is, because the bonds between the atoms differ[17] and matter itself is eternal, a thing remains with its body un-

[15] As will be seen below (I. 532–39), one of the reasons why the atom is indestructible is that it contains no void. Since all objects of the sensible world are made up of atoms moving in the void, they contain empty spaces into which foreign matter may penetrate and cause their dissolution.

[16] The meaning of lines 242–43 is obscure. Two other translations are possible: "for any force would be enough to dissolve the fabric of things in which there was nothing of eternal body," and "for none of these things, whose structure any force would be enough to dissolve, could be of eternal body."

[17] The bonds between the atoms differ because the atoms are of different shapes (II. 100–104).

injured until assailed by a force whose keenness is a match for its own structure. Therefore no thing is reduced to nothing, but all things when destroyed change back into particles of matter.

250 Finally, the rains perish when Father Aether sends them down into the bosom of Mother Earth; yet the shining crops rise up, the branches grow green on the trees, and the trees themselves become laden with fruit. In this way our race and the races of wild beasts are nourished. From this we see cities flourishing, happy in their children, and the leafy woods on every side becoming melodious with new-hatched birds. Because of this, sleek cattle lie down when weary amid the abundant pastures, and the gleaming white fluid of milk drops from their well-filled 260 udders. Thanks to this, their weak-limbed young sport playfully through the tender grass, their youthful souls excited by the milk as if by wine. Thus the objects of the visible world are not altogether destroyed, since Nature makes one thing from another; nor does she permit anything to come to birth without being assisted in this by the death of something else.

Now—since I have shown that things cannot be formed out of nothing and likewise that, when once they have been formed, they cannot be reduced to nothing—lest perhaps you begin to doubt my words because the first beginnings of things cannot be seen with the eyes, learn next of bodies which you must con- 270 fess have physical existence, although they are invisible.[18]

Let us begin with the wind: when it has been roused to violence, it beats upon the sea, overwhelms great ships, and scatters the clouds; at times it passes over the plains in a rushing whirlwind, and strews them with great trees; it vexes the highest mountains with forest-destroying blasts. With such great tumult does the wind blow wildly, and rage with noisy menace. Truly, then, invisible particles of air do exist: they sweep the sea, the lands, and the clouds of heaven, assailing them with sudden 280 whirlwinds and laying them waste; they flow and cause damage

[18] The atoms are much smaller than the particles whose existence is being demonstrated here; all that Lucretius is showing now is that invisible bodies do exist.

in the same way as does the liquid water carried along in an overflowing river, swollen by the mighty flood that gushes from the high mountains after a great rain. It tosses branches and entire trees from the forests; strong bridges cannot withstand the sudden violence of the rushing water; the stream, roiled by the great rain, throws itself with violence upon the strong piers; it causes destruction with a mighty roar, and rolls and batters beneath its waves huge rocks and whatever opposes its waters. Thus the currents of the wind, too, must be moved. Like a strong river, when they have set their course in any direction, they roll things before them and overwhelm them with repeated blasts; and sometimes they snatch them up in a whirlwind and swiftly carry them away in a swirling eddy. Therefore I say again and yet again that invisible particles of wind do exist, since we find that, in what they do and in the manner in which they act, the winds rival the great streams that we can see. 290

Then, too, we are conscious of various odors given off by objects, yet we never see the odors coming to our nostrils. We do not behold heat, nor can we recognize cold with our eyes, nor is it our habit to see voices; yet all these must be of corporeal nature because they can touch our senses, for nothing except body can touch or be touched.[19] Moreover, garments hung out on the wave-beaten shore grow damp, and then become dry if spread in the sun; but we see neither in what way the moisture of the water has come into them, nor in what way it has fled before the heat. Therefore moisture is divided into small parts that the eyes can in no way behold. Indeed, after many annual circuits of the sun the ring upon the finger imperceptibly becomes thin by being worn; the drops falling from the eaves hollow out the stone; without our perceiving it the curved plowshare, though it be of iron, becomes diminished in the fields. We see the stone pavements of the streets worn away by the feet of the crowd, and the bronze statues beside the city gates show right hands that are being worn thin by the repeated touch of those who salute them as they pass. When these things have been 300 310

[19] That all sensation is due to contact and that contact is possible only for corporeal existences will be developed in detail in Book IV.

320 rubbed away, we see that they have become less; but the nature of vision has jealously prevented our seeing what particles are removed in any given period of time. In short, the vision of our eyes, however it may strain to do so, cannot behold that which time and Nature add little by little to living things, causing them to grow slowly; nor can you see what is lost in each moment by that which is growing old through time and wasting, or by the rock hanging over the sea, being eaten by the bitter brine. Nature, then, carries on her affairs by means of invisible particles.

330 Yet everything is not held packed full of corporeal matter, for there is void in things.[20] This knowledge will be useful to you in many ways, and will prevent you in ignorance from doubting and being always at a loss in regard to the universe and from distrusting my words. For this reason I say again, void does exist, space that is empty and to which our senses do not respond. If there were no void, objects could not be moved in any way; for that which is the essential property of matter, namely to obstruct and oppose, would always be present everywhere. It would therefore be impossible for any object to move from its place, since no 340 one thing would be first to yield. But as it is, throughout the seas, the lands, and the heights of heaven we perceive many things before our eyes moving in many ways and various manners. If there were no empty space, the result would not be that things would be deprived of restless motion and exist without it, but rather they would not have come into existence at all, since matter, pressed together from every side, would have remained at rest.[21]

20 Or "void is among the things that exist." Lucretius, like his master, is not consistent in the use of the term here translated "void." Sometimes it is the space in objects or outside them not occupied by atoms; and at other times it is all space, whether or not temporarily occupied by the ever-moving atoms. See Epicurus, *Letter to Herodotus* 39b–40a.

21 Parmenides, to whom motion was an illusion, supposed that the real world was a single, solid, spherical mass, in which motion was impossible, and outside of which there was nothing, not even empty space. See Introduction, pp. xi–xii.

Furthermore, however solid you suppose objects to be, you will understand from what follows that they are of open texture. Water seeps through the rock of caves, and the entire cave weeps with copious tears.[22] Food divides and makes its way into every living body. Trees grow, bearing fruit in the proper season, because food is distributed from the lowest roots into the whole tree through the trunk and all the branches. Voices fly through walls of houses and pass into closed rooms, and numbing cold makes its way to the bones.[23] There is no way in which you would see these things happen, if there were not empty spaces through which these several bodies could pass. 350

Next, why do we see that some objects weigh more than others, although they are of no greater size? If there were as much matter in a ball of wool as in one of lead, it would indeed weigh the same, since it is a property of matter to cause all things to press downward, while on the contrary empty space is always without weight. Therefore that which is of equal size and is seen to be lighter surely gives evidence that it has more void within itself. The heavier thing, on the other hand, asserts that there is more matter within itself and less void. Therefore that which we are seeking with keen mind does certainly exist; we call it void. 360

That you may not be drawn aside from the truth, I am forced at this point to raise and ănswer an argument falsely framed by certain philosophers.[24] They say that, as scaly fish struggle forward, the water yields and opens paths for them through the liquid, and that this is possible because the fish leave spaces behind themselves into which the yielding waves flow together. They say that other things too can move in this way, exchanging places within a group even though all space is full. Truly this 370

[22] Lucretius may be thinking of springs of water in caves; but the last words suggest that he has in mind and is wrongly explaining the drops formed by condensation on cold stone walls when warm moist air enters a cave from without.

[23] To Lucretius, sound and heat are both corporeal.

[24] Lucretius is probably thinking of his usual opponents, the Stoics; but other schools agreed with them in denying real existence to empty space.

whole argument has been accepted because of false reasoning. For how will the fish be able to advance if the water has not al-
380 ready given them space? Into what place can the waves withdraw when the fish are unable to move? Thus either each body must be deprived of motion, or we must admit that void does exist mixed among things, as a result of which each separate thing may begin to move.

Finally, if two broad bodies that have been united suddenly spring apart, certainly air must occupy the whole empty space now formed between the bodies. However rapid the current with which the air flows together, the whole space cannot be
390 filled at one time, for the air must occupy first one part and then another, until finally all parts are filled. But if anyone believes that, when the bodies have separated, the space is filled because the air condenses,[25] he is wrong; for then an empty space, which did not exist before, is formed, and likewise a previously existing empty space is filled, and air cannot be made dense and thin in this way. Even if we grant this possibility, it could not, I believe, withdraw into itself and bring its parts into one without empty space.[26]

For these reasons, however much you may cause delay by arguing, you must at length admit that there is void in things.
400 I can scrape together belief in my words by presenting you with many additional arguments, but for your keen mind these few indications are enough to let you recognize the remaining argu-

[25] That is, the space is filled because the air which had occupied the space between the bodies on some previous occasion when they were separated was condensed when they were brought together, and now that they are again separated this same air becomes rarefied and fills all the space.

[26] Lucretius denies that such condensation or compression of air and its subsequent expansion or rarefaction are possible; but the last two sentences of the paragraph are far from clear. The last part of the first of these may mean either "For then [at the moment of separation] an empty space [between the bodies], which did not exist before, is formed, and likewise a previously existing empty space [outside the bodies, into which they move] is filled"; or "For in that case [whenever air is condensed] an empty space, which did not exist before, is formed, and likewise [whenever air is expanded] a previously existing empty space is filled."

ments for yourself. As dogs very often find by their sense of smell the leaf-covered lair of a mountain-ranging beast, if once they have come upon its clearly marked track, so in matters of this sort you yourself will be able to follow from one point to another, finding your way into secret and obscure places and dragging the truth from them. If, however, you slacken and turn 410 aside even a little from the task, I can make you a straightforward promise, Memmius: my sweet tongue will pour forth from the great springs of my overflowing heart such generous draughts that I fear that slow old age may creep through our limbs and unfasten the bonds of life before the whole wealth of my arguments about any single point has been sent through your ears by my verses.

But to resume weaving with words the web I have begun, all Nature as it is in itself is made up of two things. For there are 420 bodies of matter, and there is the void in which these bodies exist, and through which they move in their various courses. The senses that are common to all men indicate that matter exists. Unless confidence in sensation is first firmly established, there will be nothing by reference to which our reason can reach any conclusions regarding things not perceived by the senses.[27] Then, if there were no space or room, which we call void, there would be no place in which the bodies of matter could exist, and nowhere at all for them to move in their various courses, as we have already pointed out above. Moreover, there is nothing 430 that you can say is separate from all body and apart from void and which might be discovered as a third basic element, for whatever really exists must be something in itself. If to the slightest degree it is subject to the sense of touch, it will increase the sum of matter—it makes no difference how great or small the addition, providing that it exists—and will belong to that total. If it is something not subject to touch, unable to prevent any moving object from passing through it in any direction,

[27] For the importance of sensation as the basis of knowledge, see Diogenes Laertius, *Life of Epicurus* 31a–32, and notes in my translation of Epicurus ("Library of Liberal Arts", No. 141).

440 truly it will be that which we call empty void. Moreover, whatever has existence in itself must, on the one hand, either act in some way on other things or submit to the action of the things that act on it; or, on the other hand, it must be such that things can exist and action take place in it. But nothing that lacks bodily nature can act or be acted on, and nothing can offer place except space and void. Therefore in addition to void and body we admit to the list of things no third independent element, either falling at any time within the range of our senses or discoverable by anyone through the reasoning power of the mind. All things else that we speak of as existing you will find on ex-
450 amination are either properties or accidents of these two.[28]

A property of a thing is that which can under no conditions be separated from the thing or placed by itself without the complete destruction of both the property and the thing.[29] For example, weight is a property of rocks; heat, of fire; fluidity, of water; tangibility, of matter in general; intangibility, of the void. On the other hand, slavery, poverty, wealth, liberty, war, peace, and other things whose addition or removal leaves unchanged the essential nature of the possessor are usually and properly called accidents. Likewise, time does not exist by itself, but from the things[30] themselves a feeling arises by which we
460 distinguish what has taken place in the past, what now exists, and what may follow hereafter. We must maintain that no one perceives time in itself apart from the motion or immobility of matter.[31] Next, when men say that "the rape of Helen" or "the defeat of the people of Troy in war" exists,[32] we must be careful

[28] See Epicurus, *Letter to Herodotus* 40b.

[29] Compare the much fuller treatment of properties and accidents in Epicurus, *Letter to Herodotus* 68b–73a.

[30] "Things" here must include events and actions, which are themselves accidents.

[31] The Stoic insistence on the real existence of time accounts for the vigor of Lucretius' argument.

[32] This caution is especially necessary since a Latin phrase such as *Troia capta est,* which normally means "Troy was captured," or "Troy has been captured," can by a change of emphasis be made to mean "captured Troy exists."

lest they cause us to admit that the actions in themselves have real existence, even now that the generations of men of whom they were accidents have been snatched away forever by the passage of time; for one may call whatever has happened an accident either of its place or of space itself. Certainly, if there had been no corporeal matter and if the place and space in which every event occurs had not existed, the flame of love which, fanned by the beauty of Helen, glowed in the heart of the Trojan Paris would never have kindled the illustrious struggle of cruel war; nor would the wooden horse, giving birth to Greeks in the night, have set fire to Pergamum while the Trojans knew it not. Thus you may say that no action whatever exists or has being in the same sense as does matter, and that actions are not spoken of as existing in the same way as is the void. You may more properly call actions the accidents of the corporeal things to which they happen and of the places in which the several actions occur. 470 480

III. The Atom

483–634

Matter exists in the form of atoms and combinations of atoms. Void and matter are mutually exclusive; matter is solid and eternal. No void exists in the atom; hence it is both indestructible and indivisible. It does consist of least parts, however; but these have never existed separately.

In the next place, matter consists partly of the first beginnings of things, and partly of what results from the combination of these.[33] As for these first beginnings or atoms, no force can destroy them; they survive to the end because their bodies are solid. Yet it seems difficult to believe that any material thing can be found which has a solid body. The thunderbolt of heaven passes through the walls of houses, and so do shouts and voices. 490

[33] For the whole section on the nature of the atom (lines 483–598), see Epicurus, *Letter to Herodotus* 40c–41a.

Iron becomes white-hot in fire, rocks break apart in the fiercely flaming heat, and hard gold is melted and dissolved in the furnace. Bronze is overcome and melted like ice by the flame, and warmth and penetrating cold pass through silver.[34] Indeed, when we have been holding cups in our hands in due form, we have felt heat or cold as the liquid has been poured in from above. Thus we see that there is nothing solid among sensible
500 things. Yet pay attention while I show you in a few verses that —as the true theory of the composition of the universe compels —there are bodies composed of solid and eternal matter, bodies that we are showing to be the seeds and first beginnings of things, from which the whole sum of Nature has been created and now exists.

In the first place, since we have discovered the existence of two separate things very unlike each other, namely matter and the void in which all things take place, it necessarily follows that each of these must exist independently, without either one adulterating the other. For wherever there is the empty space that we call void, there no matter is; and wherever matter ex-
510 tends, there empty space does not in any way exist. The primary bodies of matter, then, are solid and without void. Moreover, since there is void within objects that have been created, there must be solid matter around this void. You cannot show by right reasoning that anything can conceal void and hold it within its own structure, unless you admit that what encloses the void is solid. Now that which is able to surround the void within objects can be nothing other than a complex of matter. Therefore matter, which is of solid composition, can be eternal although all other things are dissolved.

520 Next, if there were nothing that was empty and void, everything would be solid. On the other hand, unless there were definite bodies that fill whatever places they occupy, the universe would consist of void, empty space. Since the universe is neither

[34] Sound, heat, and cold are all corporeal. Iron and stone become hot when particles of heat penetrate them, and they may melt or burst if too many such particles enter.

wholly full nor wholly empty, it follows that matter has been set apart from void discretely; thus there exist definite bodies, marking off empty space from full.

These atoms can neither be disintegrated when assailed by blows from without, nor be penetrated and unwoven from within, nor yet can they fail when attacked in any other way, 530 as we have already shown you above.[35] For it is seen that whatever contains no void can neither be crushed, nor broken, nor divided into two parts by cutting; nor can it receive moisture, disruptive cold, or penetrating fire, the means by which all created things are brought to an end. The more void an object contains, the more easily it is attacked by these means and falls in utter ruin. Therefore, if the first bodies are solid and without void as I have shown them to be, they must be eternal. 540

Moreover, unless matter had been eternal, before now every single thing would have been completely reduced to nothing, and every object that we now see would have been re-formed out of nothing. But since I have shown above[36] that neither can anything be created from nothing nor can anything that has been made be reduced to nothing, there must be atoms that cannot be destroyed, into which each object can be resolved when its last day comes, so that matter may be at hand for forming new objects and repairing old ones. The atoms therefore are of solid oneness; in no other way can they have been preserved through eternity from an unlimited past and now be creating and re- 550 newing things.

Next, if Nature had established no limit to the breaking up of things, the bodies of matter would have been so reduced by the destruction of the past that nothing could now be formed from them and within a fixed time reach its perfection, for we see that any object can be broken up more rapidly than it can be formed again. For this reason that which the long, limitless period of all past time, destroying and dissolving, had now

[35] Lucretius has not shown this specifically in regard to the atom, but it follows from the whole section on the indestructibility of matter, lines 215–64.

[36] See lines 149–264.

560 broken could never be put together in what time remains. But as it is, a definite limit to the process of breaking has surely been established, since we see that each object is made anew and that there is a definite period for each, according to its kind, within which it can attain complete development.[a]

Furthermore, although atoms of matter are most solid, we can explain how all things that are soft—air, water, earth, and fire[37]—are made, and can account for their behavior, once we 570 admit that void is mingled in created things. But on the other hand, if it is assumed that the atoms are soft, it will not be in any way possible to explain from what matter strong stones and iron can be made, for all nature will be completely without any element of solidity. Atoms, then, are powerful because of their solid oneness; through their more closely-packed unions all objects can be made firm and display great might.

Next, even if no limit has been established for the division of created things, we must still assume that each kind of atom for the making of the things that now exist has actually survived 580 from infinite time, and has not yet been attacked by any danger. But if we are assuming that the atoms are of such nature that they may be broken up,[38] it is impossible that they have been able to survive through infinite time when subject throughout that time to countless blows.

Finally, since there is a limit assigned to the growth and life of creatures according to their kinds; since the laws of Nature have decreed what each may and may not do, and nothing is changed; and since everything is so predetermined that all the 590 various birds, according to their kinds, show that the marking of each bird is fixed in its matter—truly these creatures must

[a] For this and all subsequent references indicated by superior letters, see Appendix, pp. 249–85.

[37] Since these four are the basic elements of Empedocles, we can see that Lucretius already has in mind his criticism of that philosopher (lines 705–829). Far from being basic elements for Lucretius, they are examples of what the ultimate particles cannot be.

[38] As they would be broken up if subject to infinite division. As in the preceding paragraph Lucretius had Empedocles in mind, so here he is thinking of Anaxagoras (see lines 830–920).

also have a substance of unchanging nature. For if the atoms could be overcome and changed in any way, it would be uncertain what could come into being and what could not, and on what basis there was a limited power and a firmly fixed boundary for each, nor could the offspring, generation by generation, so many times repeat the nature, habits, mode of life, and actions of the parents.

Next, since there is an extreme point of that atom which our senses cannot discern, this point surely is without parts and is of the least possible magnitude;[b] and it never has been separated by itself nor shall it be hereafter, since it itself is a part, the primary and single part, of the atom. Other similar parts in order, one after another in close-packed formation, make up completely the nature of the atom. Since these least parts cannot exist by themselves, they must cling together in the atom, from which they can in no way be separated. The atoms are therefore of solid oneness, held together by the close-packed union of these least parts, not having been formed by their coming together but rather strong in eternal oneness. Nature, preserving the seeds for things, does not permit that anything be torn away from the atom, or that the atom be made less. 600 610

Moreover, unless there is something that is least, every smallest body will consist of infinite parts, since indeed the half part of a half will always have its own half part and there will be no limit to this division. Then what will the difference be between the greatest and the smallest? They will not differ at all, for although the whole universe is absolutely unlimited, nevertheless the parts that are least will like it consist of infinite parts.[c] But since true reason revolts against this and denies that the mind can believe it, you must yield and agree that there are things that have no parts and are of the least possible magnitude. Since these least parts do exist, you must also admit the existence of atoms, solid and eternal.[39] 620

If Nature, the creator of the universe, were accustomed to force all things to be resolved into their least parts, this same 630

[39] Since the least parts exist only as parts of the atom, the existence of the former proves that of the latter.

Nature would not now be mighty enough to form anything from them, for the reason that whatever has no parts cannot have the attributes that life-giving matter must have—the various unions, weights, blows, meetings, and motions through which all is accomplished.[40]

IV. Earlier Philosophers

635–920

Heraclitus, Empedocles, and Anaxagoras were all mistaken in their account of the source of all created things. Heraclitus' fire could not create such a variety of things without itself being changed. If Empedocles' four basic substances, which are of the same order as sensible objects, undergo change, they are not elements; if they retain their own natures, they can form only mixtures, not new substances. The "seeds" of Anaxagoras are too fragile to be first beginnings. It is none of these, but the atom, which is the source of all created matter.

For this very reason those who believe that the basic material of the world is fire and that the universe is made up of fire alone have obviously strayed far from the truth. The first to enter the lists as their leader is Heraclitus,[41] whose obscure sayings have 640 won him fame among the foolish rather than among serious Greeks who seek the truth. Indeed, the senseless particularly admire and love all that they see hiding behind distorted words, and they accept as true whatever pleases the ears and has been painted over with charming sound. How, I ask you, could cre-

[40] The important word is "various." If the least parts could exist separately, they would all be the same and would have the same unions, weights, etc.; and from this homogeneous mass of identical particles Nature, Lucretius says, could not form the variegated world we see about us. The permanent differences of the atoms and the way in which these differences control the formation of complexes of atoms will be discussed in Book II.

[41] For the system of Heraclitus, see Introduction, pp. x–xi. Lucretius is actually aiming much of what follows at his own rivals, the Stoics (the "senseless" of line 641), rather than at Heraclitus.

ated things be of so many kinds if they had been formed from simple fire alone? It would be of no use that hot fire be made dense or thin if the parts of fire have the same nature as the whole; for the heat would only be more intense when the parts 650 were brought together, and less intense again when they were separated and scattered. Beyond this there is nothing that you can imagine brought about in such a way; far less could so great a variety of things be composed of thick and thin fire. Here is another point: if they should assume that void is mingled in objects, fire could become thick and thin, but because they see many obstacles before them, they keep quiet[42] and shrink from supposing that there is empty space within objects. While avoiding a hill, they lose the true path and again fail to see 660 that if void is removed from matter, everything becomes solid and a single body is formed from all, which single body can emit nothing from itself in the way in which hot fire sends forth light and heat. You can therefore see that fire is not made of parts closely bound together.[43]

But if perhaps they think that another way is possible and that particles of fire are extinguished and change their substance when they are condensed (at least if they assume that this happens to all the particles without exception), then all the fire will be completely reduced to nothing, and whatever is formed will be created from nothing. For whenever a thing is changed 670 and departs from its proper limits, that is at once the death of that which was before.[44] It is therefore necessary that something of the fire survive unchanged; otherwise you are forced to assume that all sensible things are reduced utterly to nothing and that the whole store of things that are flourishing has been reborn

42 Reading *mussant* for the *muse* of the better mss. Should we read *quae sint* with Martin, we would translate: "but because they see before them many things that are obstacles and shrink from supposing that there is empty space within objects, while avoiding a hill, they lose the true path. . . ."

43 The fact that fire sends out part of itself as heat shows that it is subject to division and therefore, according to Lucretius, contains void. Anything containing void cannot, in his view, be a permanent basic substance.

44 Lines 670–71 appear again at I. 792–93, II. 753–54, and III. 519–20.

from nothing.[45] But in fact, since there are certain very definite bodies which always preserve the same nature, bodies by whose departure, addition, and transposition things alter their nature and objects change themselves, surely these bodies of which
680 things consist are not like fire. It is of no importance that certain particles of fire separate and go away and others are added, and that some of them change their order, as long as they all retain heat as their essential quality; for whatever is formed of them will be in every respect fire. The truth is, I believe, as follows: there do exist certain particles whose meetings, motions, order, position, and shape create fire, and when their order is changed they change the nature of what they create; but they are not like fire nor like any of the other things which can throw off bodies that come to our senses, and which can arouse sensation by contact.

690 Next, it is sheer madness to say, as this man does, that all things are fire and that except for fire none of the things of sense has real existence. Basing his argument on the senses, he fights against the senses, and destroys the agency upon which all belief depends and through which the very thing that he calls fire is known to him. He believes that the senses are right when they recognize fire, but he does not believe their evidence concerning other things that are no less clear than fire. This seems to me not only useless but mad. For to what else shall we refer?
700 What can we have more sure than the senses themselves by which to discern the true and the false? Indeed, is there any more reason to reject everything else and recognize only fire than to deny the existence of fire and assume that of some other thing? Clearly it is equally mad to claim either of these.

For these reasons, those who think that the basic substance of sensible objects is fire and that the universe can consist of fire, and those who have supposed that air is the first material for forming things, or that water by itself fashions them, or that
710 earth makes everything and is changed into every manner of being—all these have clearly wandered far from the truth. This

[45] See Epicurus, *Letter to Herodotus* 54.

is equally true of those who double the first beginnings, joining air to fire or earth to water, and of those who think that the whole universe can grow from four elements, namely, from fire, earth, air, and water.[46]

Chief among this latter group is Empedocles of Acragas,[47] born within the triangular boundaries of that island around which the Ionian Sea flows in mighty curves as it sprinkles the shores with brine from its gray waves, while the ocean with its 720 greedy current separates the island's shores from the coasts of Italy by a narrow strait. Here is the dreaded Charybdis, and here the murmurs of Aetna warn that she is again gathering together her flaming wrath, so that her violence may a second time vomit forth the fires that break from her jaws, raising her flashing lightnings again to heaven. Although this land seems to mankind great and wonderful in many ways, and is said to be worthy of being visited,[48] although it is opulent in good things and strengthened with a great force of men; yet it seems to have had within itself nothing more famous than this man, nothing more 730 holy, wonderful, or beloved. Indeed, such songs[49] sounded forth from his godlike heart and proclaimed his glorious discoveries that he seems hardly to have been of mortal stock. Truly he and the others whom we mentioned above, men far inferior to him on many counts and of much less worth, discovered many things in noble and godlike fashion, and uttered responses as if from

[46] Water was the basic substance in the theory of the first of the monists, Thales; air in that of Anaximenes; and earth and water in that of Xenophanes. The familiar four elements belong to the system of Empedocles. For this whole development, see Introduction, pp. ix–xiv.

[47] For Empedocles, see Introduction, pp. xii–xiv. Actually only lines 770–81 and 803–29 are directed against what we suppose to have been the particular teachings of this philosopher. Most of the rest applies to the theories of everyone before Leucippus, with the exception of Parmenides.

[48] There may be an autobiographical note to these words. If so we can add to our scanty knowledge of the poet's life the fact that he had never visited Sicily, and we may conjecture that he was no traveler.

[49] Empedocles' poem *On Nature,* of which some fragments are extant (Diels, *Fragmente,* 31 B 1–111), may have served Lucretius as a model, and it certainly gave him a warrant for his use of verse. This may account for the warmth of his praise of the Sicilian.

a shrine deep within their hearts in fashion more holy and with reason more certain than does the Pythia, who speaks from the 740 tripod and laurel of Phoebus. Nevertheless in explaining the first beginnings of things they met with disaster; great as they were, into great ruin they fell.

In the first place, they admitted motion although they had excluded void from Nature; and they assumed the existence of things that are soft and of open texture, such as air, sunlight, rain, earth, animals, fruits, yet did not mix void in the structure of these things. Then, they taught that there is no end at all to the cutting up of things and no limit set to their division, and that there is nothing at all in Nature that is the smallest possible; yet we see that in each visible object there is that extreme 750 point which seems to our senses to be the smallest possible, from which we may conjecture that what the atom, which we cannot see, has as its extreme point is the smallest possible in it as well.[50] Another reason for their failure is that they have assumed as first beginnings soft things, which we see have bodies subject to both birth and death, as a result of which it should follow that the whole universe is being reduced to nothing and the store of things that are flourishing has been reborn from nothing. You will understand by now how far each of these statements is from the truth. Furthermore, their first beginnings are hostile to each other in many ways, and are mutually destruc- 760 tive. Therefore either they will come together and perish, or they will separate as widely as we see lightning, rain, and wind separate when a storm has risen.

Finally, if all things are created from the four elements and are dissolved into them again, how can these four elements be called the first beginnings of things with any more reason than the things in their turn can be called the first beginnings of the four elements? Truly they are being born in alternation and have been exchanging their colors and their whole natures from 770 the beginning of time. But on the other hand, if you believe that the particles of fire and earth, the winds of heaven, and the dew of water come together in such a way that as they unite no

[50] See I. 599–614.

one of them changes its own nature, then truly nothing—neither any breathing thing nor any inanimate body, like a tree—can be formed from these. Indeed, in the complexity of the discordant heap, each element will still display its proper character, and you will see air existing there mixed with earth, and fire mixed with water. The first beginnings that form the objects of sense ought themselves to possess a hidden, invisible nature, so that no quality of theirs may show forth to resist and prevent 780 that which is being formed from being of its own proper kind.[51]

They even start from the sky and its fires, and suppose that fire first changes itself into the breezes of the air, that rain is born from this, and that earth is created from rain; then, in reverse order, that everything is re-created from earth, first water, then air, and finally heat. These do not cease their mutual changing, going from heaven to earth and from earth to the stars of the sky.[d] But first beginnings ought by no means to undergo such changes, since it is necessary that something un- 790 changeable survive lest all things be reduced utterly to nothing; for whenever a thing is changed and departs from its proper limits, this is at once the death of that which was before.[52] Since these four that we named above do undergo such changes, they themselves must be composed of other particles that never change, lest all things be reduced utterly to nothing before your eyes. Must you not rather assume that if bodies endowed with such unchanging nature have by chance formed fire, these same 800 bodies can, a few being added to them or taken from them and their order and motion being changed, make the breezes of the air, and that it is in this way that all things are changed into other things?

[51] See Epicurus, *Letter to Herodotus* 54. Lucretius develops his theory that the atoms possess no secondary qualities at II. 730–990. The atoms have size, shape, and mass, but they lack color, scent, temperature, etc. This is an essential point of difference between the atomic theory and the theories that had preceded it.

[52] Lines 789–93 are repeated at II. 750–54; and lines 792–93 have appeared before at I. 670–71, and will be found again at III. 519–20. They form an axiom or credo of the Epicurean school. See Epicurus, *Letter to Herodotus* 54.

"But it is perfectly clear," you say, "that all living things grow into the breezes of the air and are nourished from the earth, and that grains, trees, and animals could not grow unless the weather favored them with rains at the proper seasons so that the forests quiver as the clouds dissolve, and unless the sun on its part aided them and gave them heat." True enough; and should dry food 810 and water not aid us, our bodies would be wasted away, and all life would depart from our muscles and our bones. Beyond any doubt we are strengthened and nourished by certain particular foods, and every other thing as well is aided by what is proper to it. But it is because many atoms, common to many created things, are mixed together in many ways in Nature that various creatures are nourished by various foods. And in the case of the same atoms, it often makes a great difference with what other atoms they are in contact, in what arrangements they are held, and in what ways they set others in motion and are moved 820 themselves;[53] for the same atoms are found in the sky, the sea, the earth, the rivers, and the sun, and again in grains, trees, and living creatures, but they are mixed with different atoms and are moved in different ways. Why, anywhere in these verses of ours you may see that there are many letters common to many words, yet you must admit that as you pronounce them the verses and words differ from each other in sound and meaning; so much can the letters accomplish simply by changes in their order. But the units that are the first beginnings of things can provide more variations from which sensible things in their several kinds can be created.

830 Now let us examine the *homoeomeria* of Anaxagoras,[54] as the Greeks call his principle. The poverty of our national speech

[53] Lines 817–19, with slight changes in 817, are repeated at three places: I. 908–10, II. 760–62, 1007–1009.

[54] For Anaxagoras, see Introduction, pp. xiv–xv. Lucretius' treatment of his theories is certainly most inadequate. The word "*homoeomeria,*" which is as difficult to translate into English as into Latin, means in the singular "the "the principle of having parts like to itself to each other," or more concisely, "like-partedness." In the plural, it is used of the parts themselves. The word is not found in the extant fragments of Anaxagoras.

does not allow us to name it in our native tongue; but yet it is easy to find words to explain the system itself. Let us begin with what he calls the *homoeomeria* of things: he believes that bones are made up of tiny little bones, and flesh of tiny bits of flesh; that blood is formed from many drops of blood coming together, that gold can be made from separate flakes of gold, that earth 840 grows from bits of earth, and that fire is formed of fires and water of waters. In his thought he pictures the remaining things as formed in the same way. But he does not grant that void exists in any way in Nature,[55] nor does he believe that there is any limit to the divisibility of matter. It seems to me that he errs on both these points, just as did those others of whom we spoke before. Add the fact that he imagines first beginnings that are too weak—if indeed the term "first beginnings" should be used of seeds which have the same qualities as the created things themselves, which like them suffer misfortune and perish, and 850 which nothing holds back from destruction. When they are violently crushed, which of them will be strong enough to escape death under the very jaws of fate? Fire or water or air? Which of these? Blood or bone? Not one, I believe, where each without exception will be as completely mortal as those things that we see clearly are overcome by an appropriate force and perish out of our sight. But I cite again a fact that we have proved before:[56] matter can neither be reduced to nothing nor be created from nothing.

Moreover, since food increases and nourishes the body, we 860 may know that veins, blood, bones, ⟨and muscles are made up of parts different from themselves;⟩[57] or if they say that all foods are of mixed substance and have in themselves small particles of muscles, bones, and veins, as well as bits of blood, it will follow that all food, both solid and liquid too, will itself be thought to consist of things unlike itself, that is, of bones,

[55] Meaning either that he did not admit the existence of void within sensible objects, or that he completely denied the existence of void.

[56] See I. 146–264.

[57] There appears to be at least one line lost here. I translate Lambinus' supplement.

muscles, serum, and blood intermingled. Moreover, if whatever bodies grow from the earth are present in clods of earth, the earth must consist of things unlike itself, that is, of whatever 870 grows from its clods. If we carry the argument further, we can use the same terms. If flame and smoke and ashes are hidden in firewood, the wood must consist of particles unlike itself,[e] that is, of the unlike things that come into existence from the pieces of wood.

There remains one slight chance of escaping from the dilemma, a chance that Anaxagoras grasps for himself: namely, to think that every kind of thing lies hidden mixed in every other kind, but that in the mixture only the one thing is visible whose parts are most numerous, nearest to the surface, and most ex- 880 posed to view. This is, however, far removed from the truth; for on this theory grains of wheat, when broken by the threatening blow of the pestle, ought to show signs of blood or of some of the things that develop in our bodies,[f] and when we grind the grains between millstones, gore ought to ooze out. In the same way grass and water ought to give forth drops, sweet and of a savor like that of the rich milk of sheep; and when clods of earth are broken, herbs of different kinds and grain and leaves ought 890 to be seen hiding, scattered in minute particles amid the earth. Finally, when wood is cut, one ought to see lurking in it ashes, smoke, and tiny sparks of fire. Since clear fact shows that none of this is true, one may know that things are not thus mingled in things; but seeds common to many objects must be hidden mixed in many ways in things.

"But," you say, "it often happens on high mountains that the adjacent tops of tall trees, forced by storm winds, are rubbed 900 against each other until the flower of flame is roused and the treetops blaze." True; nevertheless there is no fire deeply hidden in the wood. Rather, there are many seeds capable of making heat, and when these have come together because of the friction, they create fire in the woods. If the flame already created were concealed within the trees, the fires could not long be hidden, but would destroy the forests everywhere and burn the trees to ashes. Now do you see that, as we said a little earlier, in the case of the same atoms it often makes a great difference with what other atoms they are in contact, in what arrangements they are held, and in what ways they set others in motion and are moved themselves; and do you not see that the same atoms with slight changes among themselves create flames and beams? Just so, the words themselves have letters only slightly different although we pronounce them with distinct sound: "flames" and "beams."[58] Finally, if you think that whatever visible objects you observe can come into being only on the assumption that there are first beginnings of matter endowed with qualities like those of the objects, by this belief you cause the destruction of the first beginnings of things. Shaken with laughter they will make sport of you, and bedew their cheeks and faces with salty tears.[59]

910

920

V. The Infinity of the Universe and the Void

921–1117

The poet here turns to a new subject, emphasizing its difficulty and its importance by a new introduction. The universe must be unlimited, since there is nothing outside the whole to bound it. The void, too, is limitless, and the atoms are infinite in number. Matter does not, as the Stoics believe, tend toward the center; nor does it all fly apart and scatter, as it would have to do if matter were finite and space infinite.

Come now, learn what follows and heed a loftier theme.[g] It does not escape me how obscure these matters are, but a great hope for praise has struck my heart with its sharp goad and at the same time planted within my breast the sweet love of the Muses. Driven by this I boldly cross the remote regions of the

[58] The play on words is a trifle better in the translation than in the original: the Latin words in question, *ignis* and *ligna,* have only three letters in common, while the English words have four.

[59] By giving the atoms the qualities of sensible objects, we make them as perishable as those objects; and if we men are made up of little men, these *homunculi* will laugh at us. See II. 973–90.

Pierides, hitherto untrodden by the foot of man.[60] It gives me joy to draw near the untouched fountains and to drink; it gives
930 me joy to pluck new flowers and to seek a fair wreath for my head from a source from which the Muses hitherto have veiled no brow: first, because I am teaching about mighty matters and pressing on to free man's soul from the tight bonds of superstition; then, because I am composing such clear verses about a dark theme, touching all with the charm of the Muses. This use of poetry does not seem to be without reason. As healers, when they intend to administer bitter wormwood to children, first touch the cup around its brim with the sweet yellow liquid of
940 honey so that the innocent child, tricked as far as his lips, may drink the bitter dose of wormwood and, although deceived, be not betrayed but rather in this way be refreshed and helped to grow strong. So now—because this system of belief usually seems harsh to those who have not tried it and because the common lot of men shrink from it—I have desired to set forth my teachings to you in sweet Pierian song and, as it were, to moisten my doctrine with the sweet honey of the Muses, to see if perhaps in this manner I can hold your attention upon my verses until you
950 see the whole nature of the universe and the form that it possesses.[61]

Since I have demonstrated that the atoms are completely solid and that they fly about forever through time without being hindered,[62] let us now consider whether or not there is any limit to their total number. Likewise in the matter of the void (or place or space) in which we have discovered that all things move, let us see whether this as a whole is firmly limited or is boundless in area and vastly deep.

To proceed, the universe is bounded in no direction, for if
960 it were, some part of it would be outermost. It is obvious that nothing can have an outermost edge unless there is something

[60] Lucretius was the first to compose a philosophical poem in Latin.

[61] Note the order of importance of the objectives: the poet's first purpose is to free men's souls from superstition; his poetry is only a means to this end.

[62] Actually the motion of the atoms is not discussed until the next book, beginning at line 62.

beyond to define it and to make apparent the reason why our senses can trace it no farther. Now since we must agree that there can be nothing external to the whole, the whole does not have such an outermost edge; it therefore lacks end and limit.[63] It makes no difference where in the whole universe you stand; nay, whatever place you occupy, you leave the universe extending equally without limit in every direction. But let us assume for the moment that the universe is limited. If a man advances so that he is at the very edge of the extreme boundary and hurls 970 a swift spear, do you prefer that this spear, hurled with great force, go whither it was sent and fly far, or do you think that something can stop it and stand in its way? You must admit and accept one of these two alternatives; and either of them cuts off all escape and forces you to confess that the universe extends without end. For whether there is something that hinders the spear and prevents it from going where it was sent and reaching its aim, or whether it flies far, it was not sent from the extreme limit. I might continue with this line of argument and, where- 980 ever you place the outmost boundary, ask you what happens in the case of the spear. The result will be that the boundary can be fixed nowhere, and that opportunity for flying always extends the flight.[h]

Furthermore, if the total extent of the entire universe were bounded on every side by fixed limits and were finite, the whole supply of matter would, because of its solid weight, by now have flowed from all sides to the bottom, and no single thing could now be moving beneath the covering sky; in fact the sky itself and the bright sun would not exist, since all matter, hav- 990 ing settled down through endless time, would lie piled in a heap. But as it is, no rest is given to the atoms for the very reason that there is no bottom at all to which the atoms can, as it were, flow and there can come to rest. All things are driven in constant motion from every direction, and atoms sped from infinite space are supplied from below.[64]

Finally, in the visible world we see one object limit another: air forms the boundary for the hills, and mountains for the

[63] See Epicurus, *Letter to Herodotus* 41b.

[64] The motion of the atoms is discussed at II. 62–332. There we are told

1000 air; earth limits the sea and on the other hand the sea bounds all the earth; but there is nothing outside that may bound the whole.[65]

The nature of space and the extent of the abyss are such that bright flashes of lightning, gliding in their courses through a perpetual expanse of time, could not cross it nor even lessen, by their movement, the remaining distance; such is the great abundance of space that lies open for things, extending without limit, in all directions and on every side.[66]

Nature herself prevents the sum of things from being able to 1010 form boundaries for itself; she requires that matter be bounded by void and void by matter, so that in this way she makes the universe infinite by their alternation; otherwise one of the two, not bounded by the other, would extend in its own single nature without end.

⟨If void were limited and the atoms unlimited, there would be no room for the atoms. On the other hand, if we assume that the atoms are finite in number and that the void is infinite in extent,⟩[67] then neither the sea, the earth, the bright expanse of the sky, the human race, nor the sacred bodies of the gods could exist for the brief space of an hour. All their atoms, driven from their combinations, would be carried abroad and scattered throughout the great void; or rather the atoms would never 1020 have united or formed anything, since the widely scattered particles could not have been forced together.

Surely the atoms do not individually put themselves in their proper places as a result of deliberation with conscious intent,

---

that the primary motion is downward with respect to us, but that this downward motion is varied and in part offset by the innate tendency of the individual atom to swerve from its course. From this swerving result the collisions and complex motions of the atoms that create the sensible world.

[65] This sentence concludes the discussion of the infinity of the universe in almost the same terms with which it was begun.

[66] See Epicurus, *Letter to Herodotus* 41b. If the universe, including both atoms and void, is infinite, Lucretius feels that no proof of the infinity of the void is needed.

[67] There appears to be a lacuna after line 1013, and some such supplement as that given is needed by the argument; see the last sentence of Epicurus, *Letter to Herodotus* 42a.

nor have they agreed, we may be sure, what motions they shall produce;[i] but it is because many atoms undergo many changing conditions throughout all space during limitless time, and are moved and stirred by blows, that, after having tried every kind of motion and combination, at length they chance to fall into such groupings as those from which this world of ours is formed and continues to exist.[68] This gathering of matter, preserved through many a great year after it has once been thrown into the 1030 proper motions, brings it about that rivers renew the greedy sea with abundant streams of flowing waters, the lands warmed by the heat of the sun bring forth new fruits, the species of wild beasts that have been produced flourish, and the gliding fires of the heavens live. These things would not take place at all if there could not arise out of infinite space an abundance of matter from which each of these might repair its losses in due time. For just as animals deprived of food lose flesh and waste away, so the world is destined to be dissolved as soon as its supply of 1040 matter, turned aside from its course in some way, has failed. Blows coming from without on every side cannot preserve the whole that has been formed. They can strike repeatedly and prevent the loss of atoms in one part until other atoms come and are able to make good the sum; but from time to time they are forced to leap away and at the same time to allow the atoms space and time for escape, with the result that these atoms can be carried free from the union. Therefore I say again and again, it is necessary that many atoms be supplied; and indeed there 1050 is need of an infinite supply of matter on every side in order that these blows may continue.

While we are on this subject, Memmius, do not accept what is asserted by some:[j] that everything tends toward the middle of

[68] This passage anticipates the attack on the teleological view of nature found at V. 110-234, but it is not out of place here. If the visible world were the result either of some divine plan or of some inborn intelligence or bias of the atoms, its creation and preservation would be possible in an infinite universe even from limited matter. But if it results from chance and if space is infinite, as the poet has already argued, then the number of atoms and the time consumed by their undirected motions must both be without limit.

the universe and that the world therefore stands firm at the center without any blows from without; that the things above and those below can in no way be separated because, as they say, the whole presses toward the center (if you believe that anything can rest upon itself); and that all the heavy objects that are on the other side of the earth are borne upward and come to rest 1060 upside down upon the earth like the reflections of objects that we actually see on the water. In the same way they contend that living creatures walk about head down and cannot fall from the earth into the parts of the sky that are below them, any more than our own bodies can of their own will fly into the regions of the sky; and that when these see the sun, we see the stars of night, and in alternation with us they share the seasons of the sky and pass nights that are equal in length to our days.[69] But a vain ⟨error has recommended these false beliefs⟩ to fools, because they have embraced and hold ⟨this theory with false 1070 reasoning;⟩ for there can be no middle ⟨since the universe is⟩ infinite. Indeed, if actually ⟨there were a center,⟩ a thing would no more come to rest there ⟨for this reason⟩ than ⟨be repelled⟩ far from it for some other reason; for all the room and space that ⟨we call the void ought⟩ to give passage equally through center and non-center alike to weights wherever their motions tend to take them.[k] And there is no place where bodies, when they have reached it, can lose their weight and come to rest upon the void; nor ought the void to support anything, but rather, 1080 as its own nature requires, it ought always to yield. Objects then cannot be held together in a complex in such a way as this, overcome by their desire for the center.[70]

Further, they suppose that not all bodies tend toward the center, but only those of earth and water (that is, the water of

[69] When our days are long, their nights are long; in other words, our summer is their winter.

[70] This paragraph anticipates matters to be presented in the first half of Book V (lines 416–770 in particular); but it is pertinent here since if matter seeks a center, a limited system such as ours might be formed and continue to exist even from limited matter in infinite space. One may already observe that the greatest weakness of Epicurean science is in astronomy.

the sea and the great streams of the mountains, and whatever is held, so to speak, in an earth-like body); and they claim on the other hand that the thin winds of the air and the hot fires are carried away from the center, and that the whole sky about us twinkles with stars and the flame of the sun feeds on the blue pastures of the sky for the following reason, namely that all heat, fleeing from the center, gathers itself there;[71] and they claim that the highest branches of trees could not put forth leaves unless food for them from the ground, bit by bit ⟨rose up. . . .[l] 1090

. . . Finally, if space is infinite, matter too must be infinite,⟩[m] lest like winged flames the walls of the world fly suddenly apart, let loose through the great void, and other things follow in the same manner; and lest the thundering spaces of the sky above rush upwards and the whole earth be suddenly dissolved beneath our feet. Amid the mingled, body-shattering ruin of earth and sky all would scatter through the limitless void, so that in an instant of time nothing would be left except empty space and invisible atoms. On whatever side you suppose that the atoms are first lacking, this side will be the gate for the destruction of the world; from this point the whole mixed mass of atoms will cast itself out.[72] 1110

These things you will learn led along with little effort. For one fact will gain light from another, nor will blinding night force you from the road and prevent you from beholding the final secrets of Nature, and, in this way, one thing shall illuminate another.

71 Lucretius' criticism is hardly justified. According to the Stoics the strength of the tendency toward the center depends upon the weight of the substance. Fire and air tend toward the center like all other things, but since they are relatively light they are forced out by heavier matter and take a permanent position on the periphery of the spherical system. See passage from Zeno in Appendix note *j*, p. 254. The Epicurean view as given at II. 184–215 is not very different.

72 Lucretius suggested above (lines 1042–48) that even if the atoms were limited in number, their pressure on the world from outside might hold it together for a time. He pictures here what would happen if that pressure were relaxed, as it would be in time if matter were not infinite.

BOOK TWO

I. The Motion of the Atoms

1–332

After a short introduction in praise of philosophy, the poet considers the motion of the atoms. This motion, more rapid than that of sunlight, is an unchanging property of the atoms. If atoms collide, they sometimes leap far apart and go their separate ways, but sometimes they harmonize their motions, forming fluids or solids. These collisions are possible because the atoms, although normally moving downward like all matter, may swerve from this downward course without previous cause. This swerve also makes possible the freedom of the will; and the freedom of the will proves the presence in nature of some uncaused motion. The sum of matter is unchanging; the individual atoms are invisible.

When on the great sea the winds are tossing the waters, it is sweet to watch from the land the great struggles of some other —not because it gives you pleasure and delight that anyone is distressed, but because it is a joy to discover from what misfortunes you yourself are free. It is also sweet to behold armies drawn up on the plains for the great conflict of war, if you yourself have no share in the danger. But nothing is sweeter than to occupy the high and quiet places fortified by the teachings of the wise, from which you can look down upon other men and watch 10 them as they wander to and fro, seeking in their wanderings a way of life, rivaling each other in genius, contending in rank, and struggling day and night with unceasing effort to rise to the greatest wealth and to become powerful in the state. O wretched minds of men! O blind hearts! Amid what shadows of life, amid what grave perils, do you spend your years, few as they are! Are you blind not to see that a man's nature demands nothing for itself except that in some way pain be banished and kept far from his body, and that, with a mind freed from anxiety and fear, he enjoy a sense of happiness? Thus we see that our physi- 20 cal bodies need little to satisfy them, namely, only those things that remove pain (although they may also bring many pleasures). Nor at any time does our nature itself require anything more pleasing than this, even though there are throughout the house no golden statues of youths holding in their right hands bright lamps to illuminate nocturnal banquets; though the house does not gleam with silver and shine with gold, nor do fretted and gilded beams echo back the harp! It is enough for friends to lie together in groups on the soft grass beside a stream 30 of water, beneath the branches of a tall tree, and to find comfort for their bodies in simple ways, especially when the weather smiles and the season of the year scatters flowers upon the grass as it grows green.[1] Burning fevers depart from the body no more quickly if you toss about amid embroidered coverlets or glowing purple than if you have to sleep beneath a common quilt. Therefore since our bodies gain no advantage from riches, rank, or regal glory, we must go a step further and believe that these are likewise of no aid to the soul; unless, indeed, when you see 40 your legions swarming through the plain as they stir up mimic war, when you draw them up, equipped with arms and all alike filled with courage, strengthened with great reserves and a force of horsemen, then your superstitious fears, frightened by this display, flee in panic from your mind, and dread of death departs from your heart and leaves it clean and free from anxiety.

[1] In lines 20–33 Lucretius has in mind Epicurus' triple division of desires, as given, for example, in the *Letter to Menoeceus* 127b: "You must consider that of the desires some are natural, some are vain, and of those that are natural, some are necessary, others only natural." Lucretius here mentions first the satisfaction of the desires that are natural and necessary in order to remove pain (lines 20–23), next those that are vain and should not be satisfied (lines 24–28), and finally those that are natural but unnecessary, the satisfaction of which will vary the quality of one's contentment without adding to its quantity (lines 29–33). Compare *Letter to Menoeceus* 127b–132a, and *Principal Doctrines* XVIII, XXIX, and XXX.

But if it is clear that all this is foolishness and worthy of scorn, and that in truth men's fears and the cares that haunt them
50 respect neither the din of arms nor fierce weapons, but move boldly among kings and potentates and have no reverence for the gleam of gold or the bright hue of purple garments—if this is clear, why do you doubt that the power over men's fears and cares lies altogether in philosophy, especially since our whole life is a struggle in the dark? Like children in the blinding darkness, who tremble and fear everything, so at times we, although in the light, fear things no more worthy of being feared than the phantoms at which children in the darkness shudder, imagining they are upon them. This terror, this darkness of the soul, must
60 be dispelled neither by the rays of the sun nor by the bright weapons of the day but by an understanding of the outer form and the inner law of Nature.[2]

Come now, I shall set forth by what motions the creative bodies of matter produce the various objects of sense, and destroy them after they are produced; and also what force compels them to do this, and what velocity has been given them for moving through the great void. Do you give heed to what I say.

Surely matter is not held tightly packed together; for we see that each individual thing becomes less, and we perceive that all things are flowing away, so to speak, in the long passage of
70 time, and that old age makes them vanish from our sight. Yet in spite of this, we see that the sum of things[3] remains constant, for the reason that the atoms departing from any thing diminish that from which they go but increase that to which they have gone, and they make the one grow old and the other flourish; yet they do not remain with it. In this way the sum of things

[2] Lines 55–61 are found twice more, at III. 87–93 and VI. 35–41; lines 59–61 have already been used at I. 146–48.

[3] The words that here, and again in line 75, are translated "the sum of things" usually mean the universe, that is, the total of atoms and void; but, as Robin has pointed out, the emphasis on visual evidence here makes that meaning inappropriate. The poet must mean that the sum of sensible things remains the same, some being destroyed and others being formed to maintain a balance.

is constantly renewed, while creatures of a day live by borrowing from each other. Some kinds become greater and others less, and in a brief space the generations of living things are changed and, like runners, hand on the torch of life.

If you think that the atoms can come to rest, and by resting 80 can produce new motions of things, you are wandering far from the truth.[a] Since the atoms move in empty space, all of them must be borne along,[4] either by their own weight or else, perhaps, by the blow of another. For when, as constantly happens, the atoms strike together in their swift motion, they leap apart suddenly; and this is no cause for wonder, since they are very hard because of their solid mass, and nothing opposes them from the rear.[5] That you may better perceive that all the atoms are tossed about, remember that in the whole universe there is 90 no lower limit, and that the atoms have no place where they may rest together, since space is without end or bound and—as I have shown in many words and proved by sure reasoning—extends without measure on all sides and in every direction.[6] Since this is established, surely no rest is given to the atoms throughout the whole void. Rather, they are kept in continuous and varied motion; when they have come together, some leap back to a great distance, but there are also others which, after a collision, contain their rapid motions within a limited space. All the atoms that have been brought together into a 100 closer complex and are vibrating within a narrow range, since they themselves are held by the interweaving of their forms, constitute the firm structure of rock, the cruel substance of iron, and other such materials. Of the others that range through the great void, a few move apart to a great distance and then return,

[4] See Epicurus, *Letter to Herodotus* 43–44, 61–62, 47a.

[5] In more modern terms, they are both perfectly rigid and perfectly elastic (although these terms are contradictory) and are moving in a frictionless medium. Lucretius thinks of two atoms, possibly of different masses, colliding and separating, each retaining its original velocity although changing its direction. Actually if two elastic bodies collide and separate, the total energy of the two will remain the same, but the velocity as well as the direction of each may change. See Epicurus, *Letter to Herodotus* 61.

[6] Compare I. 958–1007.

with wide expanses between them. These give us the thin air and the bright light of the sun. But in addition to these, there
110 are many atoms ranging through the great void that have been rejected from the complexes by which things are formed and have not anywhere been able to win their way into unions or to harmonize their motions.[b]

A likeness and image of this of which I speak frequently hovers before our eyes and presents itself to us. Whenever the rays of the sun stream in and pour light through the dark places of the house, look and you will see many minute particles darting about in many directions through the empty air in the light of the rays, as if in endless contest fighting wars and battles,
120 struggling like troops of cavalry and never ceasing, coming together and separating in continual motion. From this you may picture the constant tossing of the atoms in the great void; to this extent can a little thing serve as an example of great ones, and put us on the track of an idea. For the following reason, also, you would do well to observe these motes which you see dancing in the sunbeams: this dancing indicates that beneath it there are hidden motions of matter which are invisible. You
130 will see that many motes, struck by unseen blows, change their courses and are forced to move now this way and now that, on all sides and in every direction. Truly this change in the direction of all the motes is caused by the atoms. The atoms first move by themselves; then the complexes, which are small gatherings of atoms and are, so to speak, next to the atoms in force, are moved when struck by the invisible blows of the atoms; and these, in turn, set in motion particles that are a little larger. Thus motion, starting from the atom, ascends little by little and comes within the range of our senses, so that finally even
140 those motes that we are able to see in the sunlight are moved, although the collisions that cause this motion do not appear to our sight.[c]

From what follows, Memmius, you may learn in a few words what velocity has been given to the atoms.[7] In the first place,

[7] See Epicurus, *Letter to Herodotus* 61, 46b.

when dawn sprinkles the earth with new light, and in the solitary groves birds of brilliant hues flying through the yielding air fill the region with their limpid song, it is readily manifest to the eyes of all with what rapidity the risen sun at such a time pours out his light and clothes all things. But the radiant heat 150 and clear light that the sun sends forth do not travel through empty space. Therefore the light is forced to move more slowly while it cuts its way, so to speak, through the waves of air. Each atom of heat is not alone by itself; rather, the atoms move intertwined together and formed into complexes. They therefore hold each other back; at the same time they are resisted from without, so that they are forced to move more slowly. But since the atoms, which are of solid oneness, move through empty space and nothing outside delays them, and since each one of them, being a single unit made up of inseparable parts, is carried forward 160 in whatever single direction it has begun to move—surely they ought to excel the light of the sun in velocity and to move with far greater speed; and in the time in which the brightness of the sun fills the heavens, the atoms ought to traverse a space many times as great.[d]

. . . and not to examine with care each separate atom so that they may see by what reason each thing is carried on.

But in opposition to this, certain men,[8] ignorant of the structure of matter, hold that without the aid of the gods, Nature could neither change the seasons of the year in a way so fitted 170 to the needs of men, nor produce crops for their use, nor prepare those other things that divine Pleasure, the guide of life, persuades men to undertake, herself leading them on and enticing them to propagate their generations through the acts of Venus, lest the race of men perish. But when they suppose that the gods have established all things in the interests of mankind, they clearly have fallen far from the truth in every respect; for even if I did not know the nature of the atoms, yet I would still

[8] That is, the Stoics, who believed that the world was created by the "World Spirit" for the use of men. This paragraph now seems a digression, but it may be a natural development of something that has been lost in the lacuna above.

venture to assert from the very ways of the heavens—and to
180 prove from many other examples—that by no means was this
world created for us by the gods, with such imperfections is it
filled. We shall make this clear to you later, Memmius;[9] now
we shall set forth what remains about the motions of the atoms.

Now is the time, I believe, to prove to you, in this connection,
the following as well: not one corporeal substance can raise
itself or go upward by its own force—I say this in order that
flames may not deceive you in this matter.[10] For they come into
being and make their growth upward, and bright crops and
190 orchards grow upward, although weights in themselves all tend
downward. When fire leaps to the roofs of houses and its swift
flame eats away beams and timbers, you must not think that it
does this of its own accord, driven upward without the aid of
any external force. In this same way, when blood is let from our
bodies, it shoots forth spurting high and scattering gore. Do you
not see likewise with what violence beams and timbers are disgorged
by water? For the more strongly we force them down
deep, many of us together struggling with great effort to thrust
them below the surface, the more violently does the water drive
200 them upward and send them forth so that more than half their
length rises above the surface and leaps out. Yet we do not
doubt, I think, that these things in themselves all tend downward
through empty space. It must be in this way, then, that

[9] This promise is fulfilled at V. 195–234, a passage that begins with a sentence almost identical with the one beginning "For even if I did not know . . ." (lines 177–81 above).

[10] Lucretius is combating (and misrepresenting) the Stoic view (compare I. 1052–95 and notes). This paragraph and those that follow are open to the obvious objection that in infinite space the terms "up" and "down" are meaningless. Epicurus is conscious of this difficulty and tries to counter it (*Letter to Herodotus* 60); Lucretius prefers to ignore it. He seems to think of infinite atoms moving with constant velocity through infinite space in a single direction (before the swerve), and that direction is the one which to us is down. The cause of the motion, even though he calls it weight (*pondus*), is not an external force like gravity, which would cause acceleration rather than motion with constant velocity, but rather something internal (see *Letter to Herodotus* 61).

flames too when pressed upon gain the power to rise through the air, although their weight in itself would tend to force them downward. Do you not see how meteors, flying high in the sky by night, drag their long trains in whatever direction Nature has opened a way? Do you not see stars and heavenly bodies sinking to the horizon? From the very summit of the sky the 210 sun sends down its heat in every direction, and scatters its light through the fields; thus, too, it is toward the earth that the heat of the sun is directed. You see lightning flash through the rain crossing its path; now from this side, now from that, course the flashes that have broken from the clouds. Everywhere the force of flame falls toward the ground.

Also, in this connection, I would have you understand the following: when the atoms are being carried, each by its own weight, straight downward through the void, at utterly unfixed times and places they swerve a little from their course, just 220 enough so that you can say that the direction is altered.[e] If the atoms did not have this swerve, they would all fall straight down through the deep void like drops of rain, and no collisions would occur nor would the atoms sustain any blows. Thus Nature would never have created anything. If by chance anyone believes that the heavier atoms, by falling more rapidly in a straight line through the void, can strike the lighter ones from above and thus bring about collisions capable of causing the creative motions, he wanders far away from right reason. It is 230 true that whatever things fall through water or thin air must fall with a velocity that varies with their weights, since the water and the thin air cannot delay all things equally, but give way more readily when overpowered by heavier things; but on the other hand at no time or place can the empty void oppose anything; rather, as its own nature demands, it always yields. For this reason, in the unresisting void all things, though they be moved by unequal weights, must be carried along with equal velocity.[11] Therefore the heavier atoms have never been able to 240

[11] That falling bodies would move through empty space with equal velocity regardless of differing weights was well known to the ancient physicists

strike the lighter from above, nor of themselves to produce the impacts that cause the various motions by means of which Nature does her work. So I say again and again, it is necessary that the atoms swerve a little, but no more than the least bit, lest we seem to imagine oblique motions, and the plain facts prove this false. For we see that this is clear and obvious: when masses fall from above, as far as is visible to the eye, they cannot of themselves move in an oblique course; but who can tell,
250 by means of his senses, that the atoms do not veer at all from the straight path?[12]

Finally, if every motion is connected and the new motion arises in a fixed manner out of the old, and if the atoms do not swerve and cause a certain beginning of action that may break the chains of Fate and prevent cause from following cause through infinite time, whence comes this power of free will for living creatures throughout the earth?[13] Whence, I say, this liberty wrested from Fate, by virtue of which we each go where pleasure leads us and, like the atoms, swerve in our courses at
260 no fixed time and in no predetermined direction, but when and where the mind itself impels? Beyond a doubt, in decisions such

(see Epicurus, *Letter to Herodotus* 61) in spite of the statements found in most physics textbooks, which credit this discovery to Galileo. For an interesting and, at times, amusing discussion of this see *Aristotle, Galileo, and the Tower of Pisa*, by Lane Cooper (Ithaca, 1935).

[12] According to Epicurean *Canonicê* or scientific method, a theory dealing with matters not perceptible to the senses can be accepted if (*a*) it explains the phenomena that can be observed, and (*b*) it is not contradicted by observed facts (Diogenes Laertius, *Life of Epicurus* 34a). In this passage, after showing that the swerve is necessary to explain certain visible phenomena (in the next paragraph he will show that it is also necessary to explain the freedom of the will, a more important point), Lucretius claims in the last sentence of the paragraph that, as here limited, the swerve does not contradict the evidence of the senses.

[13] For the importance that Epicurus attached to freedom of the individual will, see his *Letter to Menoeceus* 134. According to Cicero (*On Fate* 23; *On the Nature of the Gods* I. 69–70), Epicurus' prime purpose in introducing the swerve into his system was to secure this freedom. For the relation between the swerve and the act of will, see Bailey, *Greek Atomists*, pp. 319, 435–37. The present passage incidentally makes it clear that an atom may swerve within a created thing, as well as when it is moving freely in the void, and also that the same atom may swerve more than once.

as these, it is the will of the individual that takes the lead, and from the will the impulse moves through the limbs. Do you not see that at the point of time when the barriers are opened, the strong horses, eager though they be, cannot rush forth as suddenly as the mind itself desires? The whole mass of matter through the entire body needs to be stirred so that, thus stirred through all the limbs, it may strain and follow the desire of the mind. Thus you see that the beginning of motion springs from the heart and comes first from the mind's volition, whence it is 270 spread through the whole body and the limbs. This is not the same as when we are impelled by a blow, by some great compelling force outside ourselves; for then it is clear that all the matter of the whole body moves and is carried along, even against the will, until the will has regained control of the matter throughout the limbs. Do you not therefore see that, although violence from without often compels and forces many men to advance and be hurried along against their wills, yet there is something in the human breast that can struggle against this and resist it? 280 At the bidding of this something the matter throughout our members and our limbs is sometimes forced to turn, and after it has rushed forth is checked and settles back again.

Therefore this same thing must be granted in regard to the atoms: since we see that no thing can result from nothing, there must exist some other cause for motion in addition to collisions and weight, and from this other cause comes the inborn power of the will. Weight, indeed, makes it impossible that everything takes place as a result of blows, as if by external force. But that the mind itself shall not have an inner necessity as its master 290 in all its acts and be compelled like a prisoner to do and to undergo—this is the result of the slight swerve of the atom in a direction and at a time that are in no way predetermined.[f]

The total supply of matter was never more compacted than it is today, nor again was it ever spread out with greater spaces between; for nothing comes to increase the supply of matter, nor is anything lost from it.[14] Therefore the atoms have been for all time past in the same motion as they are now, and in the

[14] See Epicurus, *Letter to Herodotus* 39a.

300 same way they shall ever move hereafter; and what things have normally come into existence shall continue to come into being in the same way, and shall exist, grow, and flourish to the extent granted each by the laws of Nature. Nor can any force change the sum of things; for there is no place outside into which any kind of matter can escape from the universe or from which a new supply can arise and burst into the universe, changing all Nature and altering its motions.

Nor is it any cause for wonder that, although all the atoms are 310 in motion, still the whole appears to be completely at rest, except insofar as a sensible thing begins to move with its entire body; for the atom in its own nature lies far below the reach of our senses. Accordingly, since you cannot see the atoms themselves, it is natural that their motions also elude your sight, especially since the motions of bodies that we can see are commonly imperceptible when they are distant from us. Often, for example, as woolly sheep crop the fertile pasture on a hillside, each drifts along wherever the tempting grass, shining with fresh 320 dew, beckons; and the lambs, when they have eaten their fill, play about and butt each other for sport. Yet when we see all this from a distance, it appears blurred, and the whole flock seems to rest like a single white cloud on the green hillside. Again, when great legions fill the area of the plain with their passing as they stir up mimic war, then the gleam rises to the sky, all the land about shines with bronze, a sound rises up from beneath the feet of the marching men, and the mountains, struck by the clamor, re-echo their voices to the stars of heaven; 330 and horsemen wheel about and suddenly charge through the center, shaking the ground with their violent onset. Yet there is a place in the high mountains from which all this seems to stand still and to lie like a gleam at rest upon the plain.

II. The Forms of the Atoms

333–729

The atoms differ widely in their forms. Since all sensation is due to contact, the differences in sensations must be explained by differences in the atoms that impinge upon our senses. A substance's nature depends upon the nature of its atoms. The number of atoms of each form must be infinite, but the number of forms is limited. Although all kinds cannot combine with each other, each created thing contains atoms of many kinds. The earth, from which all things grow and are nourished, alone contains atoms of every kind; and the earth may with reason be called the Great Mother—but must not be worshipped as divine.

Now learn of what sort are the atoms of which all things are formed:[15] how widely they differ in shape, how varied they are, with forms of many kinds—not that only a few are of a like pattern, but that the atoms in general are not all like to all. And this is not strange; for, since the number of them is so great that, as I have shown, they have neither limit nor fixed quantity, truly they ought not all to have the same size or be endowed 340 with the same shape. Moreover, the human race, the silent schools of scaly swimming creatures, the contented herds, the wild beasts, and the birds of many species that fill the joyful watering places about the river banks, springs, and lakes, and throng the pathless groves as they fly about—take any that you wish, one by one from species after species, and you will find that they differ in shape among themselves. In no other way could offspring recognize mother and mother offspring, and 350 yet we see that they do so and that they appear to recognize each other no less than do men. It often happens that a calf, sacrificed before the fair shrine of the god, has fallen beside the incense-burning altar, breathing out a warm stream of blood from its breast; but the bereft mother, wandering through the green pastures, seeks on the ground for the marks imprinted by those cloven hoofs, searching all places with her eyes to see if she can catch sight anywhere of her lost nursling. As she halts, she fills the leafy groves with her laments; and constantly she returns to her stall, pierced through with longing for her calf. 360 Neither the pliant willows, the grass quickened by the dew, nor the familiar streams that glide along bank-full can give pleasure to her heart or take away the recurrent pang; nor can the forms

[15] See Epicurus, *Letter to Herodotus* 42b.

of other calves throughout the joy-giving meadow distract her spirit or relieve it of its sorrow. So eagerly does the mother seek a certain form known to her as her own. In the same way the young kids with timorous cries recognize their horned mothers, and the frisking lambs know the bleating sheep. Thus with rare
370 exceptions kids and lambs, each as Nature demands, gambol back to the proper udder of milk. Finally, take any kind of corn you please, yet you will find that even within a particular kind each grain is not like to each, but certain differences in form distinguish them. We see that this same rule holds of the species of shells that paint the bosom of the land where the sea with its gentle waves beats the thirsty sand on the curving shore. Therefore I tell you again and again that in the same way, since the atoms are of natural origin and not artificially made after the
380 fixed image of a single model, certain ones of them must fly about with mutually differing forms.[16]

It is very easy for us to discover by reasoning of the mind why the fire of the lightning moves with greater penetrating power than does the fire that comes from our terrestrial torches; for you might say that the fine heavenly fire of the lightning is made from smaller atomic shapes, and for this reason passes through pores that cannot be traversed by our fire, which rises from wood or is born of the pitch pine. Again, light passes through a sheet of horn, but rain is turned aside.[17] What reason is there
390 for this unless it is because the atoms characteristic of light are smaller than are those of which the life-giving water is composed? We see that wine passes quickly through a strainer, but sluggish olive oil, on the other hand, is retarded because the oil consists of elements that are larger or are more entangled be-

[16] That is, certain classes of atoms differ in form from other classes. The clumsiness of the concluding sentence may arise from the fact that the illustrations, although among the most beautiful in the poem, actually lead to a conclusion opposite to the one desired. The atoms within a class are identical, but the atoms of different classes differ. In the supposed parallels the emphasis is on differences between individuals of a single class.

[17] In the ancient lantern the flame was protected by plates of more or less translucent horn. Light comes through the horn, but rain cannot penetrate it.

cause they are hook-like, as a result of which the individual atoms cannot so easily separate themselves so that each may pass individually through its own opening.[18]

Moreover, liquid honey and milk, when rolled about in the mouth, cause the tongue a pleasant sensation;[19] bitter wormwood and harsh centaury, on the other hand, torment the mouth 400 with their revolting taste. Therefore you may easily perceive that those things that can give pleasure as they touch our senses are composed of smooth, round atoms; but that on the other hand whatever things seem bitter or harsh are firmly bound together and held by hooked atoms, so that they commonly force their passage to our senses with violence, and lacerate our flesh as they enter. Finally, the things that the senses as they touch them find good or bad are at war with each other, having been fashioned from atoms of unlike shapes. Do not, then, suppose 410 that the shrill shriek of the rasping saw consists of atoms as smooth as those that form the sweet music which artists call forth and fashion, as their nimble fingers move over the strings; and do not suppose that atoms of similar shape penetrate men's nostrils when noisome corpses are burning and when the stage has just been sprayed with Cilician saffron and the nearby altar breathes forth Arabian incense. Neither should you assume that atoms of the same kind make up both the pleasing colors that soothe our eyes and the colors that impede our vision, causing 420 the tears to flow, or seeming dire and shameful because of their vile appearance; for no object that soothes the senses has been

[18] This paragraph presents certain difficulties. In the last sentence Lucretius uses one of his regular terms for the atom, but the argument suggests that the particle in question is almost as large as the openings in the strainer, which is out of keeping with all that he says elsewhere about the size of the atom. The terms used earlier in the paragraph in regard to lightning and fire are ones that he applies both to atoms and to complexes of atoms, and the argument would hold for either. Since the general course of the discussion is such that he ought to be treating of individual atoms, we may assume that he means atoms throughout the paragraph and that the last example is unhappily chosen; or possibly that what started out as a parallel from the visible world finally took form as a third example.

[19] For sensation, see IV. 216–352, 522–721.

formed without a certain smoothness of the atoms, but on the other hand none that is injurious and harsh is found to lack some roughness in its matter. Moreover, there are some atoms that are properly thought to be neither smooth, nor altogether hooked with barbs bent, but rather to have slightly projecting
430 points so that they stimulate but do not injure our senses; tartar and elecampane have tastes of just this sort.[20] Finally, that hot fire and chill frost prick our bodily senses with different kinds of teeth, is evidenced to us by the individual touch of each; for touch, by the sacred powers of the gods, touch is the sole cause of bodily sensation. This is true, whether it be when something from without forces its way into the body, or when something naturally arising in the body makes its way out, either causing us pain or, as in the life-giving acts of love, bringing pleasure; or finally when, through some collision from without, the atoms in the body itself are disturbed and disturb the senses by their
440 turmoil among themselves—you might try this yourself by striking any part of your body with your hand. The atoms must differ widely in form, then, since they can produce different sensations.

Thus things that we see to be hard and firm must be formed from atoms that are hooked together, and must be held firmly compacted as if by interwoven branches. Among substances of this sort diamonds[21] accustomed to despise blows stand in the first line of battle, and with them stubborn flint, iron of unyield-
450 ing strength, and the bronze sockets that scream as they resist the bars.[22] But liquids of fluid nature should consist of smoother, rounder atoms; for a stream of poppy seeds moves as smoothly as one of water, and these seeds when poured out flow down a slope in the same way, since separate spherical forms do not

[20] Tartar is a salt deposited as a pale red crust in wine casks; elecampane is a coarse herb of the aster family. Both have a taste that is tart rather than bitter.

[21] "Diamonds" is a probable but not certain translation of a phrase which literally means "unconquerable stones."

[22] The "stubborn flint" may be the basalt used in ancient Rome for paving blocks; the last phrase, literally "the brazen things that shriek as they resist the bars," defies certain interpretation.

cling to each other.[23] Finally, all things that you see vanish in a moment of time, like smoke, fogs, or flames, even if they are not entirely formed from atoms that are smooth and round, cannot be hampered by atoms that are interwoven; as a result they 460 are able to pierce the body and penetrate the rocks, yet they cannot cling together.[24] Thus you can easily tell that whatever seems to the senses to have teeth consists not of tangled but of pointed atoms.[25] But it ought not to appear at all strange that you find that some of the same substances that are fluid are also bitter, like the brine of the sea. . . .[26] For because it is fluid it is formed from smooth, round atoms, and with these are mixed rough atoms that cause pain, which however must not be hooked and held together. You must know that, although they are rough, still they are round, so that they can roll about and at 470 the same time rasp the senses. That you may more readily believe that rough atoms are mixed with the smooth as in the bitter water of the sea, there is a way of filtering them out and seeing how, when the same sea water is passed many times through the earth as if through a filter, it flows into the trench sweet and fresh; this is because it leaves the nauseating brine behind, since the rough atoms can stick in the earth more readily.[g]

Since I have shown this, I shall proceed to add a matter that depends upon it, and gains credence from it: although the atoms do vary, the number of different forms is limited.[27] If this were 480

[23] Lines 454 and 455 are transposed, following Brieger. Lucretius here as often is arguing from the visible to the invisible. Poppy seeds, which are round and smooth, flow like a liquid; a liquid therefore consists of smooth, round atoms.

[24] Smoke causes sensation when it gets into the eye, and fire when it heats the body. We must remember that heat is regarded as corporeal, and that an object can be heated by a flame only when it is penetrated by the atoms emitted from the flame in the form of heat.

[25] The text of this sentence is very doubtful and the meaning quite uncertain. I have translated Martin's text.

[26] A lacuna of at least one line occurs following line 465.

[27] See Epicurus, *Letter to Herodotus* 42b, 55b-56a. The argument of this

not so, I say once more, certain atoms would increase in bulk and become of unlimited size; for within an atom of whatever limited compass you propose, the shapes cannot vary much. Suppose that the atoms are composed of three least parts,[28] or increase this a little; surely when you have tried all these parts of a single atom in every arrangement—placing them above and below, transposing the right with the left—and have found 490 what appearance of the whole is given by each arrangement of the parts, if you should wish then to vary the forms further, you must add another part. From this it will follow by the same reasoning that, if you still wish to vary the patterns, the new arrangement will demand other parts; thus an increase in bulk is a necessary consequence of novelty in pattern. Therefore you cannot believe that the atoms exist in an infinite number of different patterns, for if this were true some of them would need to be of great size—a thing that I have shown above cannot be admitted.

500 If the atoms varied infinitely in form, your oriental dress and gleaming Meliboean purple dyed with the color of Thessalian shells, and the golden race of peacocks touched with laughing grace—all would lie in neglect, surpassed by objects of new colors; the odor of myrrh and the sweetness of honey would be despised, and the songs of the swans and Apollo's intricate music on the lyre, overwhelmed in like manner, would become silent; for some new thing superior to the old would keep coming into being. Likewise all things could change in the opposite direction, becoming worse just as we have declared that they could 510 become better; for there would also be something inferior to the old, more noisome to nose, ears, eyes, and to the taste of the mouth. Since this is not so, but rather a definite boundary has

---

section assumes that the smallness of the atom has just been proved. Lines containing this proof may have been lost, or else they may never have been written. The use of the same lines (not found elsewhere in the poem) to introduce this section and the next (lines 478–79 and 522–23) suggests that the poet had not given the final touches to this part of the poem.

[28] For the "least parts" of the atom, see I. 599–634.

been set for things limiting the range in each direction, you must agree that atoms differ within a finite number of patterns. The range from fire all the way to the cold frosts of winter is limited, and is measured back again on the same scale; for every degree of heat and cold and all the moderate temperatures lie between the limits, filling the whole scale in order. Thus all temperatures that exist are spaced within a definite scale, since 520 they are marked by a pair of limits, one on either hand—on this side beset by flames, on that by the unyielding ice.

Since I have shown this, I shall proceed to add a matter that depends upon it and gains credence from it: the number of atoms formed in the same pattern is infinite. For since the diversity of patterns is limited, either the atoms that are alike must be infinite, or the total sum of matter must be limited—a thing I have proven is not true, showing in my verses that from infinite space the atoms still maintain the sum of created things 530 by an uninterrupted succession of blows from every side.[29]

Although you see that certain kinds of living creatures are rather rare, and perceive that Nature is less productive in respect to them, yet it is possible that in some other quarter and region, in distant lands, there are many of that species and the number is made complete.[30] Among the four-footed beasts we see that this is especially true in the case of the snake-handed elephants, for a wall of ivory from many thousands of these beasts protects India so well that no one can penetrate to the interior;[31] so great is the number of these beasts, of which we see 540

[29] See I. 1009–51. For the principle that the parts of an infinite whole may themselves be infinite, see appendix note *c*, p. 251.

[30] In Book V Lucretius often returns to the thesis briefly stated here. Since created things are the result of chance combinations of atoms of certain kinds, and since the number of atoms of each kind is infinite and therefore equal, the various created things ought to be formed in more or less equal numbers—if not where we are, than in some other land, or (he adds in Book V) in some other world.

[31] Lucretius seems to refer to an otherwise unknown story of an actual wall of ivory protecting India.

very few specimens. But yet let me grant this also: let there be a certain thing as unique and solitary as you please, possessing its one peculiar body, to which there is nothing similar in the whole world; yet unless there is an infinite supply of matter for the formation and production of this unique thing, it will not be created, nor yet will it grow and be nourished. Even if I should also assume that a limited number of atoms proper for the creation of this one thing is being tossed about through the universe, whence, where, by what force, or by what agreement
550 will they come together and unite in such a sea, such a confused mass, of alien matter? They have, I am sure, no means of uniting. Just as when many a great shipwreck has taken place, the mighty sea long tosses transoms, ribs, yards, a prow, masts, and drifting oars hither and yon, so that stern ornaments are seen floating along all the shores of the earth, giving witness to mortal men to shun the treachery, violence, and trickery of the inconstant ocean and not trust it at any time, not even when the deceitful charm of the quiet sea smiles upon them—just as these
560 are widely scattered, in the same way, if once you assume that atoms of a certain kind are limited in number, they must have been scattered by the tides of matter driving in every direction throughout all time, and must now be tossing so far apart that they can never be driven together and join in a complex, or if joined in a complex, receive increase, and grow. But facts visible to all show that this does happen, that things can be born, and that having been born, they can increase. It is therefore clear that there are infinite atoms of each and every kind from which all things are constituted.

570 The motions that cause destruction cannot prevail forever, and entomb well-being for all time; nor yet can the motions that bring life and increase to things preserve forever what they have created. Thus in this even struggle of the atoms, a war that began in the limitless past is still being waged. Now here, now there, the forces that give life are victorious and likewise are defeated. The wail that babies utter when they first see the light is mingled with the funeral; nor has any night followed day nor any sunrise followed dark, that has not heard, joined

with the infants' feeble crying, the lamentations that accompany 580
death and the gloomy grave.

It is proper at this point for you to have the following well established, and to keep it fixed in your memory: among the things that are perceptible to the senses none consists of a single kind of atom—there is not one that is not composed of mixed seeds. Moreover, the thing that has in itself greater force and more capabilities shows thereby that it contains atoms of more kinds and of more varied patterns. In particular, the earth has within itself atoms from which the springs pour forth cold waters and constantly renew the sea; she has also those atoms 590 from which hot fires come, for in many places the surface of the earth is hot with burnings from below, and Aetna in eruption rages with fires from the depths. Earth also has atoms from which she can bring forth for mankind the shining grain and the cheerful orchards, and from which, too, she can supply water, fodder, and pleasing pasture to the wild beasts that range the mountains.

For this reason the earth alone has been called the Great Mother of the Gods,[h] the mother of wild beasts, and the parent of our bodies. Of her in ancient times the learned poets of the 600 Greeks sang that, seated on the throne in her chariot, she drove a yoke of lions; thus in their poems they taught us that earth cannot rest upon earth, but hangs in midair. They yoked wild beasts to her car because the young, however wild, ought to be made gentle and tame by their parents' care. They encircled the top of her head with the mural crown because with her shrines established upon high places she sustains cities. The statue of the divine Mother endowed with this emblem is today carried in dread-inspiring manner through great lands. Various races, 610 following their ancient rites, call her the Idaean Mother and give her as companions groups of Phrygians; for they proclaim that it was from the Phrygian lands that the cultivation of grain first spread through the whole earth. They assign Galli to her because they wish to show that those who have violated the divinity of the Mother and have been found ungrateful to their

parents should be considered unworthy of bringing living off-spring into the light. Taut tambours thunder in their hands
620 and concave cymbals clash, horns threaten with harsh noise, and the hollow pipe spurs their minds with Phrygian music; and they carry before them knives as the signs of mad rage, that through the power of the goddess they may strike fear into the ungrateful hearts and impious breasts of the people. And so when she is first borne through great cities and voicelessly blesses men with her silent greeting, they spread the whole roadway of her route with bronze and silver, enriching her with generous gifts; and they send over her a snow of rose blossoms, giving shade to the Mother and to the throng of her companions. On this occasion the armed band, whom the Greeks call the Curetes,
630 whenever they sport among the Phrygian crowds and leap in the dance, made joyful by blood and shaking their fear-inspiring crests with the tossing of their heads—this band recalls the Curetes of Mount Dictê, who are said once to have concealed that famous wailing of Jupiter in Crete when in rapid dance, armed boys about a boy, they beat bronze with bronze in rhythm so that Saturn might not seize him and champ him with his jaws, planting an eternal wound in the heart of the
640 Mother.[32] It is for this reason that armed men escort the Great Mother; or else it is because they show that the goddess admonishes men to be willing to defend their fatherland by valor in arms, and to make ready to be a guard and an honor to their parents.

But although this tale is well devised and excellently told, it is far removed from the truth; for it is necessary that the gods in their whole beings and from their own power enjoy unending life in perfect peace, far removed and separated from our ex-
650 perience. Free from every grief and from all dangers, powerful

[32] According to the myth that Lucretius here follows, Zeus (Jupiter) was the son of Cronus (Saturn) and Rhea (Earth, here identified with Cybelê), and was born in Crete. Knowing that Cronus planned the destruction of his son, who was destined to supplant him as chief of the gods, Rhea preserved the infant by hiding him in a cave, and the Curetes by their noisy dancing prevented his wailing from being heard. With most editors, line 636 is omitted.

in their own might, and with no need of us, they are neither won nor angered by our services.[33] As for the earth, truly it is without consciousness through all time;[34] and it is because it possesses the atoms of many things that it brings forth many things in many ways into the light of the sun. If then anyone wishes to call the sea Neptune and grain Ceres, and prefers to misname wine Bacchus rather than to utter its proper title, let us permit him to declare again and again that the earth is Mother of the Gods—provided that, in spite of these words, he avoids, in actual fact, staining his very soul with shameful superstition. 660

Thus[35] the woolly flocks, the martial offspring of horses, and the herds of horned cattle often eat the grass of a single field beneath the same quarter of the sky, and quench their thirst from a single stream of water, yet they are living beings of unlike species, retaining the characteristics of their parents and following their peculiar ways of life, each after its own kind. Such is the diversity of atoms in every kind of grass and in every stream as well. Moreover, any living creature you select is formed of bone, blood, veins, warmth, moisture, flesh, sinews 670 —a single being made from many; and from many, too, that are far different from each other, since they are made of atoms of unlike forms. Then again, whatever objects are burned and consumed by fire, if they have no other elements concealed in their bodies, certainly have those from which they can toss forth fire, send out light, make sparks fly, and scatter ashes far and wide. As you consider other things in this same way, you will find that they too hide within their bodies seeds of many things and hold within themselves atoms of various shapes. Finally, 680 you see many things, especially most of the fruits, which have been given at the same time both color and taste, together with

[33] Lines 646–51 are repeated from I. 44–49.

[34] As the previous sentences denied the validity of the popular conceptions of the gods, so this sentence denies the pantheistic belief of the Stoics, who taught that the Divine Spirit pervaded all the natural world.

[35] This section follows naturally, and without any break in sense, after line 597.

odor. These must therefore be composed of atoms of different shapes, for smell penetrates to organs to which color does not go. Likewise color and taste make their separate ways to the senses, each for itself, so that you may be sure that the different sensations are due to atoms of different shapes.[36] Unlike atoms, therefore, come together into a single whole, and things are composed of mixed matter. Nay, anywhere in these very verses
690 of mine you see many letters common to many words, although you must nevertheless admit that each of the verses and words is formed of its own particular letters. This does not mean that there are not many letters common to many words, or that no two words are composed of exactly the same letters, but in general all the words are not alike in all their letters.[37] So too in other fields: although many atoms are common to many things, yet the things can exist with mutually unlike wholes, so that one may properly say that the human race and grain and charming trees are composed of different atoms.

700 Yet you must not suppose that all atoms can be joined in all possible combinations. If this were true, you would often see monstrous beings created: a race arising half man and half beast, tall branches growing sometimes from living bodies, many limbs of land animals grafted upon creatures of the sea, and finally Nature throughout her all-productive lands giving pasture to Chimaeras breathing flame from hideous mouths. It is obvious that none of these monsters is created, since we see that all things, fashioned from particular atoms and sprung from a particular mother, are able to retain their types as they grow.
710 Surely this must be the result of a definite law. From all the food within the body, the suitable atoms go off into the members and, entering into combinations, move in the required ways. On the other hand, we see that Nature thrusts unsuitable atoms back to earth, and many in invisible form are driven from the body by blows and escape; for they have been unable to enter in any way into the combinations or to harmonize with and repeat the life-giving motions within the body. But do not

[36] For the sensations, see IV. 216–721.

[37] See I. 197, 823–29, 907–14.

suppose that only living creatures are governed by such laws; the same rule limits all things. For just as each created thing differs from every other thing when they are considered as wholes, so it is necessary that the atoms be of different forms—not that there are not many of the same form but that in general every one is not like every other one. 720

Next, since atoms are different, there must also be differences in the spaces between the atoms within which the atoms move, and differences too in their unions, weights, and collisions, and in their meetings and motions. These differences not only keep the bodies of living beings in separate classes; they also distinguish the lands and the whole ocean, and hold the whole sky apart from the earth.

III. Secondary Qualities Lacking in the Atom

730–1022

An object's secondary qualities—color, heat, hardness, and the like—are caused by the combinations of the atoms that compose it, and are all subject to change as these combinations change. Such qualities are lacking in the atom, for it cannot change. Since sensation is caused by internal motion, it too is impossible for the solid, unalterable atom. All things that change, perish; the atom alone is eternal.

Come now, heed my words, which are the result of happy labor, that you may not suppose that the white things you see shining before your eyes are composed of white atoms, and that those that are black come from black seed, nor believe that what is stained with any other color whatever has this color because its atoms are dyed with a like hue; for the atoms have no color at all, either like or unlike that of the things they form.[38] If it seems to you that the mind cannot visualize colorless bodies, you are far from the truth; for men born blind, who have never seen the light of the sun, recognize objects by the sense of touch, 730 740

[38] See Epicurus, *Letter to Herodotus* 54, and scholium on 44.

although from birth they have never associated the objects with any color; and surely we too can form in our minds a concept of bodies never touched by any color. Finally, when we ourselves touch objects in blinding darkness, we do not recognize them as dyed with any particular hue.

Since I have convinced you that this is so, I will now prove ⟨that the atoms have no color at all⟩; for absolutely every color changes, and everything[i] ⟨that changes its color is changed
750 itself⟩; but first beginnings ought in no way to change, since it is necessary that something unchangeable survive lest all things be reduced utterly to nothing. For whenever a thing is changed and departs from its proper limits, this is at once the death of that which was before.[39] Therefore do not touch the atoms with color, lest all things be reduced utterly to nothing before your eyes. Further, you can explain changes in color if the atoms have no color but do have differences in form, and if it is because of these differences that they produce colors of every
760 sort and change them; for with atoms of each particular kind it makes a great difference with what other atoms they are in contact, in what arrangements they are held, and in what ways they set others in motion and are moved themselves. Thus you could very easily and quickly explain the reason why that which a little while before was dark can suddenly be given a marble brilliance, as the sea, for example, is changed into bright waves of brilliant marble when great winds have stirred its surface.[40] You might say that the sea, which we usually behold as dark, at
770 once is seen to become a gleaming white when its substance has been stirred, the arrangement of its atoms changed, and certain atoms added or taken away. But if the surface of the sea were composed of dark blue atoms, there would be no way for it to grow white; for in whatever way you disturbed atoms that were

[39] Lines 750–54 are repeated from I. 789–93. Line 756 is found also at I. 673 and 797, and II. 864. Lines 760–62 are found with slight variations at I. 817–19 and 908–10, and II. 1007–1009.

[40] This metaphor, which seems strained to us, was natural in Latin, since the word *marmor,* which properly means "marble," was often used by poets to mean the bright surface of the sea.

blue-black, they could never change into the color of marble. Suppose that atoms stained with dyes of various colors were combined to make up the pure, clear brilliance of the sea, in the way in which a figure that is square and has a single outline is often put together from pieces of various different shapes and forms. Just as we see the different outlines within the square, so we ought to see different, violently contrasting colors on the surface of the sea or on any other thing that is of a single, unmixed whiteness. Also, the parts of dissimilar shapes in no way prevent the whole from being externally square; but the various colors make it quite impossible that the thing as a whole be of a single whiteness. Then next the argument that at times leads us astray and tempts us to attribute colors to the atoms[41] is destroyed, since white things are not made from white, nor are things that are called black made from black, but both are made from things of various colors. Truly, things that are white will be formed more easily from atoms of no color than from black atoms or those of any other color that resists whiteness and struggles against it. 780 790

Moreover, since colors cannot exist without light and since light itself is colorless,[42] we may know how untouched by color are the atoms. For what sort of color can there be in the blinding dark? Further, the color of an object may be changed by the light itself, according as it shines forth when struck by direct or by slanting rays; in this way the plumage that forms a bright halo about the neck and throat of a dove is seen to change in the sunlight. Sometimes it is red, with the bright color of garnet; but again as we look at it in a particular way it seems to mingle green emeralds with lapis lazuli. So too the tail of the peacock, when it is flooded with much light, changes its colors as it is moved. Since these colors result from a certain impact of light, surely we 800

[41] That is, the assumption, which he states is false, that white objects are made from smaller things that are white, and black in the same way from smaller black objects.

[42] Reading *luce* for *lucem* (i.e., *luce* for *lucē*), and changing the punctuation of the usual texts. This reading does not appear to have been suggested before.

must believe that without this impact the color could not exist.[j]

810 Since the eye receives in itself a particular blow when it is said to perceive white, and blows of a different sort when it perceives black and other colors, and since in the case of things sensed by touch it makes no difference what color they have but only with what shapes they are endowed, we may be sure that the atoms have no need of color, and that it is by reason of their various shapes that they cause the varying sensations.[43] Moreover, on the theory that a particular color does not belong to a particular atomic shape, and that all shapes may occur in any 820 color whatever, why are not the things that these atoms compose marked by colors of every kind? In that case it is probable that even crows as they fly would dart white color from white wings, and that there would be black swans formed from black seed, or that swans might be of any other color you please, either solid or variegated.[44]

Moreover, as you divide any thing into smaller and smaller parts, you can see the color slowly fading and disappearing, as happens for example when purple cloth is torn into tiny shreds. 830 When the cloth is divided thread by thread, the purple or scarlet, by far the brightest of colors, is all destroyed, so that from this you can know that before division reaches the level of the atom the parts lose all their color.

In the last place, you agree that not all things utter cries or give forth odors, and therefore you do not assign sound and smell as attributes to all things. Thus since we cannot see all

[43] All sensation, including sight and the recognition of color, is due to touch. Since touch cannot recognize color, the sensation of color must be due to the shape, not the color, of that which impinges on the eye.

[44] Bailey calls this, with reason, a "very condensed and consequently obscure paragraph." Lucretius here supposes that his opponents, although assigning color to the individual atoms, made color independent of atomic shape. But the shape of the individual atom is the major factor in controlling the combinations into which it can enter. If the color of an object, like its other secondary characteristics, depends ultimately on the shape of the atoms that compose it, color will be as consistent as the other characteristics; but if color is a property of the atom and independent of its shape, then crows may be white and swans parti-colored.

things with the eyes, we may know just as surely that certain things exist without color as that certain ones are without odor or sound, and the intelligent mind can recognize these no less 840 clearly than it can mark down those that are without the other qualities.

But that you may not believe that the atoms lack nothing but color, they are also totally without warmth, cold, and glowing heat; they are incapable of sound and lack taste; and they do not give forth from their bodies any odor of their own. When you intend to prepare the bland liquid of marjoram or myrrh, or the essence of spikenard that breathes perfume to our nostrils, it is of greatest importance that you seek out an oil that is odorless 850 and sends to us no aroma of its own, as far indeed as this is practical and attainable, so that it will to the least possible extent infect with its own smell the scents that are mixed with it as a base and cooked with it, thus destroying them. So for the same reason, since the atoms can emit nothing from themselves,[45] they of themselves surely bring to the creation of things neither odor nor sound of their own, and for the same reason no scent, nor any cold or heat, either moderate or great. Since the other secondary qualities are such as belong to mortal things (for example, 860 pliability to what is soft, fragility to what crumbles, sponginess to what is porous), the atoms can have no part in them if we are to have beneath the visible world an immortal foundation upon which the safety of all may depend, so that all things may not be reduced utterly to nothing before your eyes.

Now you must admit that all the things we see endowed with sensation are nevertheless formed from insentient atoms.[46]

[45] As solid, indivisible units, the atoms cannot give off anything from themselves. Sensible objects formed from these atoms give off atoms in such combinations as to affect our different senses. For the rest of the paragraph I have translated as best I can the text as printed by Bailey except for changes in punctuation; but it is not very satisfactory, and there may well be a lacuna between lines 858 and 859, i.e., before the sentence beginning "Since the other secondary qualities."

[46] Lucretius here reduces sensation (and, at least by implication, the mental processes that follow sensation) to the level of the secondary quali-

Phenomena that can readily be recognized by the senses, far from disproving this or tending against it, rather lead us by the hand 870 and force us to believe, as I have said, that living creatures spring from things that have no consciousness. Indeed you may see living worms come into being from vile dung when the earth, wet with excessive rain, has become rotten.[47] Moreover, we see that all things change in the same way. Streams, leaves, and pleasant pastures change themselves into cattle, the cattle change themselves into our bodies, and often from our flesh the strength of wild beasts and the bodies of winged birds gain increase. Thus Nature changes every kind of food into living 880 bodies, and from it she produces all the powers of sensation possessed by living creatures in almost the same way as she unfolds dry wood into flames and turns it all into fire. Do you now see that it is of great importance in what order atoms of each kind are placed and with what other atoms they are mingled as they move others and are moved themselves?

Again, what is it that strikes your mind, moves it, and forces it to express changeable opinions, preventing you from believing that the sentient is sprung from the insentient? Truly, 890 it is the fact that when stones, blocks of wood, and earth are mixed together they cannot produce a living capacity for feeling. Therefore in this matter it will be well to remember that I do not say that on every occasion sensory power instantly arises from all the matter that may form sentient creatures; rather I say that the fineness of the matter that forms them, the shapes of

---

ties just discussed and denied to the atoms. There are, however, certain essential differences, which he passes over. The qualities mentioned are due to certain motions or combinations of the atoms within sensible objects, which cause those objects to emit atoms in films (color) or in streams (sound, heat, etc.) that can be recognized by sentient creatures external to the objects. Sensation and perception are caused within the sentient creature by motions or combinations of its own atoms induced by something external to the creature.

47 See lines 898 and 928 of this book, and also III. 719 and V. 797–98. This belief in the spontaneous generation of worms from warm mud was held even by Aristotle; see *History of Animals* V.1, 539a22, and also Robin's note on this passage.

the particles, and their motions, arrangements, and positions are of great importance. None of this is visible to us when pieces of wood or clods of earth are mingled; and yet when pieces of wood or clods of earth have been rotted, so to speak, by the rain, they do give birth to worms because the atoms, having been thrown out of their previous motions by what has been added, come together in such a way that it is natural that living creatures be produced. 900

Some assert that it is possible for the sentient to be formed out of sentient parts, and these in turn from other parts that enjoy sensation ⟨and so on to the very atoms themselves. But those who believe this make the atoms mortal⟩ since they make them soft;[48] for all sensation is joined to flesh, sinews, and veins, all of which we see are soft and made of substance that is destined to perish. However, let us grant that particles capable of feeling can be eternal; even so we must suppose them either to have the sensation proper to a part of the body or to be like whole living creatures. But of necessity the parts of the body are unable to have sensation by themselves; for every sensation of our members depends upon us as entire bodies, and the hand apart from the rest of the body cannot be conscious of any sensation whatever, nor can any part of the body feel by itself. There remains the other possibility, that the sentient particles are each of them like a whole living creature. They must then feel what we feel, so that they can on all occasions share in our vital sensations. How then will these sentient parts be called first beginnings of matter, and how will they avoid destruction, since they are living beings and since to have life is one and the same thing as to be subject to death? Yet grant again that they can be immortal. In that case by their coming together and joining they will make nothing but a tumultuous crowd of living things, just as men, cattle, and wild beasts cannot create a single 910 920

[48] The manuscripts as transmitted cannot be translated, and most editors agree that there is a lacuna after line 903. The argument here, as in lines 963–90, is against Anaxagoras; Diels' supplement, based on the earlier attack on that philosopher (I. 830–920, especially 847), makes acceptable sense.

being by joining together. But if by chance each of these particles gives up from its own body its own sensations and takes those of another, what reason is there for ascribing to it that which must be taken away? Then finally there is the argument to which we appealed before—since we see the eggs of winged birds changing into living chicks, and since we see worms swarm out when earth has given way to mud in time of unseasonable
930 rains, we may know that it is possible for sentient creatures to arise from insentient matter.

But perhaps someone[49] will say that at any rate the sentient can come from the insentient by a transformation or by some sort of birth by which it is thrust out; it will be enough to demonstrate clearly to him that no birth takes place nor is anything changed unless there has previously been an act of union. First, no body can have feeling before the living body itself has been born, because obviously the atoms that are to form it are still
940 widely scattered through air, water, earth, and those things that grow from the earth, and have not yet come together and produced the proper life-giving motions in relation to each other, roused by which the watchful senses guard over every living thing.[50]

Moreover, when some living creature is suddenly struck by a blow heavier than it can endure, then all the senses of the body and the mind are thrown into confusion; for the positions of the atoms are disturbed and their life-giving motions far within are interrupted until the trembling of the matter through all
950 the limbs shakes loose from the body the vital bands of the soul, scatters the soul atoms, and forces them from the body through all the pores. What else should we think that a blow from with-

[49] The difficulty of interpreting this section is greatly increased by our ignorance of the theory, or theories, that Lucretius is attacking (see Bailey on this passage).

[50] The argument is obscure; but apparently there was a theory (probably Stoic) according to which the first beginnings normally have no power of sensation, but each of them gains such power when it becomes part of a living organism. But this would be a change on the part of the unchanging atom, which is, to Lucretius, impossible. The earlier arguments against sensation in the atoms would also apply in large part to this theory.

out can do but scatter the soul atoms and dissolve their combinations?[51] It sometimes happens that, when a less violent blow has been struck, the surviving life-giving motions win their battle, calm the great tumult caused by the blow, call each of the parts back into its own path, shake off, so to speak, the motion of ruin that was gaining supremacy in the body, and rekindle the senses that were almost lost. In what other way could the 960 living creatures gather together their souls and turn themselves back to life from the very threshold of destruction, instead of completing the almost finished journey and perishing?

Next,[52] since pain comes about when the atoms throughout the living flesh and limbs are disturbed by some violence and tremble in their places within, and soothing pleasure comes when they return to their seats, we may know that the atoms can neither be touched by any pain nor receive any pleasure of their own, since they are not made up of any lesser bodies from a 970 change in whose motions the atoms might feel pain or receive some profit of life-giving joy. Therefore the atoms cannot be endowed with any sensation.

Then, if we must attribute sensation to the atoms that compose every kind of living creature in order that the creature itself may feel, what shall we say of the particles by virtue of which the human race makes its peculiar growth? Surely they are shaken with deep laughter as they jeer at us and wet their faces and cheeks with a dew of tears, and they have the wit to say much about the mixture by which things are made and to ask of what smaller parts they themselves are formed; for surely these 980 particles, since they are assumed to be like complete men, ought also to be formed of other elements, and these in turn from others, so that you would never venture to call a halt. I will

[51] A blow can bring unconsciousness if consciousness depends on the combinations of the atoms, but not if it is a property of the unchanging atoms themselves. In the rest of the paragraph a similar argument is based on the fact that recovery from such derangement is possible. It is not clear whether this paragraph is part of the argument against the unknown theory of lines 931–43, or whether some new theory is being opposed.

[52] Like lines 902–30, this section is directed against Anaxagoras.

push your argument to this point: whatever you say speaks and laughs and thinks must be formed from particles that do the same. But if we see that this is foolish and mad, and that a man can laugh though he be not formed from laughing atoms, and can be wise and express opinions in learned words although not made from atoms that are sapient and fluent, why cannot all 990 sentient creatures of the visible world have been built up from seeds that altogether lack the powers of sense?[53]

Finally, we are all sprung from heavenly seed; that same sky is father to all; and when the fostering mother earth has received from the sky the flowing drops of moisture, she is made fertile and brings forth the bright crops and the pleasant groves. She also produces the human race and all the generations of wild beasts, since she furnishes the food by which all living things nourish their bodies, retain sweet life, and produce offspring; therefore she has properly won the name of mother. 1000 Likewise whatever has once come from the earth returns into the earth, and what was sent from the heavenly regions is carried back to the temples of the sky and is received by them. Death does not destroy things in such a way as to annihilate their matter; it merely separates the combinations. Then it puts the atoms together in new combinations and causes all things to change their shapes and alter their colors, and to receive the powers of sensation and to give them up in an instant. Thus you may know that in the case of the same atoms it makes a difference with what other atoms they are in contact, in what arrangements they are held, and in what ways they set other 1010 atoms in motion and are moved themselves;[54] and you may not suppose that the qualities that we see changing on the surfaces of things, born at intervals and suddenly perishing, are permanent properties of the eternal atoms. Nay, in these very verses of ours it makes a great difference with what other letters and in what order the several letters are placed; for the same letters that express the words for sky, sea, lands, rivers, and

[53] See I. 915–20.

[54] See I. 817–19, 909–10, II. 760–62, 894–96.

sun also express the words for crops, trees, and animals; if all the letters are not identical, at least the greater part are the same, but their different orders give different meanings to the words.[55] So likewise in things themselves: when the unions, motions, order, position, and pattern of the atoms are changed, the things formed from them must be changed as well. 1021

IV. The Infinite Worlds

1023–1174

Our world is not unique in the universe; it was formed by the combination and separation of atoms, and conditions making this possible have existed and will exist elsewhere. In forming the world the atoms moved subject only to their own laws, not under the guidance of a god. The earth has already passed its prime; like a field that is becoming barren, it will one day decay and crumble into ruin.

Now pay attention, I beg you, to a true teaching; for a disturbingly novel matter is making its way to your ears, and a new view of Nature is about to reveal itself. Yet there is nothing so simple that it does not at first appear rather difficult to believe, and likewise nothing so great and wonderful that all do not gradually cease to marvel at it. Think of the clear, pure color of the 1030 sky and all that it holds, the stars in their courses, the moon, and the splendor of the sun with its brilliant light; if all these were now first visible to men, if they should appear suddenly and without warning, what could be named more worthy of wonder than these, or what in whose existence men would less have ventured to believe beforehand? Nothing, I am sure, so worthy of wonder would this appearance have been held. But you see that now, since all are weary of beholding it, no one

[55] Of the thirteen different letters used in the Latin words of the first group and the twelve used in the second, ten are common to both. For similar illustrations from the letters of the alphabet, see I. 823–26, 912–14. Line 1020, which is identical with line 726, is out of place in this context and is omitted by most editors.

1040 deigns to raise his eyes to the bright regions of the sky. Therefore do not thrust my doctrine from your mind, terrified by its mere novelty; but rather weigh it with keen judgment, and if you see that my arguments for it are true, then yield to it; or if it is false, prepare to resist it. For since the totality of space outside the walls of the world[56] is infinite, the mind seeks to know what there is beyond, to which the spirit may wish to look, and which the free projection of the mind may reach.[k]

First, therefore, in every direction, on every side, above and 1050 below, throughout the whole universe, there is no end—as I have proved, as the fact itself proclaims, and as the nature of the void clearly shows.[57] Since empty space extends without limit in every direction and since, throughout the whole void, atoms countless in number fly about in many ways sped by eternal motion, we can by no means regard it as probable that only this one earth and sky have been created, and that all the many particles of matter on the outside are doing nothing. This is especially true since this world was made by Nature;[58] for after the atoms themselves, of their own accord and by chance, 1060 had been striking together in many ways and at random, uselessly and to no purpose—at length those came together which, at such times as they are joined, are the first step toward the sudden formation of great things: earth, sea, sky, and living creatures.[59] We must therefore admit again and again that elsewhere there are other gatherings of matter such as is this one

[56] In this section (as throughout the whole translation, where the distinction is essential) the term "world" will be used to mean the earth and the heavenly bodies that Lucretius regarded as belonging to it (i.e., sun, moon, stars, planets), as distinguished on the one hand from the "earth," which does not include any of the heavenly bodies, and on the other from the "universe," which includes not only our world but all the others that may exist, and also all the infinite matter and space outside these worlds (see Epicurus, *Letter to Pythocles* 88b).

[57] See Epicurus, *Letter to Herodotus* 45b; and for the argument that the universe is infinite, see I. 958–1113.

[58] That is, by natural law, which is the same throughout the whole infinite universe, and not by some divine design, which might have limited itself to the formation of a single world.

[59] As Lucretius pictures it here, after long eons of undirected and unproductive motion, the atoms in a given portion of the universe fall into the

which our sky holds in its eager embrace. Moreover, when much matter is ready, when there is space at hand and neither any thing nor any cause hinders, truly then things ought to be begun and completed. Now if the atoms are so abundant that all generations of living creatures could not count them, and if the same force and nature remain with the power to throw each kind of atom into its place in the same way as they have been thrown here, you must admit that in other parts of the universe there are other worlds and different races of men and species of wild beasts. 1070

Next is the fact that in the whole there is no single thing that is born and grows, unique and alone, without belonging to some species and being one of many individuals of the same kind. Turn your mind first to animals. You will find that the mountain-ranging breeds of wild beasts are subject to this rule; so too are the offspring of mankind, the silent schools of scaly fish, and every creature that flies. Therefore you must agree that, by the same reasoning, the earth, the sun, the moon, the sea, and the rest are no one of them unique, and that each of them belongs to a countless multitude; for they have a firmly fixed limit of life and possess bodies that have been formed by birth, just as does any one of the species that is abundantly represented in our world by many individuals of its own kind.[60] 1080

If you understand this and hold it well in mind, you see at once that Nature is free, and that, released from haughty rulers, 1090

particular combination and assume the particular motions that quite rapidly bring about the formation of a world such as ours. In this same way, to take examples from our own experience, under proper conditions a salt will suddenly precipitate from a solution or a cloud will quickly form from invisible water vapor. And just as the salt or the cloud will be formed whenever and wherever the conditions are right, so, Lucretius says, a world will be formed whenever and wherever the atoms chance to fall into the proper motions and combinations.

[60] Lucretius appears to argue that if the sun, for example, were eternal, without beginning or end, it might be unique; but since it had a beginning and will have an end, since, in other words, it is a temporary combination of atoms, it will be subject to the same rule as other combinations and will be one of many. Lucretius returns to the problem of the formation of the world in V. 416–508.

she herself does everything through herself and of her own will without regard to any deities. For, by the sacred hearts of the gods who pass a quiet and serene life in tranquil peace, who has the power to rule the boundless universe? Who can take in his hands like a driver the mighty reins of deep space? Who can turn all the skies with steady motion, and warm all the earths[61] into fruitfulness with heavenly fires? Who can be present in all 1100 places at all times, to make darkness with the storm clouds and shatter the peace of the sky with thunder, often overthrowing his own temples with the lightning he sends, or withdrawing into the deserts to rage as he practices with the weapon that often passes over the guilty and kills the innocent and undeserving?[62]

After the birth-time of the world, the first day of sea and land, and the first rising of the sun, many bodies have come in from without, many atoms have been added round about; by its tossing, the great whole has brought these together, so that from 1110 them the sea and the land might increase, the mansion of the sky gain additional space and raise its lofty roof far from the lands, and the air rise up. For from every side all the atoms proper to each thing are distributed by blows, each to its own kind, and they draw together in their own classes: water is added to water, earth grows with earthy matter, fires forge fire and sky forges sky, until Nature, creator and perfecter of things, has brought all to the final end of growth, that is, to the point where no more matter is poured into the life-giving veins than 1120 flows out from them and is lost. At this time the life of all things ought to stand fast; at this point Nature, by her own laws, checks the increase. For these things that you see growing with cheerful increase, ascending step by step to maturity, are taking more matter into themselves than they are sending forth, while the

[61] That is, the many skies and earths that compose the many worlds of the universe.

[62] Compare VI. 387–422, for a similar ironical treatment of the thunder and lightning of Jupiter. This paragraph is parenthetical and interrupts the thought, line 1105 logically following line 1089. Compare the anti-teleological argument in lines 167–83, and the long passages in V. 110–234 and VI. 379–422.

food still passes easily into all their veins, and they are not yet so extended that they lose much, wasting more than they use as life-giving food. Surely we must admit that many atoms do flow and depart from things; but the number that is being added to them must be greater until they have reached the highest point of growth. Thereafter, little by little, old age shatters their strength and full-grown vigor, and life wastes away along the downward path. Indeed, when once growth has ceased, the larger a thing is and the greater its extent, the more atoms does it scatter and send forth from its body in all directions; and food is not easily distributed into all its veins, nor is there a large enough reserve from which matter can well up and be at hand to compensate for the great tide the body pours forth. Therefore they all have good cause to perish, when they have been wasted by the outflow and succumb to the blows from outside. For then, in old age, food fails them; nor are the hostile atoms that hammer on each thing from without slow to overcome it and destroy it with their blows.[63] 1130 1140

In this way too even the walls of the great world round about, overwhelmed, will decay and crumble into ruin. Food ought to refresh and renew all things, food ought to prop them up, food ought to sustain them—but all is useless, since the veins do not admit enough nor does Nature supply a sufficient quantity.[64] Even now the age is broken; the spent earth, which once created all races and brought forth the great bodies of wild beasts, now creates little creatures with difficulty. As I believe, no golden rope let down living things from on high into the fields, nor did the sea and the waves that beat upon the rocks create them; rather, this same earth that now nourishes them from herself gave them birth.[65] Moreover the earth herself of her own accord first created for mortals the shining fields of 1150

[63] The growth and decay of worlds is like that of all other created things (see I. 551–64, 1038–51).

[64] This sentence does not apply very well to the world, and it may be out of place.

[65] See V. 783–836. For Lucretius, birth and growth are practically identical processes; both are due to the addition of atoms. And decay and death are a reversal of the process.

grain and the cheery vineyards; she herself gave sweet fruits and
1160 happy pastures. Now these grow with difficulty even when aided by our labor; and though we wear out cattle and robust farmers and waste away the plow, we are scantily sustained by the fields. To this extent the fields make their produce less and our toil greater. Now all too often the aged plowman shakes his head and laments that his great labors have been spent to no purpose; and as he compares the present with times that are past, he often praises the good fortune of his father. Likewise the gloomy cultivator of the old and withered vine finds fault
1170 with the times and piles complaints upon the age; he grumbles, telling how the men of old, since they were filled with piety, easily sustained their lives on small farms, for the measure of the field was then less for each man; he does not understand that everything is slowly wasting away and going to the grave, worn out in the last days of existence.[l]

BOOK THREE

I. The Nature and Structure of the Soul

1–416

Following Epicurus, the poet turns from the world's mortality to that of the soul, hoping thereby to free men from the fear of death. The soul is divided into the spirit, which pervades the whole body, and the mind, which is more subtle in nature and resides in the breast. The spirit receives sensations which it passes on to the mind; the mind receives these, and through the spirit it controls the actions of the body. The soul in both its parts is corporeal, consisting of smooth, round, finely divided particles of air, warmth, and wind, together with particles of a fourth, nameless matter, far surpassing the others in fineness and mobility. The proportions in which these four elements are mingled in the soul of any creature determines that creature's character. The soul is held together by the body, and neither can long exist without the other.

You, who first were able to lift so bright a light from amid such darkness, and to illuminate the blessings of life—you I follow, O glory of the Greek race; and in the tracks you once trod I now firmly place my footsteps, not so much desiring to vie with you as yearning to imitate you because of my love; for how should the swallow contend with the swan, or in what way can the kids with trembling limbs equal in a race the strength of a mighty steed? You are our father, the discoverer of our doctrine; you supply to us the teachings of a parent; and 10
as bees sip from all the blossoms in the flower-bearing meadows, so from your writings, O glorious one, we feast upon all the golden sayings, golden and most worthy of everlasting life. For as soon as your philosophy, springing from your inspired soul,

begins to proclaim the truth about Nature, the terrors of the mind flee away, the walls of the world open, and I see Nature in action throughout all space. I behold the majestic gods and their peaceful abodes, which are neither beaten by any winds
20 or rainstorms, nor violated by any fall of snow, white and hardened by keen cold; rather, they are covered by a cloudless sky, which smiles with light spread far and wide. Nature, moreover, supplies the gods with everything, and nothing at any time disturbs the quiet of their minds. But on the other hand, the regions of Acheron are nowhere to be seen, although the earth does not prevent the inspection of all things that go on beneath our feet through the void below. At these teachings a certain divine pleasure and awe run through me; for by your might
30 Nature has thus been unveiled in all her parts, and made so manifest and visible.

Inasmuch as I have shown the nature of the first beginnings of all things, how they differ from each other in their various forms as, sped by eternal motion, they fly about of their own accord, and have shown, too, in what way each thing can be created from them, it seems needful that I next make clear in my verses the nature of the mind and the spirit,[a] and drive away in headlong flight the fear of Acheron, which throws human life at its very foundations into utter turmoil, and, covering every-
40 thing with the blackness of death, permits no pure and unmixed pleasure to exist. Men frequently say that disease and disgrace are more to be feared than Tartarus, the abode of Death, that they know that the soul is composed of blood (or even of wind, if that theory chance to please them), and that they therefore have no need at all of our philosophy; but you may conclude from the following that they make this boast in order to gain applause, and not because they accept these theories as established. For these same men, exiled from fatherland and banished far from the sight of men, defiled by shameful crime,
50 afflicted with every calamity, still go on living; and wherever they have wandered in their misery, they still make sacrifices to their ancestors, slaughter black victims, and send offerings to

the spirits of the dead, turning their minds to religious observances far more eagerly in the midst of misfortune. Therefore it is proper to examine a man amid doubt and danger and to learn of what sort he is amid disaster; for only then true words are drawn from his inmost heart; the mask is snatched away, and the real features remain.

Next, greed and blind ambition, which compel unhappy men 60 to go beyond the limits of right, at times becoming principals or accomplices in crime and striving night and day with unceasing effort to attain to the greatest resources—these sources of evil in life are in no small part nourished by the fear of death. For to most men shamefaced humiliation and bitter poverty seem to be far distant from the happy and secure life, and appear to hover already, as it were, before the gates of death. Overwhelmed by false terror, in their wish to flee and remove themselves far away from these misfortunes, they acquire wealth 70 through the blood of citizens and greedily double their riches, piling murder upon murder; they cruelly rejoice in the tragic death of a brother and hate and fear the food served on the tables of their kin. In the same way and because of the same fear of death, jealousy often devours men when they see that such and such a one is powerful, or when another walks in the bright array of office and is honored, while they themselves, according to their complaints, are buried in darkness and mire. Some pine away for the sake of statues and fame. It even happens that, because of the fear of death, such weariness of living 80 and of beholding the day lays hold on men that with grieving hearts they inflict death upon themselves, forgetting that fear of this very thing is the source of their troubles. This fear persuades one man to stain his honor, and another to break the bonds of friendship and, in short, to overthrow his sacred obligations; for men have often betrayed their native land and beloved parents while seeking to avoid the regions of Acheron. For like children who in the blinding darkness tremble and fear everything, so at times we, although we be in the light, fear things no more worthy of being feared than the phantoms at 90 which children in the darkness shudder as they imagine that they are upon them. This terror, this darkness of the soul must be dispelled neither by the rays of the sun nor by the bright weapons of the day, but by an understanding of the outer form and the inner law of Nature.[1]

First I say that the mind (which we often call the reason), in which resides the rational power that guides life, is a part of a man, just as much as the hand, the foot, and the eyes are parts of the whole living creature. . . .[2]

⟨Some have said that⟩ the mind, with its power of feeling, is not located in any fixed spot, but is rather a sort of life-giving
100 condition of the body, called by the Greeks "harmony," which makes us live and have the power to feel although no "mind" exists in any part—as when the body is said to have good health, yet health does not form any part of the body possessing it. Thus they do not place in any definite spot the mind and its capacity to feel; in this it seems to me that they have wandered far from the truth. Often a part of the body that is easily visible is in pain, when nevertheless we are happy in another part that is invisible; and on the other hand it often happens that the reverse occurs, when one unhappy in mind experiences well-being
110 in his whole body. In just the same way, when the foot of a sick man is in pain, the head at the time may suffer no discomfort. Moreover, when the limbs have been surrendered to gentle sleep and the overburdened body lies spread out and unconscious, there is nevertheless something else in us that at such a time is stirred in many ways, and experiences to no purpose all the joys and sorrows of the heart.

From what follows, also, you may learn that spirit dwells in the limbs and that the body does not experience sensation be-

[1] Lines 87–93 have been used at II. 55–61, and will appear again at VI. 35–41.

[2] A lacuna of unknown length occurs here. Where the text begins again, Lucretius is presenting a view believed to be that of Aristotle's pupil, Aristoxenus, who was a musician as well as a philosopher (Cicero, *Tusculan Disputations* I. 19–21). In some form, however, the theory that the soul is a harmony is older, since Plato is at pains to combat it in the *Phaedo* (91c–95a).

cause of a harmony. In the first place, it sometimes happens that even when a large part of the body has been removed, life still lingers in our members; and again, when a few particles of warmth have fled and the breath has made its way out through the mouth, this same life at once deserts the veins and abandons the bones. From this you may be sure that all the particles do not play equal parts or maintain our safety equally, but those that are composed of air and warmth have the greater responsibility for retaining life in the limbs. Therefore there exist in our very bodies warmth and life-giving air, and these desert our dying members. Since, then, the mind and spirit have been found to be, so to speak, a part of a man, give up the name "harmony," whether it was brought down to musicians from lofty Helicon, or whether they themselves borrowed it from some other source and then transferred it to a thing that up to that time lacked a name of its own. However that may be, let them have it; but do you heed my further words. 120 130

Now I say that the mind and the spirit are held in mutual union,[3] and by themselves form a single nature; yet the understanding, which we also call the mind and the reason, is, as it were, the head, and lords it over the whole body. It is located in the central region of the breast, and there it remains.[4] Here throb dread and fear, joy soothes this region; here, then, are the reason and the mind. The remaining portion of the spirit, scattered through the whole body, obeys the reason, and is moved at its bidding and impulse. The reason alone has understanding for itself and through itself; it alone rejoices for itself when neither the spirit nor the body is moved by anything. And as 140

[3] See Epicurus, *Letter to Herodotus* 63a–68a, and scholium on 66.

[4] The location of the reason and the emotions had been much debated by ancient philosophers. Epicurus and Lucretius regard both as arising from the same source, the *animus* or mind (often called by the double name *mens animusque*, "reason and mind"), which they place in the breast. Today we tend, when speaking in popular or poetic language, to place the reason in the head and the emotions in the breast. It has been noted that the examples Lucretius gives, in the following lines, to show that the mind is in the breast are examples of emotions.

we are not tortured through the whole body when the head or the eye is attacked by pain and suffering, so at times the mind
150 suffers, and again abounds in joy, while the rest of the spirit, which is in the members and the limbs, is stirred by nothing new. But when the mind is more violently moved by a pressing fear, we see the whole spirit throughout the members join in the feeling; sweat and pallor occur over the whole body, speech is broken, words fade away, eyes are darkened, ears ring, limbs give way, until we often see men collapse from terror of the mind. Thus anyone might readily know from this that the spirit is closely joined to the mind; for when it has been shaken by the
160 mind, it finally drives and strikes the body.

The same reasoning shows that the mind and spirit are corporeal in nature. Indeed, when the mind and spirit are seen to move the members, stir the body from sleep, change the expression of the face, and direct and turn the whole body, must we not admit that they are corporeal? For we know that none of these things can be accomplished without contact, and that there cannot be any contact without material body.[5] Moreover, you see that the mind within the body suffers with the body, and
170 joins with it in feeling. Even if the hostile violence of a weapon, driven in through sundered bones and sinews, does not reach the life, still faintness follows, and a welcome collapse upon the ground, a whirling of the wits there on the ground, and at times an uncertain wish to rise. Thus the mind must be corporeal in nature, since it suffers from the blows of corporeal weapons.

I shall proceed to explain to you in my verses of what substance the mind is, and of what it is composed. In the first place,
180 I say that it is very tenuous and is made from the most minute particles.[6] Pay attention so that, from the proofs that follow,

[5] The way in which the mind is stirred by external matter, and the way in which the mind acts through the spirit to move the body, will be developed later.

[6] See Epicurus, *Letter to Herodotus* 63a and scholium on 66. In this section and the one that follows, Lucretius is not speaking of the atoms that compose the soul, but of larger particles or complexes. All atoms in or out of complexes move with the same speed, but the motions of the complexes

you may be able to understand that this is so. It is clear that nothing is done as quickly as the mind imagines it done and begins to do it.[7] The mind thus stirs itself more rapidly than do any of the things that are openly visible to our eyes. But anything so swift must consist of particles that are so perfectly round and so very minute that they can be moved when acted on by the slightest impulse. For example, water flows when moved by a very slight force, since it is formed of parts that are small and easy to roll; but on the other hand, the structure of honey is more viscous, its liquid more sluggish, and its movement slower, for its whole stock of matter clings more closely together because, we may be sure, it consists of particles that are not so smooth, so fine, or so round. With a light and trembling breath you can scatter a high heap of poppy seed from top to bottom, but you cannot do this to a heap of stones or of ears of grain; thus bodies enjoy mobility in proportion as they are very small and smooth. But on the other hand, whatever things you find to be heavier and rougher are for that reason more stable.[8] Since then we have found the mind to be wonderfully mobile, it must consist of particles that are very small and smooth and very round.[9] If you understand this fact, my good friend, you will find it useful and advantageous in many ways.

190

200

---

differ (see II. 80–166 and notes). We shall see in lines 231–57 below that the soul (and probably each of the particles in the soul) contains atoms characteristic of four different elements; heat, still air, air in motion, and a fourth unnamed element. Although in this section Lucretius is considering the composition of the whole soul, in this paragraph he is thinking primarily of the mind, and in the next of the spirit.

[7] Voluntary action is explained in IV. 877–906. The mind first visualizes the completed action, then stirs the spirit, which in turn sets the body in motion. It is assumed that the minute delay between the mental conception and the beginning of the physical action is due to the body, and that the invisible motions of mind and spirit are practically instantaneous.

[8] See II. 444–55.

[9] The poet argues from the mobility of the mind to its composition. As a matter of experience, nothing is swifter than the mind. Therefore like other things that are easily moved, it must consist of small, smooth, round particles. And as its mobility surpasses that of any other known thing, so must its particles surpass all others in smallness, smoothness, and roundness.

The following also teaches the nature of the soul, showing of what fine texture it is and in how small a space it would be contained if it could be gathered together. When the quiet peace of death has laid hold of a man and the mind and spirit have departed, you see nothing withdrawn from the whole body as regards appearance, nothing as regards weight; death preserves everything except the living sense and the warm breath. Therefore the entire spirit, interwoven through veins, flesh, and sinews, must consist of very small seeds, seeing that, when all of it has departed from the whole body, the outer surface of the members is still unbroken and not a bit of the weight has departed. In this way when the bouquet of wine has vanished, when the sweet fragrance of an ointment has escaped into the air, or when the savor has departed from any body, the thing itself seems to the eyes undiminished by the loss, nor has anything been subtracted from its weight. This is surely because it is by many minute seeds that savor and fragrance are created throughout the whole substance of the things. Therefore you may know most certainly that the mind and the spirit are composed of very minute particles, since when they flee they take no weight away.

Yet we must not suppose that the composition of the soul is simple.[10] For a slight breath mixed with warmth departs from the dying, and the warmth in turn carries air with it.[b] There is no warmth with which air is not mixed; for because the structure of fire is open, many particles of air must be in motion within it. Now we have found that the nature of the soul is threefold; yet all these together are not enough to create sensation, since our reason does not admit that any of these three can originate the motions that produce sensation, and the thoughts that stir in the mind. It is therefore necessary that a certain fourth element be added to them.[11] This element is entirely without a name; nothing exists more mobile or finer than

[10] See Epicurus, *Letter to Herodotus* 63a.

[11] In *Letter to Herodotus* 63a, we read: "But there is also a part of the soul that goes far beyond even these two in fineness, and for this reason it is more ready to share in the feelings of the rest of the body."

this, nothing that is made of smaller, smoother atoms. This is first to arouse in our members the motions that are sensation. Since it consists of small particles, it is the first to be moved; then warmth and the invisible particles of wind receive their motions, then the air, and finally all the parts are moved, the blood is stirred into motion, all the flesh feels it, and finally the 250 bones and the marrow[12] receive the sensation, be it pleasure or its opposite. Pain cannot penetrate to the marrow without risk, nor can keen suffering make its way there without everything being so disturbed that the opportunity for life fails, and the portions of the soul flee away through all the pores of the body. But as a rule the motions do not penetrate below the surface of the body; for this reason we are able to retain life.[c]

Although I am eager to explain how the four elements are mixed and in what fashion they are arranged as they function, the poverty of our native tongue checks me against my will; but 260 yet I shall touch upon the main points as best I can. The atoms speed about among themselves with the motions proper to atoms, in such a way that no one of the four can be separated, nor can the powers of one act when it is spatially separated from the others; rather, they exist as the manifold power of a single body.[13] Similarly, in the flesh of any living creature, there is usually odor and a characteristic warmth and taste, yet from all these is formed a single mass of body. In this way a single nature of the soul is created by the mixture of warmth, air, invisible 270 particles of wind, and that mobile element which gives from itself to the others the beginning of that motion from which the motion that is sensation throughout the flesh first arises.

[12] Both in popular language and in some of the medical writers the marrow was regarded as the center and source of life.

[13] Elsewhere in his discussion of the composition of the soul, Lucretius speaks of the particles of the four elements of which it is composed, not of the atoms that make up these particles. In this sentence he uses a term that is proper to the atoms themselves, not to the complexes. The apparent meaning is that the atoms that make up the complexes of each of the elements are constantly being interchanged (some kinds of atoms being found in all four), and this interchange binds the elements more closely together.

For this fourth element lies wholly hidden deep within and far beneath, nor is there anything in the whole human body more deeply buried;[14] and finally, it is the very soul of the whole soul. Just as the mind and the spirit, mixed in our members and in the entire body, are concealed because they are made of particles that are small and few in number, so the nameless element, 280 since it is made of minute particles, is hidden. It is, in short, like the very soul of the whole soul, and it holds sway in the entire body.

In a similar fashion, it is necessary that wind, air, and warmth exert their powers intermixed through the limbs, and that one now be inferior to the others and now rise superior to them, yet in such a way that all together are seen to form a certain unity, so that neither warmth nor wind separately, nor yet air by itself, may destroy and dissolve sensation by their independent action.[15] For there is that heat in the mind also, which it assumes when it boils over in anger and when fire flashes keenly 290 from the eyes. There is also much cold wind, the companion of dread, which rouses a shudder in the members and makes the limbs tremble. Finally there is the condition of quiet air that occurs when the breast is peaceful and the face calm. Those beings have more of heat whose violent breasts and passionate minds easily boil over in rage. To this group belong in the first place the violent lions, constantly growling and bursting their

14 Although Lucretius here uses terms descriptive of location, he is thinking of something more difficult to express. Even though we cannot perceive by the senses the particles or complexes of air, warmth, and wind, we can at least perceive the things ordinarily formed by such particles, from which the particles get their names. The terms "air," "warmth," and "wind" have meanings to us. But the particles of the fourth essence form no such perceptible matter, and we can give that essence no name nor can we visualize it in any way. Thus it is further "below" the range of our senses than are the other three elements of the soul.

15 Sensation results from the action of the fourth element, which sets the other three in motion. Neither air, wind, nor warmth can create sensation; and if air, for example, predominated in the soul and controlled it, the soul would function as air rather than as soul and could not receive from the fourth element the motions that are sensation. In an extreme case, sensation would cease; should the disproportion be less serious, it would merely affect the character of the soul, as described in the rest of this section.

breasts with their roarings, who cannot contain the tide of wrath within their hearts. But the cold mind of deer has more of the wind and more quickly stirs chill currents through the flesh that cause a trembling to appear in the limbs. The life of the ox depends rather on the calm air. No smoky torch of anger applied to his heart stirs him too much, while beclouding his mind in the shadow of its blinding murk; nor does he become numb, transfixed with the chilling darts of fear. He stands in the middle between the deer and the cruel lions. So it is with the human race. Although a given group of men may receive an equal polish from education, yet each is left with the basic marks of his native disposition. One must not think that evil tendencies can be so eradicated that one man will not turn too readily to cruel wrath, another be daunted a little too quickly by fear, and the third undergo certain things more calmly than is right. In many other respects, too, men inevitably differ in their inner natures and the dispositions that depend on these; but I cannot now set forth the hidden causes of these differences, nor invent names enough for the combinations of elements from which this variety of natures arises. But I see that in this situation this one sure statement can be made: the remaining traces of native faults that our philosophy cannot dispel are so small that nothing prevents us from living lives worthy of the gods.

300

310

320

Thus the soul[16] is held together by the whole body, and is itself the guardian of the body and the cause of its safety; for soul and body cling together with common roots, and it is clear that they cannot be separated without being destroyed. As it is not easy to extract the odor from pieces of incense without destroying the whole, so it is not easy to tear the mind and spirit from the whole body without the destruction of all three. Thus with their beginnings interwoven from their very origin, they are endowed with a life that is shared among them, and it is evident that neither the body nor the mind has the capacity to experience sensation by itself, without the aid of the other; but the sensation that has been kindled in our flesh by the common motions of the two is fanned into flame from either side. More-

330

[16] See Epicurus, *Letter to Herodotus* 63b–66.

over the body neither is born by itself, nor does it grow by itself, and it is clear that it does not endure by itself after death. The 340 body is not like water, which often releases the heat that has been given it and is not injured by this, but remains unharmed. The limbs, I say, cannot remain behind and survive the dissolution of the soul; rather, they perish, shattered to their depths, and rot away. From the very beginning of their existence the body and the soul in mutual contact learn life-giving motions, even while hidden in the body and womb of the mother, in such a way that dissolution[17] cannot occur without rack and ruin; so you see that, since their preservation depends on their union, the nature of the body and soul are linked together.

350 Next, if anyone denies that the body has the capacity to feel and believes that it is the spirit mixed in the whole body that receives the motion that we call sensation, he is contradicting things that are clear and sure.[18] For who would explain what the sensation experienced by the body is, if it is not that which experience itself demonstrates and teaches to us?[19] It is objected that the body completely lacks feeling when the spirit has left it. Yes, for it loses what was not an inseparable property of it during life; and it loses many other things in addition to this, when it is driven from life.[20] It is hard to maintain that the eyes see 360 nothing and that the mind[21] looks through them as if through open doors, since the feeling in the eyes leads us against this

[17] Probably the dissolution of the soul, since the word is the same as that found five lines above; but possibly the separation of the soul and the body.

[18] See Epicurus, *Letter to Herodotus* 64.

[19] We have here the typical Epicurean appeal to the senses as the source of knowledge. We may draw false conclusions from the senses, but the senses themselves never lie. The views combated in this paragraph and the next are those of the Stoics.

[20] Sensation is an accident, not a property, of the body (see I. 449–82 for the meaning of these terms).

[21] In using the term "mind" (*animus*), rather than "spirit" (*anima*), Lucretius is simply following the terminology of the Stoics, whom he is refuting. In his own theory it is, of course, the particles of *anima* in the eye that receive the sensation and transmit it to the *animus*. So too in the next section, he uses *animus* in stating Democritus' theory, but *anima* when answering this by giving his own.

belief; for this feeling carries us and drives us to the very pupils themselves, especially when, as often happens, we are unable to see gleaming objects because our eyes are hampered by the glare. This would not happen in the case of doors; for opened doors through which we ourselves see do not experience difficulty. Moreover, if our eyes serve as doors, it seems that the mind ought to see things more clearly if the eyes were removed, yes, the very door and the doorposts as well.

In this connection you could not accept what is proposed by (370) the venerable opinion of Democritus—an honored man—namely, that the individual particles of body and mind alternate one by one, succeeding each other in juxtaposition and binding the frame together. For not only are the seeds of spirit much smaller than those from which our bodies and flesh are composed, but also they are inferior in number and are sown here and there far apart through the frame. You may at least assert this: that the minute particles of spirit maintain among themselves intervals as great as the size of the smallest bodies which, when they fall on us, are just able to stir in our bodies (380) the motions that cause sensation. For sometimes we are not conscious of the resting of dust upon our bodies or of the settling of the powder that has been shaken upon our limbs, nor do we feel the mist at night, or the slender threads of the spider's web that touch us as we tear it in passing. We do not know that the flimsy web of the spider has fallen upon our heads, or the feathers of birds, or the flying down that as a rule settles slowly because of its lightness, nor do we feel the passage of every living creature and the separate imprint of the feet that gnats and (390) other insects place upon our bodies. And thus many particles of body must be set in motion in us, before the particles that form the spirit and are diffused in our frames throughout our limbs begin to feel that the body particles have been shaken, and before the particles of spirit in their turn, vibrating through the intervals between the particles of body, are able to run together, join, and leap apart again.[d]

The mind is better able to maintain the stronghold of life than is the spirit, and it has more power for life's preservation.

Without the reason and mind, no part of the spirit can remain
400 in the body for an instant, but readily follows the mind as a companion and dissipates into the air, leaving the limbs cold in the chill of death;[22] but he who retains his mind and reason remains alive. However much a man's trunk has been mangled and the limbs cut off on all sides, although spirit has been torn from him all about and taken from his body, he still lives and breathes the life-giving air of heaven. Deprived not of all but of a great part of his spirit, yet he delays and clings to life; just as the living power of sight remains if the pupil of the eye is un-
410 injured when the iris is lacerated, provided that you do not destroy the circle of the eye, cutting all around and leaving the pupil isolated, for that cannot be done without the destruction of both. But if that little central part of the eye is injured, at once sight comes to an end and darkness follows even though the bright orb is otherwise intact.[23] By such a compact as this the spirit and the mind are always bound.

II. Proofs of the Mortality of the Soul

417–829

Composed of the finest atoms, the soul is too tenuous to survive the body's death, and is subject to the body's ills. When the body decays after death, the soul atoms are scattered; thus, since the spirit can be divided, it is not immortal. We have no memory of a former existence, nor any other evidence that the soul either existed before the body or will exist after it. A mortal body cannot be united with an immortal soul; only those things are immortal that contain no void, are intangible, or occupy all space.

[22] See Epicurus, *Letter to Herodotus* 65, where Epicurus describes the fatal effect of the loss of soul even if the body is intact, in much the same terms that Lucretius uses for the loss of the mind while the spirit is uninjured.

[23] Dr. William B. Clark of the Victor C. Smith Memorial Eye Clinic comments: "I am afraid Lucretius was a little inaccurate in his description. . . . Even at that I think it was a very astute observation for the time."

Come now: so that you may know that living creatures possess fleeting minds and spirits subject to birth and death,[24] I shall go on to set forth verses won by sweet toil after long seeking, a gift worthy of you. Join spirit and mind under a single name; and when I say, for example, "spirit," and show that it is mortal, imagine that I also say "mind," since they are one thing and the same.[25] 420

In the first place, I have shown that the gentle soul is composed of minute seeds and of much smaller particles than is water or mist or smoke; for the soul is far superior to these in mobility and, when impelled by a slight cause, is more deeply moved. Indeed, it is even moved by idols of smoke or mist when, for example, we are deep in sleep and see the offerings on the altar send up smoke and breathe steam on high; for there is no doubt that thought and dreams are caused by idols that are brought to us. Since you see that milk or water pour out in all directions when a container is broken, and since mist and smoke are dissipated into the air, you must believe that the soul, being composed of seeds more mobile than are these, also is poured out and perishes much more quickly than these and is more rapidly separated into its original elements when once it has been taken from the body of a man and has departed from it.[e] Truly, when the body, which constituted a sort of jar for the soul, is not able to hold it because it itself has been shaken by some blow or has lost the blood from its veins and become porous, how do you think that the soul can be held together by the air, which is a container more porous than the body? 430 440

Moreover, we feel that the mind is born at the same time as the body, grows along with it, and becomes old at the same time.

[24] The proofs of the mortality of the soul (lines 417–829) form the most important part of Book III, if not of the whole poem. It is safe to assume that most, if not all, of the separate proofs came directly or indirectly from Epicurus, but it is impossible to be more specific. It should however be noted that, although Epicurean terminology is used from time to time, only the first of the arguments really depends on the atomic composition of the soul.

[25] In the translation of this part of the poem, "soul" will be used unless there is particular reason for distinguishing between "spirit" and "mind."

For just as children totter with weak and tender bodies, so the judgment of their minds is unsure. Then when life reaches ma-
450 turity and the physical powers become robust, the understanding is greater and the capacity of the mind is increased. Afterwards, when the body has been shaken by time's fierce force and the limbs sag with their strength blunted, then the intellect limps, the tongue wanders, the mind totters, all things fail and come to naught at the same time. So it is natural that the whole structure of the soul be dissipated like smoke into the high air of heaven, inasmuch as we see that it is born with the body, grows up along with it, and becomes, in old age, weary and weak at the same time, as I have shown.

Next, we see that as the body itself undergoes dire disease and
460 cruel pain, so the soul undergoes carking cares, grief, and fear; therefore it is natural that it partake also of death. The soul often wanders from its course when there is disease of the body; for it ceases to function and speaks raving words, and at times a deep coma carries it into a sound and endless sleep, while the eyes close and the head nods. While in this condition the soul hears no voices, nor can it recognize the faces of those who stand about their friend, calling him back to life and bedewing their
470 faces and cheeks with tears. Therefore you must admit that the soul, too, is dissolved, inasmuch as the touch of disease makes its way into it; for pain and disease are each of them devisers of death, as we have already been taught by the fate of many.[26] When the power of wine has penetrated a man and the glow imparted by it has gone down into his veins, a sluggishness of the limbs follows; his legs get in their own way as he staggers; his
480 tongue hesitates; his mind is sodden; his eyes swim; shouting, sobbing, and brawling grow louder; and now many other symptoms of the same sort follow—why is this, unless it be because

[26] The lines that appear in the manuscripts as 474 and 475 are omitted by all editors. Line 474 is identical with line 510, which was in some way copied here by error; and then line 475 seems to have been added in a not very successful effort to make sense. These errors occurred in some manuscript earlier than that of which all the extant manuscripts are copies, direct or indirect.

the violent vigor of the vine regularly throws the soul into confusion even while it remains within the body? But whatever things can be thrown into confusion and be hindered in their functions thereby give evidence that they would perish and be stripped of all life to come if they were assailed by a slightly stronger power.

Often a man overwhelmed by the sudden violence of disease falls before our eyes as if struck by lightning, foams at the mouth, and groans; his limbs twitch, he loses consciousness, his muscles become tense, he writhes, he gasps, and he wearies his own limbs by tossing to and fro. Surely the reason is that the soul, confused and rent asunder by the violence of the disease through the limbs, ejects foam just as the waves of the salt sea boil before the mighty violence of the winds. Then a groan is wrung from him because his limbs are overcome by pain, and in general because the seeds of sound are ejected, and after they have gathered in his mouth are thrust out as usual and where the way is ready.[27] Loss of wit follows, because the faculty of the mind and spirit is thrown into confusion and, as I have shown, is divided asunder, tossed apart, and rent in pieces by this same poison. When the cause of the disease has withdrawn and the acrid humor of the corrupted body has returned to its place of hiding,[28] then the victim, staggering at first, rises to his feet and slowly recovers all his senses and regains his soul. When even within our bodies our souls are tossed about by such great ills and, rent in pieces, are in such grievous trouble, why do you believe that the same souls can live without bodies in the open air amid the mighty winds?

Moreover, we perceive that the soul can be cured like the diseased body, and we see that it can be affected by drugs. This, too, indicates that the soul has a life subject to death; for he must add parts or change their order or remove some little bit from the whole who undertakes and begins to change the soul

490

500

510

27 Speech is discussed at IV. 524–72.

28 The conventional medical theory of Lucretius' day and for many centuries thereafter ascribed health to the proper balance of the four "humors" of the body, and all diseases to their excesses and malproportions.

or who seeks to change any other created thing. But that which is immortal does not permit that its parts be interchanged or that anything whatever be added to it or depart from it. For whenever a thing is changed and departs from its proper limits,
520 this is at once the death of that which was before.[29] Thus whether the soul be sick, or whether it be cured by medicine, it gives evidence of its mortality, as I have shown. Thus truth clearly meets false reasoning, cuts it off as it seeks to escape, and proves its falsity by a double-edged refutation.

Next, we often see that a man dies gradually and loses the vital capacity for feeling limb by limb: first his toes and toenails become black, next the feet and legs die, then the marks of chill
530 death advance slowly through the rest of the body. Since this soul is cut up and does not come forth whole at one time, it must be regarded as mortal. But if you think that the soul can draw itself through the limbs toward the center and bring its parts together into one place, thus removing sensation from all the limbs, that place at least, in which so great a quantity of soul is brought together, clearly ought to have a greater capacity for feeling. But since this is nowhere to be found, truly, as we said before, the soul is rent asunder and scattered abroad;
540 therefore it perishes. Even if it pleased us to grant what is not true, and to say that the soul can gather itself into a mass in the bodies of those who are dying little by little and leaving the light, yet you must admit that the soul is mortal; and it makes no difference whether it perishes scattered through the air or is gathered in from its usual places and becomes sottish, since the man as a whole is more and more losing his senses, and less and less life remains on every side.

The mind is one part of a man, which remains fixed in a defi-
550 nite place like the ears and the eyes and all the other sense organs that govern life.[30] Just as the hand, the eye, or the nostrils, separated from us, cannot possess the power of sensation, or even exist, but are dissolved into corruption in a brief time, so the mind cannot exist by itself without the body, that is,

29 Lines 519–20 are also found at I. 670–71, 792–93, and II. 753–54.

30 See Epicurus, *Letter to Herodotus* 63b–66.

without the man himself; for the body is clearly a sort of container of the soul, or rather some other thing you might imagine more closely bound to it, since the soul is not merely contained within the body but is interwoven through it.

Next, the living powers of the body and soul are strong and enjoy life when they are joined together; for neither can the soul by itself, without the body, perform its life-giving motions, nor can the body bereft of the soul continue to live and to enjoy sensation. Just as the eye by itself, torn out from its roots and sundered from the whole body, is unable to see anything, so the spirit and mind clearly have no power in themselves. This is certainly because, mixed throughout the veins and the flesh, throughout the sinews and the bones, they are held together by the body, and their atoms cannot leap apart freely, with great intervals between them.[31] Shut up in this way they move themselves in the motions that cause sensation, motions they cannot perform after death when they have been thrown outside the body into the open air, since then they are not held together in a similar way. For the air will be a body, and a living one, if in it the soul can restrain itself and limit itself to those motions that it once performed amid the tissues of the body itself. Therefore again and again I repeat that when the whole envelope formed by the body is dissolved and the breath of life has been cast out into the open, the conscious mind and spirit —as you must admit—are also dissolved, since the soul and the body have a condition of life that is bound together.

Next, since the body cannot endure the dissolution of the soul without rotting away with a foul odor, why do you doubt that the soul, gathered together from the inmost depths, flows out and is scattered like smoke, and that the reason why the body is changed and crumbles and falls in such ruin is that its

560

570

580

[31] This all follows from what has been said of the movements of the atoms (II. 80–141), the variety of atomic shapes and resulting variety in their combinations (II. 581–729), and the nature of the soul (III. 177–257). The soul atoms, being smooth and light, will leap apart to great distances and be unable to form a stable union or to maintain a union should one be formed by chance, unless they are firmly held together by the rougher, heavier matter of the body.

very foundations within have been moved from their places as the soul passed out through the members and through all the curving passages and the openings that there are in the body? From this you may learn that the soul was already divided in 590 many ways throughout the flesh before it came out, and that it was torn into pieces in the body before it escaped and flew into the air of heaven.

Nay, even while the soul still moves within the limits of life, we see that it is often shaken by some cause and wishes to depart and to be freed from the whole body, and as if at the very last moment, the face is seen to droop and all the weakened limbs collapse over the lifeless body. It is at a time like this that one says, "His mind is gone," or "His spirit has left him." Confusion 600 reigns, and all desire to hold fast to the last bond of life. Then the whole force of mind and spirit is shaken, and these, together with the body, are in such a state of collapse that a slightly more severe ill could bring about their dissolution. Why then do you doubt that the soul, thrust out from the body, weak, in the open air, and deprived of its covering, not only cannot endure for eternity, but cannot exist for the briefest time imaginable?

It is clear that a dying man does not feel his spirit departing as a whole from his entire body or first withdrawing to his throat 610 and then upward to his jaws; but rather, he feels it failing in the fixed place where it is located, just as he knows that the other senses are destroyed each in its own place. But if our soul were immortal, it would not thus complain at death that it is dissolved, but would rather rejoice that it is going out and shedding its skin as does a snake.

Next, why are the reason and the intellect of the mind never born in the head, the feet, or the hands; why do they remain fixed for all men in one place in a definite region of the body, unless it be because to every created thing a certain place for being born is allotted, a place where, after it has been born, it 620 may remain and exist with its many members so arranged that the order of its limbs is never reversed? So certainly does effect follow cause; flame is not created from streams of water, nor is cold born of heat.

Moreover, if the soul is immortal and can have sensation when it is separated from the body, we must suppose, I think, that it has been endowed with the five senses, and in no other way can we imagine the souls of the dead wandering about Acheron. For this reason the artists and the earlier generation of writers have represented the souls equipped with senses. But the soul 630 cannot have eyes or nostrils or even hands apart from the body, nor yet a tongue nor ears. Souls by themselves, therefore, can have neither sensation nor existence.

Since we feel that there is life-giving consciousness in the whole body, and see that the whole body is full of spirit, if some violence suddenly cuts the body with a swift blow in such a way that it divides it into two parts, beyond question the spirit, split and cut asunder, will be divided at the same time as the body. But anything that is cut, and divides into any number of parts, 640 thereby abandons its claim on immortality. They say that scythe-bearing chariots, reeking with indiscriminate slaughter, often cut off limbs so suddenly that the part that has fallen, sundered from the body, is seen to quiver on the ground, although the mind and spirit of the man cannot feel the pain because of the rapidity of the misfortune, and at the same time because his mind is absorbed by the fervor of the fighting. Sometimes one man makes for the fight and slaughter with what remains of his body and does not note that his left arm with its shield is lost, swept away amid the horses by the wheels and the 650 devouring blades; and another as he climbs up and presses on does not know that his right arm has fallen. Still another struggles to rise although his leg has been cut off, and nearby on the ground the dying foot twitches its toes. The head cut from the warm and living body preserves on the ground its look of life and its wide-open eyes, until it gives up the remaining portions of soul.[32] But in the case of the snake with darting tongue, lash-

[32] This vivid but exaggerated and admittedly second-hand account of the havoc wrought by scythed chariots interrupts the argument. Lucretius had just said that if you cut any living creature into two parts, both parts will contain portions of spirit. After the digression he goes on in line 657: "But in the case of a snake . . . , if you cut both pieces into many parts. . . ."

ing tail, and long body, should it please you to cut both the
660 pieces into many parts, you would see each of the severed parts while the cuts are fresh twisting about and bespattering the ground with gore, the front part struck by the burning pain of the wound striking back at itself in order to assuage the pain by biting at it. Shall we say then that in all these little parts there are complete souls? But on that theory it will follow that a single living creature had many souls in its body. Since this is false, we must conclude that the soul, which was one, has been divided with the body; and for this reason we must believe both body and soul to be mortal, since they are divided in the same way into many parts.

670 Moreover, if the soul is immortal and makes its way into the body as we are born, why are we not able to remember the life previously lived; why do we not retain some traces of the deeds of that life?[33] For if the mind has been so changed that all memory of the past things has fallen away, the change does not fall far short of destruction. You must therefore confess that the soul that was before has perished, and that the soul that now exists is a new creation.

Moreover, if it were the rule that after the body had been
680 completed the already living soul was brought into it from outside, at the moment of birth and of crossing the threshold into life,[34] it would not be natural for it to seem to have grown up with the body and limbs in the very blood stream; but it ought to live alone by itself in a cave, yet in such a way that the whole body is flooded with sensation. Therefore I say again and again that one must not think that souls are without any share in birth, or that they are free from the law of death; for we cannot believe that souls could be so intimately bound to our bodies
690 if they had been brought in from outside. Things clearly visible show that the relation of body and soul is quite different; for the soul is so interwoven throughout veins, vitals, sinews, and

[33] Plato, claiming that the soul does remember, uses this memory as one of his proofs of the pre-existence, and therefore of the post-existence, of the soul (*Phaedo* 72e–77a; *Meno* 81c–86b).

[34] This is the Pythagorean doctrine of the transmigration of souls.

bones, that our very teeth have a share in sensation, as we are shown by toothache, or the twinge that cold water causes, or the harsh stone that we bite upon when it is hidden in the bread. And since souls are so interwoven, it is clear that they cannot go out unharmed and safely separate themselves from all the sinews, bones, and joints.

But if, perhaps, you think that the soul is introduced from without and then blended throughout our members, so much 700 the more will the soul perish when it is fused with the body; for the soul is divided through all the pores of the body, and whatever is thus blended is dissolved and therefore perishes. Just as food, when it separates into all the members and the limbs, perishes and creates out of itself a different substance, so the spirit and the mind, however whole they may be as they enter the new body, in spreading through it are dissolved. Their seeds are scattered, so to speak, through all the pores into the members, and from these seeds is created the soul that now rules the limbs, born from that soul that at the time of birth 710 was scattered through the frame and perished.[35] Therefore it appears that the soul is neither without a day of birth nor free from destruction.

Next, are seeds of soul left in the lifeless body, or are they not? If any are left behind and remain, the soul that departed, made less by the loss of some of its parts, cannot rightly be regarded as immortal. But if the soul is carried off with its members intact and departs in such a way that it leaves no parts of itself in the body, whence do corpses exude worms from their rotting flesh, and whence does such a boneless, bloodless host of 720 living things surge through the bloated limbs?[36] But if by chance you believe that separate souls can enter the maggots

[35] Lucretius does not present this as an acceptable explanation of the formation of the soul. Answering the arguments of those who believe in the pre-existence of the soul, he claims that if such a pre-existing soul entered the body at birth (which he denies), it would completely lose its identity in the process. Just as the flesh of our bodies is not the same flesh that we have eaten, so the souls that now rule our bodies could not be the same as souls that entered them at birth.

[36] See II. 871–73, and note.

and come into their bodies from without, and if you do not marvel that many thousand souls come together in the place that a single soul has left, yet surely you must wonder about this and raise this question: whether each soul seeks out seeds suitable for worms and constructs for itself a place where it may live, or whether the souls, if you please, make their way into 730 bodies that are already completed. But no reason can be given why, of their own accord, the souls should do this, or why they should undergo the labor. Truly, when they are without bodies, they are not troubled by illness, cold, and hunger as they flit about; for it is the body that is exposed to these evils and troubled by them, and the soul suffers many evils because of its contact with the body. But grant that it be as useful as you please for the souls to construct bodies that they may enter, yet no way appears in which they can do this; therefore, souls do not make bodies and limbs for themselves. Nor yet is it possible that souls are instilled into bodies that are already formed; for 740 neither can they be intimately interwoven, nor can common sensations establish a harmony.[37]

Again, why does terrifying violence accompany the cruel breed of lions, and trickery that of foxes? Why is the instinct for flight given to the deer by their sires, and why does ancestral panic move their limbs? And why do all the other characteristics of the different species develop in the body and soul from the beginning of life, unless because a definite power of soul grows along with each body from its own seed and breeding? But if the soul were immortal and were accustomed to go from body to body, living creatures might have their characters interchanged. 750 The dog of Hyrcanian breed would often flee from the attack of the horned deer, and the hawk would tremble as it fled through the air of heaven before the onrushing dove; men would lose their minds, and the races of wild beasts would become wise. And they are again arguing falsely when they say that the soul is altered by the mortal body and yet is immortal;

[37] The meaning seems to be that the particles of soul and body could not combine in the sense-giving motions. Note that in this whole section Lucretius assumes for the sake of the argument that a soul can exist without a body, a thing which of course he denies.

for whatever is changed is dissolved and therefore perishes. For the parts of the soul are thrown about and moved from their order, and must therefore be subject to dissolution throughout the limbs in such a way that all the parts perish along with the body. But if we say that the souls of men always go into human 760 bodies, yet I will ask you why a foolish soul is made from a wise one,[38] why no child is ever wise, and why the foal of a mare is not as well trained as the strong horse is. They will, of course, take refuge in the argument that the mind becomes weak in a weak body. But if this happens, one must admit that the mind is mortal because it loses so completely the life and experiences of an earlier time, when it has been changed throughout the limbs. In what way will the strength of the mind, as it gains power, be able to reach the desired prime of life at the same time 770 as a particular body, unless it is the body's partner from its first beginning? Why will it wish for its own advantage to depart from the aged limbs? Does it fear to remain shut up in the decaying body lest its dwelling place, worn by the long time of old age, overwhelm it? But if the soul is immortal, it is not in any danger.

Next, we see that it is silly to believe that souls stand in attendance waiting for the unions of love and for the birth of beasts, and that immortal souls in countless numbers await mortal members, in breathless haste contending with each other for the opportunity to enter first and in preference to others; 780 unless perhaps in order to avoid violent disputes among themselves, they have entered into compacts that the soul that first flies up shall be admitted first.

Next, a tree cannot exist in the upper air, or clouds in the depths of the sea; nor can fish live in the fields, or blood be hidden in wood, or sap in stone. There is a fixed and determined place where each thing may grow and have its being. In the same way, the mind cannot come into being alone without the body, or exist apart from sinews and blood. Were some varia- 790 tion possible, it is more likely that the mind would be able to

[38] The souls, even of the wisest men, would always return in the bodies of infants. Line 763, which repeats line 746, is omitted.

take its place in the head, the shoulders, or the very heels, and habitually be born in any part you please, while still remaining in the same man and the same vessel. But since it has been determined and clearly established where in our bodies the spirit and mind[39] can be and grow by themselves, so much the more must we deny that they can be born or endure outside the entire body.[40] Therefore you must admit that when the body perishes,
800 the soul, torn to pieces in the whole body,[41] also perishes. Indeed, it is foolish to join the mortal to the eternal, and to believe that they can share sensation with each other and act upon each other; for what can be more unlike than mortal and immortal, and what more lacking in unity and harmony than temporal and eternal joined together, enduring as yoke-mates the cruel blasts of life?[42]

Finally, that which remains forever must either turn aside blows by virtue of its solid body, not permitting itself to be penetrated by anything that could separate the tightly packed parts
810 within, as is the case with the atoms, whose nature we considered above; or second, it must be capable of enduring through all eternity for the reason that it is immune to blows, as is the void, which remains intangible and is not at all affected by any impact; or third, it must be eternal, as is the universe, because there is no void about it into which its matter can, as it were, recede and be dissolved, and no space into which its parts may escape, nor are there any external bodies that can fall upon it and break it up with a mighty blow.[43] But if the soul is rather regarded as immortal because it is fortified by life-giving forces,
820 or because nothing at all foreign to its safety comes near it, or

39 Since the spirit is dispersed throughout the body, this argument properly applies only to the mind.

40 The first part of this paragraph recurs with minor variations at V. 128–41.

41 See lines 580–91 of this book.

42 The version given is a paraphrase; a literal translation of the last four lines is as follows: "For what can be thought more at variance within itself or more disjointed or out of harmony than that the thing that is mortal, joined in union with the immortal and eternal, endure severe blasts."

43 With minor variations the paragraph to this point recurs at V. 351–63, where it seems more appropriate.

because those hostile forces that draw near turn back, repulsed in some way or other before we are able to feel that they have done any injury, ⟨these conditions, actually, are not fulfilled. . . .⟩[44] In addition to the fact that the soul grows ill with the illnesses of the body, it often happens that it is tortured with fears about things to come, made miserable with dread, and worn out with anxiety; and although its evil deeds are past, its sins still gnaw at it. Add the madness that is the particular evil of the mind, and the loss of memory; add the fact that the mind is sunk in the black waves of lethargy.

III. Death Is Not to Be Feared

830–1094

Since we shall cease to exist after death, we need not fear it; nothing that happens subsequently will concern us. Neither the idea of our own death, nor the death of others, should grieve us; it is folly to want to prolong life, for the old must yield its place to the new. The stories of the punishments of the lower world are allegories of the evils of this life. Since the best and greatest men have died, we should not complain; since true knowledge alone can set us free, we should not seek forgetfulness through the desperate pursuit of new pleasures.

Death is nothing to us and does not concern us at all, inasmuch as the soul is mortal.[45] Just as we felt nothing painful in the time now past when the Carthaginians were pressing to the attack on all sides, when everything beneath the high shores of heaven, struck by the confused tumult of war, trembled and shuddered, and it was a question to which of the two the rule of all mankind on land and sea would fall; so when we shall not be, when soul and body by whose uniting we exist will have been sundered from each other, surely then nothing can happen to us, who shall not exist, or stir our senses, not even if the earth be mingled with the sea and the sea with the heaven. And if our 830 840

44 At least one line has been lost at this point.

45 See Epicurus, *Letter to Menoeceus* 124b–25; *Principal Doctrines* II.

mind and soul do feel after they have been torn from the body, yet this is nothing to us who exist as individuals formed by the union and association of body and soul.[46] If, after our death, time should again gather together once more the atoms of which we were formed, and should restore them to the positions that they now occupy, and if the light of life should again be 850 granted[47]—even if this should happen, it would not pertain at all to us once the chain of consciousness had been broken. Even now no concern troubles us about the selves we formerly were, no pain touches us about them. For when you consider the whole past expanse of unmeasured time and how manifold are the motions of the atoms, you could easily believe that these same atoms from which we are now formed have often been arranged in the same order in which they now are. Yet we are 860 not able to grasp this in our memory, since an interruption of life has been thrown between, and all the motions have wandered far from sense.[48] For if perchance pain and wretchedness are to occur, a man to whom they can occur must also exist at the same time. Since death removes this possibility and prevents the existence of the dead man to whom the discomfort of death would be assigned, we may be sure that there is nothing in death to be feared by us, that he who does not exist cannot be made miserable, and that a man is as if he had never been when once immortal death has taken away his mortal life.

870 Therefore when you see a man complaining that after death he will either rot away when his body has been laid out for

[46] That is, even if for the sake of the argument we grant the existence of the soul after death, this does not concern us; for each of us owes his individual consciousness to that particular combination of soul and body that will be ended by his death.

[47] According to the Stoic doctrine of great cycles, after a fixed period everything will return to its original state and the cycle will be renewed. Epicurus and Lucretius admitted the possibility of such a return but only as a result of chance, and they rejected the theory of a fixed cycle.

[48] That is, as they wandered in the void the atoms were far from the combinations that alone can produce sensation. Lines 843–61 form a parenthesis. In thought the next sentence follows directly on line 842: "When we shall no longer be . . . nothing can happen to us . . . ; for if perchance. . . ."

burial, or else will perish in flames or at the jaws of wild beasts, you may know that, however vehemently he denies a belief in any consciousness after death, his words do not ring true and that some sting is hidden in his heart. He does not, I think, accept what he professes or the ground for his belief,[49] nor does he separate himself and tear himself completely from life, but rather unconsciously imagines that some part of himself will survive. For when each man, while still alive, pictures to himself that birds and wild beasts will tear his body after death, he 880 pities himself; for he does not separate himself from the corpse nor remove himself sufficiently from that cast-out body; and he fancies that he himself is in it, and standing by it he impregnates it with his own feelings. For this reason he complains that he has been born a mortal, and does not see that when he is truly dead there will be no second self alive to be able to lament to himself that he has been killed, and to stand and suffer because he lies there torn or burning. When one is dead, if it is an evil to be torn by the jaws and teeth of wild beasts, I see no reason why it should not be bitter to be placed on the fire and roasted in 890 hot flames, to be immersed and smothered in honey, to become stiff with cold when slumbering on the surface of a chill rock, or to be buried and overwhelmed by the weight of the earth above.

"No joyful home," they say, "will now receive you, nor will your good wife and sweet children run to snatch the first kiss and touch your heart with silent joy. You will not be able to enjoy your prosperity or to be a protection to your friends. A single wretched day," they say, "has miserably taken from miserable you all the many blessings of life." But at this time they 900 do not add, "Nor will you retain any longing for these things." If they should see this clearly in their minds and follow it up in their words, they would free themselves from great anguish and fear of mind. Another says, "You, indeed, as you are asleep in death, so shall you be for all the time that remains, free from

[49] "What he professes": i.e., that there is no sensation after death. "The ground for his belief": i.e., that the soul does not live after leaving the body.

all bitter pains; but we weep without end for you turned to ashes on the dread pyre, and no day shall take the eternal sorrow from our hearts." Of him one should ask, if death amounts
910 only to a peaceful sleep, what is there so bitter that anyone should be able to wear himself away with eternal grief.

When men are reclining at a banquet and hold the cups and shade their brows with wreaths, they often express themselves from the heart and say, "Brief is this pleasure for poor weak men. Soon it will be ended, and never afterwards can it be called back." They speak as if in death this would be the worst of sorrows, that dry thirst would burn and parch the unhappy, or that longing for any other thing would torment them. But no
920 one seeks for life or for his conscious self when mind and body alike are lulled in sleep. No longing for ourselves comes to us as we slumber, although, for all we know, the sleep may be everlasting. Yet in sleep the atoms throughout our members do not wander far from the motions that are sensation, since when a man is roused from sleep he collects himself.[50] We must therefore believe that death concerns us even less, if anything can be less than what we see is nothing; for a greater disturbance of restless matter follows death, nor does anyone ever rouse
930 himself and stand up whom the chill end of life has once overtaken.

Next, suppose that Nature should suddenly send forth her voice and herself make this charge against any of us: "What, O mortal, so distresses you, that you give way too much to whimpering lamentations? Why do you groan and weep at death? For if the earlier life now past was pleasing to you and all your pleasures have not wasted away and perished without giving satisfaction as if they had been stored up in a broken bowl, why do you not depart like a guest satisfied at the banquet of life, and with a calm mind, foolish one, welcome a

[50] Sleep will be discussed below, IV. 907–1036. For the present we need to know only that in sleep the seeds of the soul leave their regular places and motions and do not cause sensation, and that when the sleeper wakes, the seeds resume their normal functions.

carefree sleep? But if whatever things you have enjoyed have been poured out and wasted, and if life has become distasteful to you, why do you seek to add more to it, that this addition in its turn may all come to evil and perish without giving pleasure? Why do you not rather make an end of life and labor?[51] For there is nothing more that I might devise or discover to please you; all things are forever the same. If your body is not now withered with years, and your limbs wearied and spent, yet everything remains the same, and will so remain even should you go on to surpass all ages in living, nay rather, should you never die." If Nature asks this, what shall we reply, except that she has brought a just accusation and has set forth a true charge in her words? 940 950

But if some older, more mature man should complain and unhappily bewail his passing more than is right, would not Nature assail him with greater justice and attack him with bitter words? "Away with your tears, you gallows bird, and put an end to your croaking. After having enjoyed all the blessings of life, you are now withering away. But because you always desire what is absent and despise what is at hand, your life has slipped away from you incomplete and unpleasing, and now death stands beside your head when you do not expect him and before you are able to depart, filled and satisfied with the feast of life. Come now, give up all these things which are foreign to your time of life, and with calm mind yield them to your sons, for yield you must."[52] Nature, I believe, would assail him with justice, and with justice rebuke and correct him; for the old is always making way when thrust aside by what is new, and one thing must be built from another. Yet no one is given over to the pit, or to black Tartarus. There is need of matter for the growth of later generations, all of which, nevertheless, shall 960

[51] See Epicurus, *Letter to Menoeceus* 124b–26; *Principal Doctrines* XIX, XX. Although the Epicureans did not recommend suicide as did the Stoics, they regarded it as permissible and under certain conditions as desirable (Epicurus, *Letter to Menoeceus* 126–27a).

[52] Reading *agedum gnatis concede, necessest.* The text of this line is very uncertain, but the general meaning is clear.

follow you when they have lived their lives; and in like manner generations before you have died, and others shall die hereafter. 970 Thus without end one springs from the other, and life is granted to no one as a possession, but to all as a loan. See likewise of how little concern to us were the ages of eternal time that passed before we were born. Nature holds this up to us as a mirror of the time that will be after our death. Does this appear in any way to be dreaded? Does it seem at all sad? Is it not more free from care than any sleep?

And[53] in truth the things reported from the depths of Ach- 980 eron are all of them here in our own life. Wretched Tantalus, numbed with vain horror, does not fear the great rock hanging in the air above him, as the tradition has it;[54] in this life, rather, an empty fear of the gods oppresses mortals, and they dread the stroke that Fortune may bring to each. Birds do not force a way into Tityos as he lies in Acheron, and certainly they cannot for all eternity find something for which to search in his great breast. However widely the vast expanse of his body might extend, if with his outspread limbs he covered, not merely nine 990 acres, but the entire circle of the earth, he still could not endure eternal torture, or forever furnish food from his own body. But our Tityos is this man whom, as he lies overwhelmed in love, vultures are rending and vexatious trouble gnaws, or whom cares aroused by any other passion tear. Sisyphus, too, exists in this life before our eyes: the man who greedily seeks from the people the fasces and the cruel axes, and always departs from the contest defeated and downcast. For to seek authority that is empty and is never given, and in the search ever to suffer cruel 1000 hardship—this is to push with great effort up the opposing

[53] This section follows rather naturally on what comes just before it, but it actually is a long parenthesis, the main thought being resumed at line 1024.

[54] Lucretius follows a less familiar form of the legend, in which Tantalus, who had stolen the food of the gods, was punished by being suspended in midair under a stone, which constantly threatened to fall. Because of his ceaseless fear he was unable to eat or drink. In the more familiar version he starves while surrounded by fruit and water that stay always just beyond his reach.

mountain the rock that in spite of you rolls back again from the very top, and headlong seeks the level places of the plain. Next, always to be feeding the thankless soul, yet never to fill it full and satisfy it with goods (as the seasons of the year feed us when they come around and bring their many charming products, while yet we are never filled full with the fruits of life)—this, I think, is the myth they tell of girls in the flower of life who pour water into a broken jar, which can in no way be filled. Cerberus and the Furies, in truth, and the lack of light, Tartarus belching dread fire from its jaws—these surely neither exist anywhere, nor can exist.[55] But in life there is great fear of punishment for great deeds of evil, and there is penalty for crimes: prison, the terrible casting from the Rock, whips, executioners, stocks, pitch, hot plates, torches; and even if these are missing, yet the mind, conscious of its deeds and fearful, applies goads to itself and burns itself with lashes, and meantime sees neither what end there can be of misfortunes, nor what limit there is for punishments, and fears lest these same become more severe in death. In a word, the life of fools becomes a hell on earth. 1010 1020

This too you might say to yourself from time to time: "Even good Ancus gave up the light of his eyes, a better man than you, shameless one, in many ways. After him many other kings and potentates have fallen, who had ruled great nations. Even he who once, having paved a road through the great sea, gave his armies a highway over the deep and taught them to cross the salty depths on foot, who with his horses prancing over the sea scorned its roaring, even he has lost the light and breathed out his soul from his dying body.[56] Scipio, the thunderbolt of war, the dread of Carthage, has given his bones to the earth like the 1030

[55] Since there is some evidence that Lucretius included Ixion in his account of the lower world, and since this sentence is grammatically incomplete in the Latin text, many editors have supposed a lacuna of several lines somewhere between lines 1010 and 1014.

[56] The bridging of the Hellespont by Xerxes (whether historical or not) was so well known that the poet did not need to mention his name. In the next line Lucretius actually writes, "the son of the Scipios," using the Greek patronymic, *Scipiadas,* since no form of the Latin name *Scipio* can stand in dactylic verse.

lowest slave. Add the discoverers of the sciences and of the arts, the companions of the Heliconian Muses; even the chief of them, Homer, after having gained the scepter, was lulled in the same sleep as the rest. Finally, after mature years warned De-
1040 mocritus that the memory-producing motions of his mind were weakening, of his own accord he offered his head to death. Even Epicurus[57] himself died, when the light of life had run its course, he who surpassed the human race by his genius and dimmed the light of all men as the heavenly sun when it has risen dims the stars. And will you hesitate to pass away and will you be indignant, you whose life is all but death while you still live and have sight, who waste the greater part of your days in sleep and snore while your eyes are open nor cease from seeing dreams, who carry about with you a mind troubled by
1050 empty fear, you who cannot discover what is wrong with yourself when, poor drunken sot, you are overpressed by many cares and wander tossed about in the uncertain terror of your mind?"

If men, who clearly feel that a burden whose weight wearies them rests upon their minds, could know with equal clarity from what causes this happens and why so great a mass of evil, as it were, comes to rest upon their hearts, they would not live such lives as we now see most of them living, when not one of them knows what he desires for himself, and each of them constantly seeks to change his place, as if he could thereby lay aside
1060 his burden.[58] He to whom being at home is utter weariness often goes out from his great mansion and suddenly returns, since in truth he feels that it is in no way better out of doors. Then madly driving his colts he hastens to his country villa, pressing on as if bringing aid to a burning building; when he has reached the threshold of his villa he yawns at once, or falls heavily

[57] This is the only place in the entire poem where Epicurus is mentioned by name. Elsewhere Lucretius uses honorific titles but seems to avoid the name as if it were too sacred to be uttered.

[58] The cause of these evils is the fear of death and the superstitious dread of the gods. The cure is the scientific Epicureanism that shows that death is nothing to us and that the gods have no power over the world and no concern with man.

asleep and seeks forgetfulness, or even, in headlong haste, seeks to revisit the city. In this way each man flees himself; but himself he cannot escape. Against his will he clings to himself and hates himself, for in his illness he does not understand the cause 1070 of his malady. If this were seen clearly, each man, giving over his affairs, would seek before all else to understand the nature of the universe, since the point at issue is not his status for a single hour but for all eternity—the state in which every mortal must pass all the time that remains after death.

Finally, what great and evil desire for life forces us to such restless activity amid dangers of uncertain outcome? Truly a sure termination of life stands near at hand for mortals, nor can we avoid the meeting with death. Moreover, we spin about in 1080 the same place and are still present there, nor do we forge, by living, any new pleasures for ourselves. But while what we desire is absent, it seems superior to other things; when we have gained this, we seek for something else, and an unchanged thirst for life still holds us open-mouthed. Lastly, there is doubt what fortune time may bring, what may be sent to us by chance, what end is pressing upon us. By prolonging life we do not diminish by a hair the period of death, nor can we take anything away from it so that we may be dead less long. Finally, although 1090 by your living you bring to an end as many generations as you please, yet the death that awaits you will be none the less eternal; and he who made an end of life today will be dead no less long than he who perished many months and years ago.[59]

[59] As Book I ended with the infinity of matter and void, and Book II with the infinite number of worlds, so Book III closes with the infinite reaches of time before and after the brief span of an individual life.

BOOK FOUR

I. The Idols

1–216

The surfaces of things emit "idols" which pass through the air; when they occur in rapid succession, they arouse the sense of sight. The idols and the atoms that compose them are extremely fine; they are formed rapidly, emitted in all directions, and capable of crossing vast distances and penetrating certain substances. Sometimes idols are spontaneously generated in the air.

I am traversing the remote regions of the Pierides, hitherto trodden by the foot of no man. It gives me joy to draw near the untouched fountains and to drink; it gives me joy to pluck new flowers and to seek a fair wreath for my head from a source from which the Muses hitherto have veiled no brow; first, because I am teaching about mighty matters and pressing on to free man's soul from the tight bonds of superstition; then, because I am composing such clear verses about a dark theme,
10 touching the whole with the charm of the Muses. This use of poetry does not seem to be without reason. As healers, when they intend to administer bitter wormwood to children, first touch the cup around its rim with the sweet yellow liquid of honey so that the innocent child, tricked as far as his lips, may drink the bitter dose of wormwood and, although deceived, be not betrayed but rather in this way be refreshed and helped to grow strong; so now—because this system of belief usually seems
20 harsh to those who have not tried it, and because the common lot of men shrink from it—I have desired to set forth my teachings to you in sweet Pierian song and, as it were, to moisten my doctrine with the sweet honey of the Muses, to see if perhaps in this manner I can hold your attention upon my verses until

you see the whole nature of the universe and perceive the value of my words.[1]

Since I have shown the nature of the soul, from what it is formed, and how it grows strong in company with the body, and also how, when it is torn from the body, it returns into its first beginnings, I shall now begin to explain to you a matter that is very closely bound to this:[2] namely, the existence of what we call the "idols" of things. Like films torn from the surfaces of objects, these fly back and forth through the air; and these same idols, coming upon us awake or asleep, terrify our minds when we behold their monstrous shapes and the likenesses of those who have departed from the light; and when we are sleeping they have often roused us in terror from our slumber. I shall explain all this, so that we may not by any means believe that spirits escape from Acheron or that ghosts fly about among the living, nor suppose that any part of us can be left after death when body and soul have alike been dissolved, each into its proper first beginnings. It is for this that I say that idols and thin shapes of objects are given off by the objects from the surfaces of their bodies, as you may learn from what follows, however dull your wit. 30 40

But since I have explained of what sort are the beginnings of all things, how they differ in their various forms and fly about of their own accord, sped on in everlasting motion, and in what way each thing can be created from them, I shall now begin to prove to you a matter most pertinent to this, the existence of 50

[1] Except for the final clause of the last verse, these twenty-five lines are repeated from I. 926–50.

[2] The introduction to this part of the poem is preserved in two forms. Lucretius seems first to have planned that this book follow Book II; and lines 45–53 form a transition from the general discussion of the atom and the void in Books I and II to the new subject, sensation. Later, when Book III was inserted, a new introduction, lines 26–44, was composed, making a transition from the doctrine of the mortality of the soul to the theories on sensation; but the old introduction was also retained.

For the whole discussion of the idols, see Epicurus, *Letter to Herodotus* 46a–50a.

what we call "idols" of things. These might also be named films or shells, because each idol presents an appearance and form like that of the particular thing from whose body it was shed before its wandering.

First, since many objects emit sensible bodies—sometimes sending them out freely diffused, as wood sends out smoke and fire heat, sometimes more interwoven and coherent, as when grasshoppers shed their smooth coats from time to time in the summer, calves at birth drop the cauls from the surfaces of
60 their bodies, or slippery snakes put off their old skins amid the briers (for we often see brambles decked with the tossing spoils) —since all this takes place, it should be possible for any object to give off a thin image from its very surface. No reason can be given why the films should not separate and depart from bodies just as readily as the coverings just mentioned,[3] especially since there are many minute particles on the surface of objects, and these can be thrown off, retaining their former
70 order, and thus preserve the outline of the form; and they can be emitted much more rapidly, insofar as particles that are few and are located on the outer surface are less subject to interference.

Not only have we seen many things emitting bodies in abundance from deep within, as we have previously said, but we have also often seen them shedding the color from their surfaces. The yellow, red, and dark purple awnings furnish common instances of this, when they have been stretched over the great theater and quiver as they are displayed, billowing, between the spars and crossbeams; for the people in the seats below, all the splendor of the stage and the dignified gathering of
80 the senators[4] are tinted and made to ripple with the color of the awnings themselves. The more the walls of the theater are

[3] See Epicurus, *Letter to Herodotus* 46a, where we find a similar, typically Epicurean, argument from non-contradiction. If a theory explains a set of observed phenomena and is not contradicted by these phenomena or by any others, it may be accepted. This seems naïve, and in the absence of exact data and rigidly controlled experiments it did lead to fantastic conclusions, but it is essentially the method of science today.

[4] Reading *patrum coetumque decorum* with Munro.

closed in, and the brilliance of the day shut out, the more brightly does all that is within smile, bathed in beauty. And so, since the awnings send color from their surfaces, we must suppose that each thing sends out thin likenesses, since in each case it is from the surface that the particles are cast. There are therefore sure indications of shapes possessing very thin texture, which fly about at random and cannot be seen one at a time and individually. Moreover, the reason that smell, smoke, heat, 90 and all like things flow out from objects in confused form is that, in coming from their places deep within, they are broken up along their winding courses, there being no straight passages along which they can gain exit as wholes. But on the other hand, when the thin film of surface color is emitted, there is nothing that can tear it up since it lies upon the very surface, and is ready to depart. Finally, whatever images appear to us in mirrors, in water, or in any other reflecting surface, since they 100 possess an appearance like that of their objects, must be made by idols of those objects, which have been sent from them.[5] There exist, therefore, thin images of the forms of things, similar to the things themselves; and although no one can see them individually, yet when they are turned back constantly and in rapid succession from the reflecting surface, they present a visible image. It is clear that in no other way can the images be so preserved as to be reflected so like each individual thing.

Come now and learn how tenuous the idol is. In the first place, 110 whereas the atoms are far below the reach of our senses and much smaller than the things the eyes are just able to see, yet to strengthen your belief in this point as well, learn in a few words how minute are the beginnings of all things. In the first place, some living creatures are so small that a third part of one of them could by no means be seen. Of what size, then, must we suppose any of their entrails to be?[6] What of the lobe of the

[5] After this line the manuscripts repeat lines 65 and 66, obviously a copyist's error.

[6] Aristotle, *On the Parts of Animals* III. 4. 1, 665a30, claimed that creatures of the sort that he calls bloodless had no intestines; and he takes Democritus to task for saying that the entrails of such creatures were invisible because of their smallness.

heart and the ball of the eye? What of the members and the
120 limbs? How small are they? Then what of the several first beginnings from which the spirit and the mind must be formed? Do you not see how fine and minute they must be? Moreover, whatever thing sends a sharp smell from its body—all-heal, bitter wormwood, sluggish southern-wood, sharp centaury—if you ⟨touch⟩ any one of these gingerly with two ⟨fingers, the smell will cling because the small particles adhere to your skin. . . . There is therefore no reason⟩[a] why you should not admit that many idols of things drift about in many ways, and that these have no power and cannot be perceived.

Do not by chance believe that only those idols drift about
130 that have come from actual objects and are likenesses of them; for there are some that are formed spontaneously and establish themselves in that lower part of the atmosphere which we call the air, putting on many forms and moving themselves about above us.[7] Just so we see clouds quickly gather on high, marring heaven's calm face and lightly stirring the air with their own motion; for we often see faces of giants flying along and spreading a shadow far and wide, and sometimes great mountains and crags torn from mountains seem to rise above the
140 sun or to pass beneath it, and again a huge beast seems to lead other clouds back and forth. Since they are fluid, they do not cease altering their shapes, and changing into outlines of forms of every sort.

Now how easily and rapidly these idols are formed,[8] and how constantly they flow from objects, slipping away from them and departing, ⟨I shall explain . . .⟩.[b] For what is on the surface of things is always welling up to be cast forth. When this impinges upon certain things, for example on glass, it passes through; but when it lights on harsh rocks or solid wood, it is at
150 once so shattered that no idol can be given back. But when surfaces that are bright but solid (mirrors are good examples) have

[7] See Epicurus, *Letter to Herodotus* 46a, 48; and for the part played by such idols in causing dreams and visions, see lines 722–76 below.

[8] See Epicurus, *Letter to Herodotus* 47b, and the first sentence of 48.

been placed in front of the films, neither of these things happens; for the films cannot pass through these as they pass through glass, nor on the other hand can they be shattered; the polished surface is ever mindful to secure the safety of the films. The result is that from the mirror the films flow back to us. And although you place each object in turn before the mirror for the briefest possible time, its image appears; so you may know that thin films or thin forms are flowing without interruption from the surface of each object. Thus many idols are given out in a short time, so that their creation may rightly be called rapid. 160 Just as the sun must send down in a brief time many particles of light, in order that all things continuously be filled with brightness, so too in like fashion it is necessary that in an instant of time many idols be carried from objects—in many ways, on every side, in all directions—since in whatever direction we turn the mirror toward the surfaces of things, there in the mirror images of the same shape and color as the things answer back.

Moreover, when the sky has been completely clear, of a sudden it becomes so darkly clouded that you might believe all the 170 darkness had left the lower world and filled the great spaces of the sky, such faces of black fear hang over us from on high, where clouds have gathered in a noisome night; yet no one can say how small a part of these their idols are, or give an explanation of this in his words.[9]

Come now and hear with what swift motion the idols are carried,[10] and what mobility is given them as they pass through the air, so that only a brief time is spent in covering a long distance in whatever direction each of them is sped by its peculiar

[9] The sense is obscure, possibly because of an unrecognized lacuna, more probably because of the unfinished condition of this part of the poem. Lucretius' argument may be something like this: the idols or films given off from the clouds are so tenuous that you cannot say how small a fraction of the whole each represents. Yet the whole mass of a cloud is sometimes formed in a brief time. Why then wonder at the rapidity with which the films are made?

[10] See Epicurus, *Letter to Herodotus* 47b.

180 impulse. All this I shall explain to you in verses that are sweet rather than many, as the slight song of the swan is sweeter than that harsh cry of the cranes broadcast beneath the south wind's lofty clouds.

First you may often see that things that are light and made from small bodies are swift. For example, the light and heat of the sun are swift for the reason that they are formed from minute particles, which are, so to speak, driven forward and do not hesitate to cross through the intervening air when struck by the blows of those that follow; for one particle of light is
190 instantly replaced by another, and gleam treads hard on gleam like cattle driven tandem. In the same way, therefore, the idols must be able to cross a distance beyond our thinking in an instant of time, because in the first place there is a minute cause behind that sends them out[11] and propels them through the space that remains, where they are carried along with such birdlike lightness; next because the idols sent forth are endowed with such porous nature that they can easily penetrate through things of every kind, passing, as it were, through the enclosed air.[c]

Moreover, if bodies of things that are sent out from deep
200 within—the light and heat of the sun, for example—are seen to glide forth and cover the whole expanse of the sky in an instant of time, and to fly across the sea and flood the earth and the heavens, what then of those bodies that are already at hand on the outer surface when they are ejected, whose emission nothing hinders? Do you not see that they must go more quickly than the sunlight and to a greater distance, and that in the time in which the light of the sun spreads across the sky, they must

[11] The meaning is uncertain, but the important word is probably *parvola*, "minute," which might almost be rendered "atomic." The idols themselves (see Appendix note *c*, p. 267) are webs of atoms spaced far apart, and the force that starts them on their journey through space is also at the atomic level, namely the motion of the atoms on the surface of the object, or rather on what becomes the surface as the idol which was the surface is ejected. For the velocity of atomic motion, see II. 142–64.

pass through an extent of space many times as great?[12] This, too, seems to be a particularly sure proof of the speed with which 210 the idols of things are borne along: as soon as a reflecting surface of water is placed under the open sky, at once, if the vault of the sky is starry, the calm stars of heaven shining in the water answer back. Do you see how in an instant the pattern has come down from the heavenly regions to the terrestrial shores?

II. Sensation and Thought

216–822

Sight is caused by contact between the idols and the eyes, and other sensations by other forms of such contact. The theory of idols also explains the mirror image, and other peculiarities and distortions of perception. Sound is caused by particles in motion; we produce speech by shaping such particles with our lips. When sound particles rebound, the echo occurs. Taste comes from particles of varying shape, pressed out as we chew food; smell, from particles that come from things to our nostrils. There are subjective differences in the reception of sensation, yet sense is our only basis for knowledge; although the evidence of the senses is true in itself, it may be perverted by the addition of opinion. Mental images are akin to visual ones; thought may be caused by a tenuous image which can affect the mind but not the senses. Idols like those causing thought may cause dreams.

Therefore I say again and again, you must confess that bodies are sent out that strike the eyes and arouse the sense of sight.[13]

[12] Since the particles of light and heat of the sun (each particle consisting of a group of atoms) must force their way to the surface of that body before they are emitted, their initial velocity is much less than that of the idols, which always start from the outer surface of the emitting body, ejected by the vibration of the atoms behind them (see Epicurus, *Letter to Herodotus* 48).

[13] See Epicurus, *Letter to Herodotus* 49–50a.

From certain things odors ceaselessly flow; so too cold comes from rivers, heat from the sun,[14] and from the waves of the sea
220 comes the spray that eats away the dikes along the shores; without pause, various sounds fly through the air. When we wander by the sea, moisture of a salty taste comes to our mouths, and on the other hand, when we watch as wormwood is diluted and mixed, its bitterness touches us. So from each thing its proper effluence arises in a flood, and these are sent in every direction and from every side; nor is there any pause or rest in their flow, for we are continuously experiencing sensations, and may see
230 and smell all things and hear them sound. Moreover, since a particular shape touched by the hands in the dark is recognized to be the same as that which is seen by the eyes in the bright clear light, the senses of touch and of sight must be stirred by a like cause. Now if we handle something square in the darkness, and its square shape impresses us, what except its idol can come as square to our eyes when it is light? It is therefore clear that the cause of seeing is in the idols, and that without them nothing can be seen.

Now these idols of which I speak are moving from all sides,
240 and are scattered abroad in every direction; but because we can see only with our eyes, it follows that all things with their shape and color impinge upon our vision from that side to which we direct it.

The idol permits and causes us to see and distinguish the distance of each object. For when it is sent out, it at once pushes on and drives before it whatever air lies between it and our eyes;[15] and all this air glides through our eyes and, so to speak, brushes
250 through the pupils and so passes on. As a result we see how far distant each thing is. And the greater the quantity of air that is driven, and the longer the breeze that passes through our eyes, the more distant and remote each object is seen to be. Truly this is done with the utmost speed, so that we perceive at the same moment both the nature of the object and its distance from us.

[14] Cold and heat are regarded by Lucretius as material substances, given off by certain bodies and penetrating others.

[15] This is obviously inconsistent with lines 196–98.

Least of all, in this connection, should we wonder that the objects themselves are perceived, although the individual idols that impinge upon our eyes cannot be seen; for when the wind strikes upon us bit by bit and biting cold encompasses us, we do not feel each individual particle of the wind and the cold that it brings. Rather, we feel them as wholes, and we feel that blows are being delivered upon our bodies exactly as if something were beating upon us and making us feel its own body from without. Moreover, when we tap a rock with a finger, we touch the color on the outer surface of the stone. This we do not recognize by touch; rather, we are conscious of the characteristic hardness far within the stone.[16] 260

Come now and learn why the reflected image seems to be beyond the mirror; for certainly we see it set apart within. In this same way do those things outside the house appear to us that we actually see through a frame, when the doorway offers unobstructed vision through itself and permits many things outside to be seen from within. In this case, just as with the mirror, the act of seeing is completed by a double train of air. First the air which is on this side of the doorway is perceived, next the doorposts themselves follow on right and left, after this the light outside and the second air brush through the eyes, and finally those things outside, which we are actually seeing through the doorway, are perceived. In this same way, when the likeness of the mirror first sets itself in motion, while it is coming to our eyes, it thrusts forward and drives on whatever air lies between itself and our eyes, with the result that we perceive all this before we see the mirror. But when we have seen the mirror itself, the image that has been carried from us to the mirror arriving there is turned about and comes back to our eyes, and it propels and rolls before itself a second column of air, causing 270 280

16 The connection of these four lines with the argument is far from clear. Perhaps it may be stated in this way: the sense of touch in our fingers does not recognize the color of an object, since the color is a single film on the object's surface, but it does recognize the hardness of the object, which is the result of a series of films, one within the other, that make up the bulk of the object itself. In the same way the sense of sight, which is merely a special form of the sense of touch limited to the eye, is not moved by a single film but responds to the repeated impact of a series of idols.

us to see this before we see the image itself. For this reason our reflection seems an equal distance removed behind the mirror. Therefore I say again and again: there is no reason to wonder ⟨that there is the same appearance of a twofold distance in the case of objects that are seen through an open door⟩[17] and in
290 that of those that are reflected from the surface of a mirror, inasmuch as in each case the act of seeing is completed by two columns of air.

Now my right hand and foot are seen on the left of the reflection in the mirror, because when the image coming to the plane surface of the mirror strikes against it, it is not turned about as a whole but is reflected straight back, as if someone should force a damp clay mask against the end of a pole or beam, and the mask itself, without its features being bent to either side, should step by step be turned inside out and refrashion itself.[d] The
300 result would be that the same eye that was the right is now the left, and that the right eye in turn is made from what was the left.[e]

It also happens that an image is passed from one mirror into another, so that five or even six reflected images may be formed. Whatever is concealed back in the inner part of a house, however far removed around twisting corners, may yet be seen to be in the house, all of it being brought out thence through winding passageways by means of many mirrors. In this way does the image reflect from mirror to mirror; and when a left-hand image is passed on, it is so turned by the next mirror that it
310 becomes right; then it is turned back again and changed into its earlier form. Moreover all the mirrors that are called *latuscula,* which have been given an angle like to that of a baked brick,[18] pass back to us right images, either because the image is passed from mirror to mirror and then comes back to us after having been twice reflected, or because the image has been reversed by

[17] Most editors mark a lacuna at this point. The words supplied complete the obvious meaning of the sentence.

[18] Reading *cocti* or *tosti* for *nostri.* The editors retain the manuscript reading and translate "like to our flank," taking *lateris* from *latus,* "side," rather than from *later,* "brick."

the time it reaches us, the bent form of the mirror teaching it to turn itself toward us.[f]

Moreover, you might think that images walk beside us, keep step with us, and imitate our gait, because when you withdraw from before any part of the mirror, from that part at once no image can be given off; for Nature forces all images to withdraw and retreat at right angles.[g] 320

Next, the eyes shun and avoid the sight of bright objects. The sun blinds you if you try to hold your gaze upon it, because its own power is great and the idols from its surface fall heavily from on high through the clear air and disturb the texture of your eyes as they strike them. Moreover, any piercing brilliance often sears the eyes because it contains many seeds of fire, which cause pain in the eyes as they penetrate. All things seen by the jaundiced become yellow because many seeds of yellow flow from their bodies to meet the idols of things, and many also are mixed in their eyes, which by their touch stain all with their sallow color. 330

From out of the darkness we see what is in the light for the reason that, when the nearer black air of darkness has first come to our open eyes and filled them, the bright shining air follows at once, which cleans them, as it were, and thrusts aside the black shadows of that other air; for the bright air is many times more mobile, more finely divided, and more powerful. As soon as this has filled the eyes with light and opened their passageways, which the dark air had previously clogged, at once the idols of the objects that are located in the light follow and stir our eyes so that we see. But on the other hand, we cannot see from light into darkness for the reason that the heavier air of darkness, coming last, fills all the openings in the eyes and clogs their ways so that no idols of any objects can make contact with the eyes and move them.[19] 340 350

When from far away we see the square towers of a city, it often happens that they appear round because from a distance

[19] Since, on his theory, the object in the dark must be giving off idols, Lucretius feels bound to explain why it cannot be seen. The difficulty is a real one to him, although to us the explanation may seem quite uncalled for.

every angle appears blunted; or rather, the angle is not seen, and its blow and impact are lost and do not come to our eyes, for while the idols are passing through much air, the air blunts
360 the angle through frequent collisions. The result is that, since each angle escapes our senses, the stone structures are seen as though turned in a lathe; yet they do not appear quite like those things near us that are truly round, but rather they seem to imitate such objects a little in shadowy outline.[h]

Our shadows seem to move with us in the sunlight, following our steps and imitating our gait—if you really believe that air bereft of light can walk, following the movements and the gait of men, for this which we are wont to call a shadow can be noth-
370 ing but air without light. Truly the earth is deprived of the light of the sun in particular places one after another as we walk along and cut it off, and in the same way the part of the ground that we leave is flooded with light. Therefore the same shadow of our body seems still to follow us from one place to another; for new light of the sun's rays is always pouring itself out, and the earlier light perishes like wool spun into fire.[20] Therefore the earth is easily deprived of light, and likewise it is filled with it again and brushes the dark shadows from itself.

Yet even here we do not admit that the eyes are in any way
380 deceived.[21] It is theirs to see where the light and shadow are; whether or not the lights are the same, and whether the same shadow that has been in one place passes to another, or on the other hand that takes place which we have described—to determine these things is the task of the rational power of the mind; and the eyes cannot understand the laws of Nature.[22] Therefore do not ascribe to the eyes the error of the mind.

[20] A proverbial expression of unknown origin but clearly meaning "to vanish suddenly" or "to be destroyed suddenly."

[21] For the following discussion of the validity of sensation, see Laertius, *Life of Epicurus* 30–34a; Epicurus, *Letter to Herodotus* 50b–52a, and *Principal Doctrines* XXIII, XXIV.

[22] The title of the whole poem is *De rerum natura,* literally, "Concerning the Nature of Things," but better translated "Concerning the Laws [*de natura*] of Nature [*rerum*]." Here Lucretius says that the eyes have not learned the *natura rerum,* i.e., do not understand the atomic theory; in par-

The ship on which we sail is moving when it seems to us to be standing still; we believe that the other ship, which is at anchor, moves beside her. Mountains and plains, beside which we steer our craft and fly along with our sails, appear to flee astern. All 390 the stars fixed in the vaults of heaven seem to stand still; yet they are in constant motion, since they rise, cross the sky with their shining bodies, and go again to their distant setting. In the same way the sun and moon, which actual experience proves are in motion, to our eyes remain fixed. Mountains that rise from the midst of the sea, between which there lies open a broad passage for our ships, appear from a distance to be a single island composed of the mountains joined.[23] When boys have whirled 400 themselves about and have come to a halt, the halls turn and the columns spin around, so that they can scarcely believe that all the buildings are not on the point of falling in ruin about them. Now when Nature begins to lift up the red disk of the sun, with its trembling fires, and to carry it above the mountains, those ranges, directly above which the burning sun seems to stand, touching them with its rays from close at hand, are in truth hardly two thousand arrow shots, perhaps less than five hundred javelin casts, distant from us; yet between them and the 410 sun stretches the vast plain of the sea beneath the great shores of heaven, and many thousands of lands occupied by various races of men and breeds of wild beasts. A pool of water no deeper than a finger, which has gathered between the blocks that pave the street, offers a view that extends deep beneath the earth as far as the yawning mouth of the lofty sky reaches above it, so that you seem to look down and see clouds and sky and bodies marvelously hidden in this sky beneath the earth. Next, when 420 our keen horse has come to a halt in midstream and we look down upon the rushing waves of the river, some force seems to be carrying the body of the standing horse against the current

---

ticular, they do not understand the nature and limitations of vision, and therefore they can only pass on to the mind that which they see (the idols that impinge on them), leaving it to the mind to interpret, or misinterpret, the sensation.

[23] One island is partially behind the other, and we fail to see the water between them.

and to be thrusting it up the opposing stream; and wherever we turn our eyes, everything appears to us to be carried along and to flow in the same way. Although a portico is of uniform width and is supported by equal columns throughout its length, yet when we look through the whole long portico from its upper end, it slowly contracts, the sides narrowing like a pyra-
430 mid, the roof meeting the floor, and the right-hand side drawing to the left, until all meet in the pyramid's vanishing point.

On the ocean the sailors see the sun both rise from the waves and set and hide its light in the waves—which is natural, for they see nothing but water and sky. (I give all these examples that you may not believe lightly that the senses are shaken on every hand.) To those unfamiliar with the sea, ships in port seem to struggle lamely against the waves with their stern-posts broken. Truly, whatever part of an oar rises above the salty brine is straight, and the rudder above the water is straight;
440 but everything plunged beneath the surface of the water seems to be bent and broken, to be twisted back and up, and almost to float on the liquid surface. When at night the winds are carrying scattered clouds through the sky, then the bright constellations seem to glide in the opposite direction and, high above these clouds, to move in a way different from that of their true motion. If by chance you place your hand below one eye and press it, because of some sensation in the eye all things that you look
450 at seem to become doubled as you see them: the bright lights from the flames of lamps are doubled, throughout the whole house the furnishings repeat themselves twofold, the faces of men are duplicated, and their bodies are doubled. Finally, when sleep has bound our limbs in sweet slumber and the whole body lies in utmost quiet, we nevertheless seem to ourselves to be awake and to move our limbs, and in the blinding darkness of the night we believe that we see the sun and the light of day and have exchanged the closed room for sky, sea, rivers, moun-
460 tains; we seem to cross plains on foot, to hear sounds although the deep stillness of the night is all about us, and to speak words when we are silent. We see a surprising number of other things of this kind, which all seek, as it were, to undermine our

faith in the senses; but in vain, since the greatest part of these deceptions occurs because of the opinion of the mind, which we ourselves have added—with the result that those things are taken as seen that have not been perceived by the senses; for nothing is more difficult than to distinguish things clearly seen from the doubtful things that the mind at once adds of itself.[24]

If a man thinks that nothing can be known, he does not know whether he can know even this, since he confesses that he knows nothing. I will not argue with this man, who himself has placed his head where his feet ought to be. Yet let us grant that he does know this; I will ask him, since up to the present he has never seen anything true among the objects of sense, from what source does he know the meaning of knowing and not knowing, and what has created in him the concept of the true and the false, and what has proved that the doubtful is different from the certain? You will find that knowledge of the true is created first of all from the senses, and that the senses cannot be refuted.[25] To do this one would need to discover something more trustworthy than the senses, something which of itself could overcome errors by means of the truth. What ought to be regarded as more trustworthy than the senses? Will reason, which springs entirely from the senses, be able to contradict them, although it itself arises from a sense that you call false? Unless the senses are true, all reason is likewise false. 470 480

Can the ears contradict the eyes, or the sense of touch dispute the ears? Or again, can the taste that belongs to the mouth find fault with touch; can the nose dispute it, or the ears convict it of error? Not so, I believe; for each sense by itself has its separate function, each has its own power. Therefore it is necessary to perceive what is soft and what is hot or cold in one way, and in another to recognize the different colors of things and to see all the qualities that are recognized along with colors. 490

24 Epicurus, *Letter to Herodotus* 50b–52a, is more emphatic and ascribes all error to the additions of opinion.

25 See Laertius, *Life of Epicurus* 31b–32; Epicurus, *Principal Doctrines* XXIII, XXIV.

Likewise the taste in the mouth has its own sphere of action; odors arise in one way, sounds in another. It follows of necessity that one sense is unable to contradict another. Nor has a sense ever been able to disprove itself, since the credibility of a sense must always be regarded as the same. Therefore, whatever
500 is perceived by the senses at a particular time is true. Even if the reason should not be able to explain why that which was square when close at hand seemed round at a distance, yet it would be better for a man to be without the true interpretation, giving false explanations of the two shapes, than for him in any way to let slip from his hands what has been grasped, and to shake the basic credit of his senses, destroying the whole foundation upon which our life and safety rest. For not only would all reason fall in ruin, but life itself would collapse at once unless you dared to trust the senses, avoiding precipitous places and whatever else
510 of this kind one ought to shun, and seeking for the opposite. Thus that whole army of words, drawn up and made ready for battle against the senses, has no validity for you.

Finally, in building, if your basic measure is faulty, if your square is not true and departs from the correct line, if your plumb line wavers the least bit to either side, the whole structure cannot escape being built awry, crooked and distorted, leaning backward or forward and out of plumb, so that parts of it seem to be on the point of falling and actually do fall, all un-
520 done by false measurements at its beginning. In this same way in your case, any reasoning about things must be distorted and false if the senses are false from which the reasoning has sprung.

There remains the by no means difficult task of demonstrating how each of the other senses perceives its own proper object.

In the first place, all sounds and voices are heard when they have made their way into the ears, and arouse the organ of hearing with their substance; for it must be admitted that voice and sound are corporeal, since they can strike the senses.[26] Moreover

[26] For the whole account of sound, see Epicurus, *Letter to Herodotus* 52b–53a.

the voice often grates upon the throat, and a shout roughens the windpipe as it passes out. This is natural, for when the particles 530 of sound have gathered together in a great whirling mass in the narrow passages and begin to go out, they fill the throat and also rasp the gateway of the mouth. There can be no doubt, then, that voices and words consist of corporeal particles of such sort that they cause pain. Likewise it does not escape you that something bodily is carried out and taken away from the sinews and the very strength of a man by continuous speaking prolonged from the splendor of the rising sun to the shades of black night, especially if the words are delivered in a loud voice. Thus the 540 voice must be corporeal since the man who speaks much loses a part of his substance. Harshness of voice is caused by a roughness of the particles, and likewise gentleness is caused by their smoothness. Particles of like form do not penetrate our ears when the trumpet blasts thunderously with low bellow and barbarously blares back with raucous roar, and when ⟨the swans from the winding vale⟩[27] of Helicon pour forth their soothing lament with saddened tone.

When we emit these sounds from deep within our bodies and 550 send them forth straight through our mouths, the mobile tongue, skilled artificer of words, divides them, and the shaping of our lips, in its turn, gives them their form. When the distance is not great from which each separate sound has set forth and come to us, the individual words too must be clearly heard and separately perceived, for the sound keeps its shape and form. But if too long a space lies between, the words are necessarily confused in passing through much air, and the speech is distorted while flying through the breezes.[28] As a result you hear 560 the sound and yet cannot understand the meaning of the words, so confused and intermixed do they reach you. Moreover, a single word uttered in a throng by the lips of a crier often moves the ears of all. One voice, therefore, divides at once into many

[27] Part of this line is hopelessly corrupt. The translation follows Lachmann's suggested correction.

[28] Compare the square tower that appears round, lines 353–63, 500–502 above.

voices, since it distributes itself into individual ears, imprinting a form and a clear sound upon the words. Part of the sound that does not fall into the ears themselves is carried beyond and per-
570 ishes, diffused to no purpose through the air. Part, dashing against solid places and being hurled back, repeats the sound and sometimes deceives with the empty echo of a word.

If you understand this clearly, you may explain to yourself and others how in solitary places the rocks return in proper order the counterparts of words, when we seek our wandering comrades on the shadowy mountains, calling with loud voices for those who are scattered. When you have uttered a single shout, I have heard places give back six or seven; thus the hills themselves, tossing the words to other hills, repeat again and
580 again what has been spoken. The neighbors imagine that in these places dwell nymphs and satyrs with goatlike feet; they say that there are fauns, by whose nightly revels and jovial play the deep silence is often broken, and that the sounds of strings are heard, and also those sweet laments that the pipe pours forth when stopped by the fingers of the player; and they add that from far away the farmers listen when Pan, shaking the piney covering of his half-human head, again and again runs over the open ends of the reeds with curved lip so that his pipes may
590 not cease to pour forth the sylvan music. They tell of other strange wonders of this sort, so that they may not by any chance be supposed to dwell in solitary places deserted even by the gods. This is the reason they boast of miracles in their tales; or perhaps they are led on by some other cause, since the whole human race is too eager to gain an audience.

Finally, you need not wonder how voices reach our ears, having passed through places through which the eyes cannot see visible objects. Men are often seen speaking through closed doors. Surely the reason is that the voice can pass unharmed
600 through the winding passages in things, but idols refuse to do so; for the latter are torn to bits unless they move through straight passages, like those of glass through which every idol flies. Moreover, sound is divided in every direction, since one sound springs from another when a single sound, having issued

from the mouth, at once splits apart into many—just as a spark of fire often scatters itself into fires derived from itself. Therefore places that are hidden out of sight are filled with voices; they are all in a fever and ring with sound. But all idols, once they have been sent out, move in straight paths;[29] therefore no one can see over a wall, although he can hear voices on the other side. But even the voice itself, in passing through the walls of a house, is blunted and reaches our ears in a confused form, and we seem to hear a sound rather than words. 610

The tongue and palate, by which we gain the sensation of taste, do not call for a long explanation nor present much difficulty.[30] In the first place, we sense a taste in the mouth when in chewing we apply pressure to food, just as one would do if beginning to dry a sponge full of water by squeezing it in the hand. Then all that we press out is distributed through the pores of the palate and the winding passageways of the open-textured tongue. For this reason, when the bodies of the spreading taste are smooth, they gently touch and stroke all the moist, sweating regions of the tongue. On the other hand, the rougher the surface of the bodies, the more they pierce and tear the sense as they assail it. Next, the pleasure of taste is limited to the region of the palate; when once the food has gone down through the throat and while it is being distributed to the members, there is no pleasure. It makes no difference with what food the body 620 630

[29] This is true of the idols that cause sight. But these same idols may wander about individually, following no set course and sometimes reaching the mind directly without the sense of sight having come into play. See lines 722–56 below.

[30] There appears to be nothing about taste in the extant works of Epicurus; in the *Letter to Herodotus* he passes directly from hearing to smelling. Democritus seems to have developed the theory of taste in some detail. A bitter taste, for example, is caused by particles that are smooth, small, and spherical, but with a sinuous surface. Tastes are not, according to him, real qualities of matter but only our interpretation of the shapes, sizes, and motions of the atoms (Diels, *Fragmente,* 68 A 135, sections 65–72. See also the Introduction to the present work, pages xviii–xix; and for Lucretius' view on the subjective element in taste, the next note.)

is nourished, provided only that what is eaten can be digested and distributed to the members, and that the moist condition of the stomach can be preserved.

Now that we may understand it, I will tell you why different creatures have different foods, and why what is bitter and acrid to one can nevertheless seem very sweet to another.[31] In this matter there are such great differences and variations that what is food for one can be bitter poison for others. For example there is a ⟨certain kind of⟩[32] serpent that dies if touched by the
640 saliva of a man, biting itself to death. Moreover, hellebore is a dire poison to us, but it fattens goats and quails. That you may learn in what way this takes place, you must first remember what we have said before. Seeds[33] mixed together in various ways are contained in sensible objects. Moreover, just as all the living creatures that take food are unlike on the outside, and each is bounded by the outline of its members after the manner of its kind, so too the seeds of which they each consist have different
650 forms. Since, then, the seeds are of different shapes, the spaces and the openings, which we call pores, must also be different in all their members, including their mouths and palates. Some of these pores, therefore, ought to be smaller and some larger; in some creatures the openings should have three sides, in some, four; many openings should be round, and some should have many angles variously arranged. For as required by the arrangements and motions of the particles, the shapes of the pores ought to be different; and the passageways ought to differ with the texture of that which surrounds them. On this principle, when

[31] Unlike sight and sound, which are objective and not defined in terms of the creature receiving the sensation (but see lines 706–21 below), taste, or at least its interpretation, is subjective. A given substance always emits taste particles of the same sort, but these may seem sweet to one and sour to another, and they may affect the same recipient in different ways as his own condition changes. The same is true of smell.

[32] This line begins with three good Latin words, two of which are completely meaningless here. They may result from a copyist's difficulty with the name of the snake. The Elder Pliny tells the same tale but does not name the snake (*Natural History* VII. 14–15).

[33] These are not atoms but complexes of atoms.

a substance that is sweet to one is bitter to another, its smoothest bodies must gently enter the pores of the palate of the creature 660 to which it is sweet, but on the other hand its rough and hooked particles surely penetrate the gateways of the pores of those beings to which this same substance is bitter when taken in. From this it is simple to understand the following as well. When fever attacks a man because of rising bile, or when for some other reason any violent disease is roused in him, then his whole body is disturbed and all the positions of the particles are changed. As a result, those substances that were formerly agreeable to his senses are so no longer, and there are others that are better fitted, which may cause an acid taste when they have 670 penetrated. For both sweetness and sharpness are mingled in the taste of honey,[34] a fact that we have often shown to you before.

Come now, I shall tell you how the coming of odors touches our nostrils. First there must be many things from which a changing tide of odors flows and spreads;[35] and we must suppose that this wave, as it is emitted and flows forth, is scattered widely; but because of the various forms,[36] one odor is better suited to one creature, another to another. For this reason the smell of honey attracts bees through the air from however great a distance, and that of dead bodies summons the vultures. The 680 pack of dogs sent on ahead leads where the cloven hoof of the wild beast has trodden; and the white goose, savior of the citadel

[34] Honey, in which we may normally recognize both a sweet and a sharp taste, is not a very apt example to illustrate the point that some foods are acceptable to us in one state of health but not in another. Lucretius has not previously spoken of honey as having a sharp taste, although at III. 191–95 he explained its slow flow by the presence of some particles not so smooth, fine, and round as those that give it its agreeable taste (see II. 398–407).

[35] See Epicurus, *Letter to Herodotus* 53b.

[36] Lucretius is probably thinking chiefly of the various forms of the particles that make up the odors; but the variations in the organs of the recipients are an equally necessary part of the argument, and they may be implied.

of the sons of Romulus,[37] recognizes from afar the scent of man. So different smells, belonging to different substances, lead each creature to its proper food and cause each to shun whatever is bitter poison to it; in this way the races of wild beasts are preserved.

It is clear that some of these smells that assail the nostrils can be sent to greater distances than others; yet none of them is 690 carried as far as are sounds and voices, to say nothing of the idols that impinge upon our eyes and cause us to see. For an odor comes slowly on a wandering course and perishes before it is perceived, scattered easily little by little into the breezes of the air. The first reason for this is that the odor is sent out with difficulty from deep within its source. That odors flow forth and are emitted from deep within is shown by the observed fact that all things do give out more smell when they are being broken, rubbed in a mortar, or destroyed by fire. As the next reason, it is clear that an odor is made of larger particles than a cry, 700 since it does not penetrate stone walls, through which voices and sounds are carried. It follows that, as you will see, it is not so easy to track out the direction in which the object that emits the odor is located; for the blows of a scent grow cold as they come hesitatingly through the breezes, and odors do not speed still hot to our senses as messengers of things. So dogs often go astray and are at a loss for the trail.

This is true not only in the case of smells and tastes:[38] likewise, all shapes and colors of things are not so equally suited to all senses of all animals that certain objects when seen are 710 not more painful to some creatures than to others. Ravenous lions, for example, cannot withstand or look upon the cock, that bird whose custom is to banish night with its beating wings, and with its clear note to welcome dawn. At once the lions think of flight, which must be because there are certain seeds in the body of the cock that, when sent against the eyes of lions, pierce

37 For the geese that saved the Capitol from the Gauls in 390 B.C., see Livy, V. 47, Virgil, *Aeneid* VIII. 655.

38 That is, that taste and smell are subjective. This section logically follows line 686.

the pupils through and cause such keen pain that the fierce beasts cannot endure it. Yet these same particles can in no way harm our eyes, either because they do not penetrate our eyes, or because, after they have entered, a free passageway out of the (720) eyes is given them so that they have no opportunity by delaying in the eye to harm it in any way.[i]

Now hear what things move the mind, and learn in a few words the source from which arise those things that enter it.[39] First I make this statement: many tenuous idols of material things are wandering about in many ways, on every side and in all directions. When these meet in the air, they are easily joined together, like spider webs or bits of gold leaf. Indeed, they are far more subtle in texture than the idols that fill the eyes and arouse the sense of sight, since they penetrate the (730) porous structure of the body, stir the tenuous mind, and arouse sensation within it. Thus we see centaurs, the limbs of monsters like Scylla, dog-like Cerberean shapes, and images of the dead, whose bones the earth embraces; for images of every kind are carried about at random. In part these are idols formed spontaneously in the air itself; in part they are idols of every kind that departs from any of the various forms, together with others that have been put together from these.[40] Certainly an idol of a centaur is not made from a living centaur, since no (740) such animal ever existed; but when by chance the idols of a horse and of a man have come together, one clings readily to the other because of their subtle nature and tenuous texture, as we have said before. The other idols of this kind are formed in this way.

When these idols are being carried about rapidly and with

[39] See Epicurus, *Letter to Herodotus* 46a–52a, where thought and sight are discussed together.

[40] Our thoughts and dreams of persons and things of the past are caused by worn-out idols, which were emitted in the regular way when the persons or things existed, and which are still floating about. Idols formed by combinations of idols emitted from real objects account for our thoughts and dreams of such unreal things as centaurs. No examples are given of thoughts caused by idols spontaneously generated in the air.

the utmost lightness, as I have already shown, any single subtle image with one blow moves our mind;[41] for the mind itself is tenuous and is stirred with wondrous ease. That this happens
750 as I say, you can easily learn from the following. Since what we perceive with the mind is like what we see with the eyes, the cause must be the same in both cases. Now then, inasmuch as I have taught that I see a lion, for example, by means of idols that rouse my eyes, we may know that the mind is moved in the same way by means of idols of lions and of the other things that it "sees," no more and no less than are the eyes, except that the idols the mind perceives are more subtle.

In the same way,[42] when sleep has relaxed our limbs, the rational parts of our minds remain awake, but with this difference: the idols that stir our minds when we are awake now stir
760 them to the point that we believe we truly see the man whom death and the earth already hold bereft of life. Nature brings this about because all the senses of the body, checked by sleep, are quiescent throughout the limbs, and cannot refute the false by the true. Moreover, the memory lies languid in sleep and does not argue that he whom the mind believes it sees alive has long since passed into the power of death and destruction.

In the next place it is not to be wondered at that the images move themselves, tossing their arms and other members in the
770 dance, as an image often does in our sleep. When the first image has perished and another image in another pose has come to take its place, the first seems to have changed its position. Truly, you must believe that this happens quickly, such are the speed and the number of things and so great the abundance of parti-

[41] That the mind can be stirred by a single idol is implied elsewhere, but only here is it expressly stated as a general truth.

[42] It is clear that lines 757–822 never received a final revision. Lines 818–22 are clearly out of place where they now stand and would more naturally follow line 767. Lines 777–817 are a reworking of lines 768–76 with considerable new material. Since it is impossible to tell what Lucretius would have done in a final revision, the only safe course is to present the passage as it stands. The reader, however, may well omit lines 768–76 and read the rest in the following order: 757–67, 818–22, 777–817. With this whole section, compare lines 962–1036 below.

cles in any perceptible period of time, that the supply of images is constantly replenished.

In this connection we raise many questions and must clarify many points if we wish to explain the subject completely. First we must ask how each man's mind at once thinks of that to 780 which his desires point. Do idols wait upon our wills, and does an image present itself to us as soon as we have a wish, whether the heart yearns to think of the sea, the land, or the sky? A gathering of men, a procession, banquets, battles—does Nature create and prepare all these at a word, especially when the mind of each of the other men in the same region and spot is contemplating far different things? Again, what do we suppose when in our sleep we see idols advance in rhythm and move their supple limbs, when alternately they gracefully extend their 790 supple arms and, in harmony with these, repeat the gestures with their feet? Are idols really steeped in art, and do they wander about highly trained so that they can present their spectacles to us in the hours of the night? Or will this be the truth? Since in the single unit of time that we recognize by the senses —that is, in the time in which a single sound is uttered—there are hidden many units of time whose existence the reason recognizes, it follows that in any period of time whatever all the various idols are everywhere ready at hand, so great is their mobility and so great their number. In this way, when the first idol has 800 perished and another in another pose has taken its place, the first seems to have changed its position. And because they are tenuous, the mind can see clearly only those that it strives to see. Thus all that are beside perish, save those for which the mind has prepared itself.[j] The mind of itself makes itself attentive, and expects that it will see what follows each thing; therefore it does. Do you not see that our eyes, when they begin to look at something that is tenuous, make themselves intent and ready, and that, unless they do this, it is not possible for us to see 810 clearly? Even in things that are plainly visible you can note that if you do not pay attention, the things are, so to speak, far removed and remote for the whole period of inattention. Why then should we marvel if the mind fails to note things other than those to which it has devoted itself? Then we base important conclusions on limited evidence and involve ourselves in the snare of self-deception.[43]

It also happens that sometimes an idol is not replaced by one 820 of the same kind, but that what was previously a woman appears still to be present but to have been changed into a man before our eyes, or varying features and ages follow one after another in the same person. But sleep and lack of memory prevent our wondering at this.

III. Some Bodily Functions in Relation to the Soul

823–1036

After a passing attack on all teleological theories of nature, the poet goes on to explain certain functions of the body, including the need for food, bodily motion, sleep, and dreams.

In this connection we are very anxious that you carefully avoid this fault, and shun this error most scrupulously: do not suppose that the bright pupils of the eyes have been created in order that we may see; that to enable us to advance with long strides, the ends of the shins and of the thighs have been furnished with joints and are supported by feet; moreover, that 830 forearms have been fitted to strong upper arms, and hands have been given us as aids on either side in order that we may do the things that are necessary for life.[44] These and all other relations

[43] This sentence is ambiguous. It may give a result of our failure to pay attention outside a narrow area; or it may cite our frequent self-deception as a further proof of the theories just advanced.

[44] See II. 167–83, V. 110–234, and VI. 379–422. If the gods created the world they must have done so with a purpose; but in a universe where all is caused by chance working under its own laws, there can be no purpose. Or to state it differently, if you accept purpose in creation, you must also accept some intelligent power behind that purpose. When Epicurus presented the arguments Lucretius here repeats, he was probably opposing the teachings of Aristotle; but Lucretius himself is aiming at the Stoics, who believed not only that their god, who was co-existent with Nature, had a purpose in creation, but also that this purpose was the benefit of mankind.

of this sort that men set forth have been turned upside down by reasoning that is inverted, for nothing in the body has come into existence in order that we may use it; rather, what has come into being has afterwards created its own function. The act of seeing did not exist before the eyes were born, nor that of speaking with words before the tongue was created; instead, the origin of the tongue long preceded speech, ears were created long before 840 a sound was heard, and, in a word, all the members existed before their several functions. Therefore they cannot have developed for the sake of being used. But on the other hand, men were joining in the struggle of war with bare hands, tearing each other's limbs and bloodying their members, long before gleaming weapons flashed; and Nature urged men to avoid wounds long before the left hand learned how to hold the protecting shield. It is true, also, that giving over the weary body to sleep is far older than the soft coverlets of beds, and that the 850 quenching of thirst is earlier born than the cup. We can believe that these things, which have been found because of the needs of life, were invented in order to be used. But all the others are different; for each of them created the concept of its function after it itself had first come into being. In particular, we see that the senses and the limbs belong to this class; wherefore I say again and again, it is in no way possible for you to believe that they can have been created for the sake of their utility.

You must not wonder that the body of every living creature naturally requires food. Indeed, I have shown that many particles 860 flow and depart from bodies in many ways, but more must flow from those that breathe.[45] Since the particles in these are kept in motion, since many are pressed up from deep within and carried off as sweat, since many too are exhaled from the mouth when the creatures pant in weariness, the bodies become porous and are altogether undermined, and pain results therefrom.

[45] See II. 1122–32. Atoms flow from all bodies, and all bodies are constantly receiving atoms. For inanimate bodies these two processes approximately balance; but creatures that move and breathe lose more than they receive and therefore need food to maintain themselves.

Food is taken in order that, when introduced into the body, it may support the limbs and restore strength, and may allay the manifest desire for eating throughout the members and veins.
870 Likewise liquid goes out into all the parts that call for liquid; and if many particles of heat have gathered together and set the stomach on fire, the liquid comes and scatters them, quenching the heat as if it were an actual fire, so that the dry heat may no longer consume our limbs. Thus panting thirst is washed away from our bodies; thus the hungry desire is filled.

Now how it happens that we are able to walk when we wish, in what way the power is given us to move our limbs in different ways, and what it is that habitually thrusts forward this great
880 weight of our bodies, I shall tell you. Do you listen to my words. I say that idols of walking[46] must first come up and strike the mind, as was explained before.[k] From this follows the will to act; for no one begins any act before the mind pictures what it wishes, and the mind foresees the action because the idol exists.[47] Thus when the mind has so stirred itself that it wishes to move and walk, it at once strikes the spirit, which is scattered in the whole body through the limbs and members, a thing easily accomplished since mind and spirit form one united
890 whole.[48] The spirit then strikes the body, and so the whole mass is thrust forward, little by little, and moved. The body, moreover, becomes more porous; and air, as is natural for a thing that is always mobile, enters through the openings and penetrates the passages abundantly, dividing itself into every little part of the body. The result is that, as a ship is moved by the sails and the wind, so now the body is moved by these two things.[49] It is no ground for wonder that such small particles

46 That is, idols of ourselves walking.

47 Literally: "That which it foresees, of that an image exists"; or "Because the mind foresees this thing, an image of it exists."

48 See, for example, III. 136–60.

49 Probably by the idol of motion and the air within; or possibly by the air within and the limbs.

are able to twist so great a body and turn our whole weight. For 900
a light breeze with its subtle body beats upon a great ship and drives it forward in spite of its huge mass; and regardless of the speed with which it is going, a single hand directs it and the one helm turns it where it wills. With slight effort, too, the crane with its pulleys and wheels moves and holds on high many things of great weight.[l]

Now the way in which sleep,[50] of which we have spoken, sends rest streaming through our members and frees the heart from the mind's anxieties, I shall tell in verses that are sweet rather than many, as the slight song of the swan is sweeter than that 910
harsh cry of the cranes broadcast beneath the south wind's lofty clouds. Do you but give discriminating ears and a shrewd mind; and do not deny the possibility of what I say, or depart with a mind that repels the truth although you yourself are at fault and cannot see.

First, sleep occurs when the spirit, throughout the limbs, is torn to pieces, when part of it is forced out and leaves the body, and part of it is pushed back and retires deep within;[m] for then the members collapse and droop. There is no doubt that sensa- 920
tion in us is the work of the spirit; and when sensation is interrupted by sleep, we must suppose that the spirit has been moved from its place and that some of it has been thrown from the body, but not all; for if all departed, the body would lie stretched out in the eternal chill of death.[51] Indeed, if no part of the spirit remained hiding in the limbs as fire hides covered by much ash, from what source could sensation quickly be kindled

[50] See the scholium on Epicurus, *Letter to Herodotus* 66. In this section and the next we have an introduction (lines 907–15), a brief explanation of sleep (lines 916–28), the end of another introduction (lines 929–31), and finally an amplified explanation of sleep (lines 932–61). Sleep has been briefly discussed earlier in this book at lines 757–91; and lines 909–11 are repeated from 180–82. All this seems to indicate that this part of the poem had not received final revision at the hand of the poet.

[51] Part of the spirit can be lost without fatal results, but death follows the loss of all of it (see III. 402–7).

again in the limbs as the flame rises up from the hidden fire?[52]

But I shall set forth the way in which this new state is brought
930 about, and from what causes the spirit can be disturbed and the body relaxed; see to it, for your part, that I do not waste my words on the winds.

In the first place, since the outer surface of the body is next to the breezes of the air and is touched by them, it must be beaten and struck by repeated blows of the air, and for this reason nearly all things are covered by skin, shell, hide, or bark.[53] In the case of creatures that breathe, this same air when it is drawn in and let out beats on even the interior parts. Since
940 the body is thus beaten on from inside and out, and since the blows pass through the small pores of our bodies to the basic particles within and to the very atoms, little by little our members collapse; for the positions of the atoms of body and spirit[54] are disturbed. As a result part of the spirit is driven outside, and part withdraws and hides itself within; and even the part that is scattered through the limbs cannot be joined together or act upon itself, for Nature blocks the passages and prevents its union. Therefore, the motions of the particles of body and spirit having been interrupted, consciousness retires deep within.
950 Since there is nothing to prop up the limbs, so to speak, the body becomes weak and all the members collapse, the arms and the eyelids fall, and as one sleeps, his legs are often drawn up with muscles relaxed.

Then, too, sleep follows eating because, when food is divided into all the veins, it does the same as does the air. That sleep is

[52] It is easy to see how the spirit particles that remained in the body might resume their normal places and motions; but how are those that were driven from the body to be recovered? Lucretius gives no answer to this, but probably we are to assume that among the atoms that are constantly raining in upon the body there are enough of the proper sort for rebuilding the spirit.

[53] To be consistent Lucretius must mean that because they chance to have been provided with protection they have survived, not that some guiding power has provided them with protection in order to make survival possible (see lines 823–57 above).

[54] Reading *animae*, "of spirit," for *animi*, "of mind," as the argument requires. This reading is suggested by Bailey in his commentary.

by far the heaviest which you take when you are full fed and weary, because then the greatest number of particles is beaten upon severely and confused. For that reason the withdrawal of part of the spirit into the body is deeper, the expulsion of another part of it is more violent, and that of it which remains in place is more divided and disturbed. 960

Each of us in sleep most often seems to follow the activity to which he is most closely bound, to carry out the occupation to which he has been devoting the most time, to pursue the line of thinking on which his mind has been most intent.[55] Lawyers believe that they are arguing cases or drawing up contracts; generals, that they are conducting wars or fighting battles; sailors, that they are carrying on their close struggle with the winds; I, that I am busy with my task, constantly searching into the nature of the universe and setting forth in Latin verse what I have discovered. Thus, too, other interests and occupations are often seen to occupy men's minds in sleep to no purpose. When men who for many days in succession have given their undivided attention to the games have ceased to apprehend them with their senses, it appears that open passageways are left in their minds through which the idols of these same things may come.[56] Thus for many days these same things are so kept before their eyes that these men, even when awake, seem to see the actors dancing and moving their supple limbs, to hear in their ears the fluid song of the cithara with its eloquent strings, and to see the same audience and even the varied decorations of the stage shining forth. So great a difference is made by one's interests and pleasures and by the matters with which one is habitually concerned. This is true not only of men but also of all beasts. In truth you will see strong horses, when their members lie at rest, sweating and struggling for breath in their sleep as if they expended the last ounce of effort for victory, or trying 970 980 990

[55] See what is said of dreams in lines 757–822 above.

[56] Since both sight and dreams are caused by similar idols from without, these "open passageways," made by idols causing sight and now available for an idol causing a dream, are probably to be taken quite literally.

to start[57] as if the barriers had just been raised. Huntsmen's dogs, in deep sleep, will often tense their legs suddenly or suddenly give voice, and they will repeatedly draw in the air through their nostrils as if they had caught the scent of a wild beast and were following hard upon it; and when awakened they often pursue empty forms of deer as if they saw them fleeing, until they shake off the error and come to themselves. Fawning house dogs, on the other hand, shake their bodies and leap from the ground[58] just as if they had caught sight of unknown forms and faces. The fiercer the breed, the more is it its nature to rage in sleep. In the night the birds of various colors flee and suddenly disturb the groves of the gods with their wings, 1010 if in their gentle sleep they have seen hawks flying in pursuit of them and attacking.

Moreover, the minds of men, which cause great actions by great motions,[59] often do and accomplish the same things in their sleep; without moving they attack kings, are captured, join in battle, cry aloud as if being strangled. Many fight and utter groans in their pain and fill the whole space with great shouts as if they were being bitten by a panther or a fierce lion. Many talk about important matters in their sleep, and many have 1020 furnished evidence of their own acts. Many meet death. Many are terrified as if they were about to fall headlong from a high mountain to the earth; and when they are roused from sleep, they are as if mad, and only with difficulty do they recover themselves from the disturbance of their bodies. A thirsty man sits beside a river or a pleasant spring, and all but takes the whole into his mouth. A cleanly person deep in sleep, thinking that he has raised his garment beside a privy or urinal, pours forth the liquid strained from his whole body, soaking the Babylonian 1030 coverlets of great splendor. Then to him into whom for the first time youth has brought together the seed, when the seasonable

[57] Reading *velle volare* with Munro for the meaningless *saepe quiete* of all the manuscripts.

[58] At this point the manuscripts erroneously repeat four lines from the description of the hunting dog.

[59] Probably the motions of the atoms are meant.

day has formed it in his members, there appears from without a likeness of no particular person, presenting a beautiful face and a fair complexion, which stirs him, exciting the organ swollen with much seed, so that, as if the act were accomplished, he emits a great flowing stream and defiles his garment.

IV. The Passion of Love

1037–1286

Sexual desire seeks satisfaction in the person who aroused it; yet it is best not to concentrate all passion on a single object. Passion always entails pain and frustration, and love is best avoided; once in love, however, it is possible to disenchant oneself by considering the defects of the beloved. Women feel desire as do men; love may be aroused by qualities other than beauty. The child resembles the parent whose seed is the stronger; fertility requires the proper mingling of appropriate seeds.

This seed, as we have said, is roused in us when maturity first gives strength to our limbs.[n] One thing moves and stirs one thing, another stirs another; but human influence alone summons human seed from a man. As soon as the semen is moved and goes forth from its places of origin,[60] it passes from the whole body through all the members and, gathering in the designated part of the tissues, at once excites the generative organs themselves. These parts, being aroused, swell with the semen, and the desire is formed to direct it where detestable lust strains.[61] It seeks that body whence the mind has received the wound of love; for wounded men for the most part fall upon the wound, blood spurts in the direction from which came the

1040

1050

[60] It should be noted that here and in several places below Lucretius speaks of the semen as being formed throughout the whole body and then being gathered in the generative organs.

[61] Line 1047, which is nearly identical with line 1034, is omitted by all editors.

stab, and red gore covers the enemy if he be near. So if anyone has been wounded by the weapons of Venus, whether the dart has come from a boy with effeminate limbs or from a woman hurling weapons of love from her whole frame, he strives in the direction from which he has been pierced, and struggles to unite with that body and to pour into it the liquid drawn from his own; for a wordless desire foretells the pleasure.

This is what we mean by love. From this desire Love receives his name, Cupid. From this, that drop of the sweetness of love 1060 steals into our hearts and is followed by chill care; for if the object of your desire is absent, yet her imagined form is before you and her sweet name haunts your ears. But you ought to shun those images, frightening off the food on which love feeds, and you should turn your thoughts elsewhere and scatter on any person whatever your concentrated passion, not holding it centered once and for all on the love of one and thereby winning for yourself anxiety and sure affliction; for the canker grows and eats more deeply as it is nourished, the passion burns 1070 hotter day by day, and the burden grows heavier unless you either obliterate the first wounds by different blows, healing them while still fresh by following some woman who welcomes all, or else are able to turn your mind to other things.

He does not miss the joy of love who avoids its passion, but rather he gains those pleasures that are free from pain. Certainly the pleasure from these things is less mixed for those who are in their right minds than for those who are lovesick; for at the very moment of enjoyment the passion of lovers wavers uncertainly, and they are not sure what they should first enjoy with eyes and hands. What they have sought they grasp tightly; 1080 they cause bodily pain, repeatedly clamping teeth upon lips and dashing mouth against mouth; for the pleasure is not unmixed and there are hidden thorns, which urge them to cause pain to that very thing whence sprout these shoots of madness. But in the midst of love Venus easily lessens their pains, and an admixture of soothing pleasure checks their bites. For hope rests on this: that the flame may be quenched by that very body which was the source of the heat. But Nature, in answer, says that it all happens in just the opposite way. This passion is unique; the more we satisfy it, the more our hearts are fired with the accursed desire. Food and drink are taken within our members; and, since they can come to rest in their proper places, the desire for water and bread is easily satisfied. But from a person's fair face and color nothing is sent into our bodies for enjoyment except the subtle idols, and even these are often tossed to the wind by unhappy love. Just as when a thirsty man, in a dream, seeks to drink and no real water is given him which could quench the fever of his frame, but laboring to no purpose he reaches for idols of liquids and is still thirsty while drinking in the midst of a torrential stream; even so in love, Venus with her phantoms makes sport of lovers, and they cannot satisfy their bodies by gazing at bodies close beside them, nor can they rub away anything from the limbs as they play with gentle hands over the whole body. Then when their limbs are intertwined and they are at the point of enjoying the flower of youth, when the body has a foretaste of its joys and Venus is about to sow the woman's fields, each greedily clasps the other's body, joining the moisture of their mouths and panting as teeth press on lips; but all in vain, for neither can take anything away, nor can one whole body penetrate and enter the other, for this is what they seem at times to desire and to strive to do. So they cling greedily together in love's embrace while limbs grow slack, wasted by the violence of pleasure. At length, when accumulated desire has burst from the tissues, there comes a brief pause in the wild passion. Then the same madness returns, and that same frenzy visits them once more when they themselves seek to learn what it is that they desire to win for themselves and can discover no device to overcome the evil. Vacillating thus, they waste away from a secret wound.

1090 1100 1110 1120

Add that the lover wastes his strength and is undone by care; add that he spends his life subject to another's whims, that his duties are neglected, and that his reputation totters to its fall. At the same time his estate is ruined in the purchase of Babylonian ointments,[62] fair Sicyonian sandals gleam on his mistress' feet, great emeralds of flashing green are set in gold, robes of sea-purple are in constant use, and as they are worn they drink in the sweat of love. The wealth honorably gained by his father 1130 is spent for ribbons and veils, or exchanged for a mantle and fabrics of Caria and Ceos. Banquets with luxurious hangings, food, games, repeated cups, ointments, crowns, and wreaths are provided; but to no purpose, since from the very midst of this flood of pleasures something bitter comes forth, a prick of pain amid the very blossoms, either because in his own mind he feels remorse, conscious that he is wasting his youth in idleness and going to ruin in a swamp of evil, or because as his mistress left she tossed out a word of doubtful meaning, which, planted in his eager heart, burns like a fire, or else because he thinks that 1140 she is turning her eyes too far afield and gazing on another, and sees on her face the traces of a smile.

These evils are discovered in a love that is appropriate and wholly successful; in an unhappy and hopeless love the evils that you can discover, even with your eyes closed, are beyond number. It is therefore better to be on guard beforehand in the way that I have shown, and to beware lest you be snared. For it is not so difficult to avoid falling into the traps of love as it is, once you have been captured, to get out of the nets themselves and to break the strong knots of love. But even after 1150 having been caught and bound you could escape the dangerous place if you would not stand in your own way, overlooking all the faults, both of the mind and of the body, of her whom you seek and desire. For most men, blinded by passion, do this very thing and attribute to their mistresses qualities that are not really theirs. Thus we see counted among favorites and held in highest esteem women who are in many ways misshapen and unseemly. One man laughs at another and bids him pray to Venus because he has been overpowered by a shameful love,

[62] The text here is doubtful. I have transposed lines 1123 and 1124 following Lambinus, and have retained *unguenta* in line 1125. Bailey keeps the order of the manuscripts and believes that *unguenta* has displaced some word for a kind of shoe or slipper.

and yet, poor fool, he himself often does not see his own great bane. The dark girl is called "honey-colored"; the slovenly and unkempt, "unaffected"; the grey-eyed, "Athena"; the sinewy and wiry, "gazelle"; the tiny is called "doll," "one of the graces," "nothing but wit"; the over-tall, a "miracle" and "full of dignity." If she stammers and cannot speak distinctly, she lisps; if she is dumb, she is modest; if she is restless, annoying, and talkative, she becomes one of the Bacchantes. She whose thinness brings her close to death is called "little darling"; and the one about to die of a cough is called "slender." On the other hand, she who is overweight and full-bosomed is Ceres herself, the mother of Bacchus; the pug-nosed is a female Silenus or Satyr; the one with large lips, a kiss. It would be a long task if I undertook to name the rest in this way. But yet, grant that she have in her face all the beauty you wish, that the power of Venus rise from all her limbs, truly there are others just as good; truly we once lived without her; truly she does, and we know that she does, the same things as the uncomely do, surrounding her wretched self with foul odors so that her maid servants avoid her and laugh in secret. But her lover, excluded and weeping, covers her threshold with flowers and garlands, anoints her proud doorposts with marjoram, and wretchedly prints kisses on the doors. If he should be admitted and only a single breath should strike him as he entered, he would seek a decent excuse for departing, forgetting his long-planned and heartfelt lament; and he would blame himself for his folly as he saw that he had attributed to her more than it is right to accord to any mortal. This does not escape our Venuses; therefore all the more with greatest care they conceal all these hidden parts of their lives from those whom they wish to hold fast-bound in love; but to no purpose, since in your mind you yourself could bring all this to light and seek the meaning of all the mockery, and then, if she has a fair mind and is not hateful, you could in turn overlook all this and grant pardon to human frailty. 1160 1170 1180 1190

Nor does the woman always sigh with a love that is feigned when she clasps the man's body with her own in embrace, and

holds him, printing wet kisses with sucking lip. For often she does this from her heart and, seeking common joys, urges him to run the full course of love. The female birds, beasts, cattle, and horses would not yield to their mates for any other reason
1200 except that their nature is in the full fire of heat and receives with reluctant joy the passion of the covering male. Have you not often seen how those whom mutual pleasure holds are tortured in their common chains? In this way at the crossroads dogs eager to separate strain avidly away from each other with all their strength, yet at the same time they cling to each other in the close bonds of love. This they would never do had they not known mutual pleasures, which are able to trick them and hold them bound. Therefore, as I have said, the pleasure is shared.

When, in the act of generation, the woman's seed has with
1210 sudden force conquered and laid hold of that of the male, then children like the mother are formed by the mother's seed, just as children like the father are formed when the male seed is the stronger.[63] But the children whom you see resembling the figures of both parents, mingling together the features of both, these are growing from the father's body and the mother's blood when a passion harmoniously shared has brought together the seeds excited throughout the limbs by the goads of love, and neither of them overcomes the other or is overcome. It sometimes happens also that children can be born like their grandparents and may often recall the features of remoter ancestors
1220 for the reason that in many ways parents hide mingled in their bodies many seeds that fathers have handed down to fathers from the beginnings of the race. From these Venus produces figures of various sorts and recalls the looks, voices, and hair of ancestors; for these are no more made from a specified seed than are our faces, bodies, and members. The father's seed is required for the birth of a girl, and the mother's body for the formation of a boy, for the embryo is always of the seed of both parents;
1230 and whatever is born is most like the parent of whose seed it has

[63] This seems to be the traditional theory of the atomists.

more than an even share. This can be seen whether the child is a boy or a girl.

Divine power does not drive away life-giving seed from anyone to the end that a man may never be called father by dear children but must spend his whole life without issue. Most men believe that the gods have this power, and in sorrow they sprinkle altars with much blood and honor shrines with gifts, praying that they may make their wives pregnant with many children. To no purpose do they weary the divine gods and the oracles; for some are sterile because the semen is too thick, and 1240 some because it is thinner and weaker than is proper. If it is thin it turns to liquid at once and comes back from the womb and fails to fertilize,[64] because it is unable to cling in place. In the case of the others, since the semen emitted is too thick and clotted, either it does not penetrate with a far-reaching blow, or it is unable to flow into the places equally, or else when it has made its way in, it does not mix readily with the female seed. The unions of love are seen to show many differences. Some men are more likely to make some women pregnant, and other 1250 women receive the heavy burden of a child more readily from other men. Many a woman, unfertile in more than one previous marriage, has afterwards found a husband from whom she can conceive children and become rich with sweet offspring. For a man whose wife, although formerly fertile, has become unable to bear a child in his home, a wife of comformable nature has been found so that he can strengthen his old age with sons. So important is it that seed fitted to seed be combined for producing life, and that thick join with thin and thin with thick. The 1260 food with which one maintains life also makes a difference, for the seed are increased in the members by some foods, and by others are thinned and wasted. The manner in which the act of love is performed is also of great importance; for it is usually thought that wives are most likely to conceive if this is performed in the manner of four-footed beasts; for thus, when the breasts are below and the buttocks are raised, the seeds can find their place. Our wives have no need at all of enticing move-

64 Reading *ab ortu* with Lachmann, for *abortu*.

1270 ments. Indeed, a woman hinders and opposes conception if, for all her pleasure, she withdraws with her buttocks from her husband's love and rouses the tide of his passion with all her soft bosom; for she diverts the furrow of the plow from its true direction and turns the sowing of the seed from its place. Courtesans for their own advantage are wont to move in such a way lest they often receive the seed and be neglected while they are pregnant, and also that their love itself may be more pleasing to their lovers; but it is clear that there is no need of this for our wives.

Sometimes without the divine aid of the arrows of Venus a 1280 woman lacking in outward beauty wins love; for it may be that by her own acts, by her agreeable manners, or by her neatly kept body a woman so wins you that you easily pass your life with her. Moreover, custom strengthens love; for what is beaten upon by frequent blows, however light, is finally overcome and yields. Do you not see that drops of water falling upon a rock in the course of a long time drill through it?

BOOK FIVE

I. Our World

1–508

After an introduction praising Epicurus, the poet explains the origins and laws of this world. Far from being immortal, it is lifeless and will someday fall into ruin; to assert this is no impiety, for the gods do not dwell in the celestial bodies, and they did not form the world for the benefit of man. All things are subject to mutation and decay, the world among them, for it fulfills none of the conditions for immortality. The elements of the world are at war with one another. It was formed when the proper atoms happened to fall into appropriate combinations and motions; the earth was formed from the heavier particles, while the lighter, in order of decreasing density, formed the water, the air, and the aether.

Whose mighty genius can compose a poem worthy of these discoveries of Nature's majesty? Who has such skill in words that he can fashion fitting praise for the merits of him who, by his genius, has sought and won such prizes and left them to us? Surely it will be no one born of mortal stock. For, noble Memmius,[1] if one must speak as the grandeur of the system revealed by him demands, he was a god,[2] a very god, who was first to discover the plan of life now called philosophy, and who by his 10 art brought our life out from such great storms and darkness into waters so calm and light so clear. Compare with this the godlike discoveries made of old by others. Ceres is said to have taught mortals the use of grain and Liber that of wine, the drink

[1] Memmius has not been mentioned since II. 182.

[2] The Epicureans regarded Epicurus as worthy of divinity (Cicero, *Tusculan Disputations* I. 48): and Epicurus said that his true followers would live like gods among men (*Letter to Menoeceus* 135b).

born from the vine; yet without these life could remain, a life such as some tribes are said to live even now. But there could be no good life without a heart made clean;[3] therefore the more de-
20 servedly do we regard him as a god from whom arose the sweet solaces of life that even now have spread among great nations and are calming their hearts. But if you believe that his labors are surpassed by those of Hercules,[4] you wander even farther from the truth. How would that gaping mouth of the Nemaean lion or the bristly back of the Arcadian boar injure us today? What could we suffer from the Cretan bull or from the Hydra, pest of Lerna, walled about with poisonous snakes? Or from the triple force of three-bodied Geryon? ⟨. . . Would the
30 birds⟩ that inhabit Stymphalia greatly injure us, or yet the steeds of Thracian Diomedes breathing fire from their nostrils near the Bistonian plains and Mount Ismara? And the guardian of the gleaming golden fruit of the Hesperides, the cruel serpent with bitter glare, coiling his huge body about the tree trunk—what harm could he do there beside the shores of the Atlantic and the forbidding expanses of the sea, regions that no man, whether of our race or that of the barbarians, dares draw near? And the other monsters of this sort that have been destroyed—even had they not been vanquished, even though still alive, how would they harm us? In no way, I believe. Even
40 as it is, the earth yet teems with a surfeit of monsters and is filled with frightening terror through groves, great mountains, and deep forests, places that for the most part we have the power to avoid. But if the heart is not purified, then in what battles and dangers must we be involved, even against our wills! What sharp anxieties caused by passion, what terrors, then tear troubled man! What shall we say of pride, lust, and petulance and the great disasters they cause? What, of luxury and sloth? He, then, who subdued all these and drove them from our
50 minds, not by arms but by words, does he not, although a man, seem worthy to be counted among the gods, especially since it was his habit to utter many good and godlike sayings about the

[3] See Epicurus, *Letter to Menoeceus* 132b; *Principal Doctrines* V.

[4] The Stoics honored Hercules as early man's great benefactor.

immortal gods themselves, and to expound by his words the whole nature of the universe?

Following in his tracks, I pursue his reasoning and show by my words how necessary it is that each particular object remain subject to that law by which it was created, and how impotent each is to override the mighty decrees of time.[5] In particular, we have already discovered that the soul is corporeal and had a beginning, and that it cannot endure unharmed for long ages, but that "idols" do exist, which often deceive us in our sleep, when we seem to see a man from whom life has departed.[6] The plan of my work has now brought us to the point where I must demonstrate that the world, likewise, consists of matter which had a beginning and will have an end. Then, too, I must explain how the union of that matter laid the foundations of earth, sky, sea, stars, sun, and the globe of the moon;[7] which living creatures have come forth from the earth, and which have never been produced at any time; how the human race by variations in sound began to employ names of things in its intercourse; and in what way men's hearts were filled with that fear of the gods, thanks to which throughout the earth shrines, lakes, groves, altars, and images of the gods are held sacred. Moreover, I shall explain by what power Nature, like a pilot, directs the courses of the sun and the movements of the moon, so that we may neither by chance believe that these bodies freely and of their own wills move through their yearly courses between heaven and earth, intent on fostering the growth of fruits and of living creatures, nor yet think that they are rolled on by some design of the gods. For if men, even those who have rightly learned that the gods pass lives untouched by care, are nevertheless left to wonder from time to time in what way each

60

70

80

[5] See Epicurus, *Letter to Herodotus* 76b–77; *Principal Doctrines* XI, XII, and XIII.

[6] See IV. 760–61.

[7] These—the earth and the bodies that seem to revolve about it—form the *mundus*, a term which will be rendered "world." This must be distinguished from the earth in a narrow sense, and from the universe which contains many worlds.

thing in Nature can be brought to pass, especially in the case of the things they see above their heads in the region of the upper air, they are again carried back into the old superstitions, and they acknowledge cruel masters, whom they in their misery believe to be all-powerful, since they do not understand what can come into existence and what cannot, and by what law there is
90 for each thing a power that is limited and a boundary that is firmly fixed.[8]

To proceed, that we may not delay you longer with promises, look first at the sea, the earth, and the sky. Their triple nature —three bodies, Memmius, three forms so unlike in appearance, three such textures—a single day will destroy; and the whole mass and mechanism of our world, after having been sustained through many years, will fall in ruins.[9] It does not escape me how new and strange to your mind is the thought that destruction awaits the heaven and the earth, and how difficult it is for
100 me to establish this fact by words. This is to be expected when a matter hitherto unknown is brought to a man's ears, and yet it cannot be placed within the range of his eyes or the reach of his hands, whence the shortest road, well-paved by confidence, leads to the human breast and to the temple of the mind.[10] Yet I shall speak. Perhaps events themselves will lend support to my words, and you will witness mighty quakings of the earth and all things shattered in a brief space of time. May ruling Fortune[11] turn this far from us, and may reason rather

[8] Lines 89–90 were used at I. 76–77, and lines 82–90 will appear again at VI. 58–66.

[9] See II. 1144–45.

[10] The figure seems to come from Empedocles: "It is not possible to draw near to it, nor can it be reached by our eyes or touched by our hands, where lies Persuasion's chief highway to the minds of men" (Diels, *Fragmente*, 31 B 133).

[11] Possibly Lucretius is thinking in atomic terms, where "chance" is what cannot be predicted although it happens according to Nature's laws; but probably he has dropped into the familiar language of poetry and has personified Fortune as a divinity.

than reality itself persuade you that it is possible for all to fall in ruin, overcome by a mighty crash.

Before I attempt to utter oracles about this matter, in fashion more holy and with reason more certain than does the Pythia speaking from the tripod and laurel of Phoebus,[12] I shall bring you much comfort with my learned words. Do not, chained by superstition, think by any chance that earth, sun, sky, sea, stars, and moon are of eternal substance and hence should exist for eternity, and therefore believe it right that, like the Giants, all pay the penalty for an impious crime who by their teachings assail the walls of the world and foretell the end of the bright sun in heaven, dishonoring immortal beings with mortal words.[13] Yet in fact these things are so far from divinity and so unworthy of being counted in the number of the gods that they may more properly be thought fit to serve as types of that which is utterly removed from living motion and sensation. It is impossible to suppose that the mind and its intelligence can exist equally well with a body of any kind whatever; for certainly a tree cannot grow in the upper air or clouds in the depths of the sea, nor can fish live in the fields, nor can blood be hidden in wood or sap in stones. There is a fixed and determined place where each thing may grow and have its home. So the mind cannot come into being alone without the body, or exist apart from sinews and blood. Were some variation possible, it is much more likely that the mind would be able to take its place in the head, the shoulders, or the very heels, and habitually be born in any part you please, while still remaining in the same man and the same vessel.[14] But since it is even determined and clearly established in which spot in our bodies the spirit and mind can be and grow by themselves,[15] so much the more must

110

120

130

140

[12] Lines 111–12 are repeated from I. 738–39.

[13] Cicero (*On the Nature of the Gods* II. 44) calls impious those who, like the Epicureans, deny the divinity of the stars.

[14] Lucretius places the mind in the breast (III. 140).

[15] This does not agree with the statements elsewhere in the poem. The mind has its fixed position in the breast, but the spirit is distributed through the whole body (III. 136–44).

we deny that they can exist wholly outside the body[16] and the living form, whether in decomposing clods of earth, in the fire of the sun, in water, or in the lofty borders of the heavens. It is clear, therefore, that these heavenly bodies are not endowed with a conscious existence like that of the gods, inasmuch as they cannot even receive the breath of life.[17]

This belief too you must reject, that there are sacred dwellings of the gods in any part of our world.[18] Since the nature of the gods is tenuous and far removed from our senses, it is
150 scarcely recognized by the perception of the mind. Since it escapes from the contact and touch of hands, it cannot itself touch anything that is subject to our sense of touch; for that cannot touch which cannot itself be touched. Therefore even the dwellings of the gods must be different from ours, intangible like the bodies of the gods themselves, which I shall prove to you hereafter in ample form.[19]

Again, to say that the gods wished to prepare the beautiful world for the sake of man, that for this reason it is proper to celebrate the work of the gods as praiseworthy, and to regard it
160 as eternal and destined to exist forever; to say it is not right that what the ancient devices of the gods eternally established for the human race should ever be shaken from its place by any violence, or vexed by words, or be overturned entirely from its very foundations; and to imagine and add other things of this sort—all this, Memmius, is folly.[20] For in what way could our thanks reward those who are immortal and blessed, so that they would undertake to do anything for our sake? By what new thing could those who had been so long in repose have been
170 induced to desire to alter the former tenor of their lives? For it is clear that he ought to rejoice in the new who is weary of the old; but when no evil has in the past befallen one and he has

[16] Lines 128–41 are repeated with minor variations from III. 784–97.

[17] This is primarily directed against the Stoics, who believed in a world-spirit present in all parts of the universe.

[18] See Bailey, *Greek Atomists and Epicurus*, 438–67.

[19] This promise is not fulfilled. Epicurus placed the homes of the gods in the *intermundia*, the space between the worlds and thus outside our earth and the celestial bodies regarded as belonging to it.

[20] See IV. 823–57.

passed his life happily, what can rouse in such a one a love for what is new? What evil could it have been for us not to have been created? Are we to believe that life lay in darkness and sorrow until the creation of the world shed light upon it?[21] Whoever has been born may well wish to remain alive as long as alluring pleasure holds him; but if a man has never tasted the love of life nor been in the number of the living, how is he 180 injured by never having been born?

Whence did the example of creation and the very concept[22] of mankind enter the minds of the gods, so that they knew and visualized what they wished to create? Or in what way did they learn of the atoms' power and of the things that the atoms can accomplish as they change their relative positions, if Nature herself did not give an example of creation? For since from infinite time many atoms in many ways, kept in motion by blows and being stirred by their own weight, were always being carried along and coming together in every possible fashion and trying 190 all the combinations that could be created as they joined each other, it is not at all strange if they also fell into arrangements and came into courses such as those from which this present world is kept in existence by constant renewal.[23]

[21] Many editors, placing lines 175–76 before 174, make this sentence refer to the boredom of the gods before the creation of the world.

[22] *Notities*, here translated "concept," is Lucretius' word for Epicurus' *prolēpsis*, a general concept resulting from repeated sense experience (see Laertius, *Life of Epicurus* 31a, and note). Such a mental concept may be translated into action, and the gods might have created man if they had had the concept "man." But before the first man was formed, the concept could not have existed. The first man, therefore, must have resulted from the undirected action of the atoms moving under their own laws, not from the deliberate action of the gods.

[23] Lines 187–94 are expanded from I. 1024–28; and lines 187–91 will be used again with variations as lines 422–26 below. They describe the critical period in the formation of a world. For infinitely long periods of time the atomic motions may have no result; then at a particular spot in the universe the conditions necessary for the formation of a world are present—the proper atoms in proper proportions going through proper motions—and the formation of a world takes place with relative rapidity; and when once a world has been formed, it tends to perpetuate itself for a time. See II. 1063, and note.

Even if I did not know the nature of the atoms, yet I would venture to assert from the very ways of the heavens, and to prove from many other examples, that the world was by no means prepared for us by the gods, with such imperfections is it filled.[24]
200 First, a half of all that the great expanse of heaven covers has been greedily possessed by mountains and forests where wild beasts make their homes, or occupied by cliffs, vast swamps, or the sea that holds far apart the shores of the lands. Of what is left, about two-thirds is stolen from mortals by fiery heat and by the ceaseless fall of the cold. What land remains Nature, if left to herself, would cover with briars, unless man prevented, accustomed as he is to maintain his life by groaning over the heavy two-pronged mattock and by cleaving the earth with the
210 deep-pressed plowshare. If we did not rouse the earth to production, rendering its clods fertile as we turn them with the plow and working over its soil,[25] plants could never of their own accord come forth into the liquid air. Even as it is, from time to time, that which we have won by great labor, at the very time when the leaves are springing up over the soil and all is flourishing, is parched by the excessive heat of the sun, overwhelmed by sudden rains and chill frosts, or spoiled by the blasts of the winds in a fierce storm. Next, why does Nature, on
220 land and sea, foster and favor the dread race of wild beasts hostile to mankind? Why do the seasons of the year bring pestilence? Why does untimely death wander abroad? Finally, the baby lies naked on the ground like a sailor tossed up by the cruel sea, speechless, in want of every life-giving aid, when Nature with the pangs of birth has first brought him from the womb of his mother into the regions of light. He fills the place round about with mournful wailings, as is right in the case of one before whom lies the journey through so many ills of life. Yet the various flocks and herds and the wild beasts grow and
230 have no need of toys; none of them require the soothing prattle of a fostering nurse, or demand different sorts of clothing for the different seasons, or need arms and high walls by which to

[24] Lines 195–99 are repeated with minor changes from II. 177–81.

[25] Lines 210–11 are repeated with minor changes from I. 211–12, where, however, their context is quite different.

defend their possessions, since for each of them the earth herself and wonder-working Nature produce all things in abundance.

In the first place, since earthy matter and moisture, the gentle breath of the winds and the warm heat—the elements from which we see that this world is formed[26]—are all of them clearly of a substance subject to birth and death, we must believe the world as a whole to be of the same character;[27] for surely, if we observe that the parts and members of a thing are of a substance that has had a beginning and is mortal, we always find that the thing itself is mortal and likewise has had a beginning. Therefore, since I see that the basic elements and parts of the world are consumed and then remade, I may also be certain that there was some time of origin both for the sky and for the earth, and that destruction will come to them. 240

Do not believe that in this argument I have seized a point for myself without proof, in that I have unquestioningly assumed that earth and fire are mortal and that moisture and air perish, and have declared that these same things are reborn and again increase. First of all, some parts of the earth, parched by continued suns and trodden on by many feet, breathe forth dust in a flying misty cloud which strong winds scatter through all the air. Part of the tilled land is washed away by the rains, and greedy streams eat away their banks.[28] Moreover, whatever the earth gives to living things, nourishing them and causing them 250

[26] The four Empedoclean elements—earth, water, fire, and air—serve Lucretius' purpose here, where he is speaking in popular terms. Moreover, while they are not the ultimate elements from which all is formed, we shall find throughout much of what follows that they represent an intermediate stage in development, phenomena being often explained in terms of these four or of some of them.

[27] See Epicurus, *Letter to Herodotus* 73b. This section logically follows lines 91–110, where the mortality of the earth was asserted before the poet turned aside to attack the belief that the gods created the earth for man.

[28] The dust, vanishing into the air, becomes air; and the soil, vanishing into the water, becomes water; or in atomic terms, the atoms that made earth now make air or water. Thus earth is destroyed and water and air are created, although the second point is not explicitly made. In the same way, the food that a plant receives from the earth becomes part of the plant, and the plant when it decays becomes once more a part of the earth.

to grow, is returned to the earth in the same measure; and since without question we see the same earth to be the mother of all
260 and the common sepulcher of all, you may be sure that she is being eaten away and is also being increased and re-created.

Next, there is no need of words to show that sea, rivers, and springs always abound with new liquid and that the waters flow ceaselessly; the great flow of waters from all sides declares this. But particles of water are successively removed, with the result that in the whole system there is no surplus—partly because the seas are diminished as strong winds sweep over their surface and the sun, from on high, unravels their fabric with its rays,[29] partly because the water is being spread out beneath all the lands; for the salt is filtered out, and the liquid parts seep
270 back and all gather together at the sources of the rivers, from which the water flows above the earth in a sweet stream wherever the path once marked by its liquid tread directs the waves.

Now then, I shall speak of the air, which every single hour undergoes changes throughout its whole body in ways that we cannot number.[30] Whatever flows away from objects is all carried ceaselessly into the great sea of the air. Unless the air, on the other hand, gave particles back to objects, renewing them as they wasted, everything would by now have been dissolved and turned into air. The air, therefore, does not cease to be
280 born from things and to change back into things, for it is clear that everything is constantly ebbing and flowing.[a]

[29] To complete the argument, Lucretius should state that the water that is changed into air is changed back into water in the form of rain. To us this paragraph may seem to indicate, not that water perishes and is re-created, but that it goes through ceaseless changes without loss; but to Lucretius, when water ceased to exist as a visible liquid, it ceased to exist at all (its atoms, of course, continuing to exist but in the form of some other thing), and when it reappeared as a liquid, it had been re-created. Lines 269–72 are repeated with minor changes at VI. 635–38.

[30] Ernout compares with this passage the statement ascribed to Empedocles by Plutarch, *Natural Questions* XIX. 916d=Diels, *Fragmente*, 31 B 89: "Know that there are effluences from all created things. Not only from animals, vegetables, earth, and sea do many streams flow, but also from stones, bronze, and iron; for all things are destroyed and perish because matter flows and is carried from them always and without interruption."

That generous source of clear light, the sun in heaven, constantly floods the sky with new light and ceaselessly replaces the old light with new; for each separate unit of light vanishes wherever it falls. This you may learn from the following: as soon as clouds begin to gather below the sun and, so to speak, to sever the rays of light, at once the whole lower portion of each ray disappears, and the earth is shadowed wherever the clouds pass. Thus you may know that there is always need of 290 new brightness, and that each sunbeam perishes as it strikes; and there is no way in which a thing can be seen in the sunlight unless the very source of light itself continuously provides a new supply.[31] Nay, even these night lights of yours that belong to earth, those hanging lamps, those torches with bright flickering flames and much pitchy smoke—in like fashion, aided by heat, these hasten to supply new light; endlessly, endlessly do they quiver with flames, nor does the light, as if broken, leave any gap in itself. So quickly is the destruction of light from every 300 fire hidden by the swift origin of new flame. You must therefore believe that sun, moon, and stars in this same way toss forth light in ever new supply and that the earlier units of flame are always perishing, lest perchance you suppose that these heavenly bodies possess an unassailable might.[32]

Next, do you not see that stones too are overcome by time, that lofty towers fall in ruins and masonry rots away, that the shrines and statues of the gods develop cracks as they grow weary, and the divine presence can neither move forward the

[31] See IV. 185–90.

[32] The destruction and creation of the first three elements—earth, water, and air—are described as changes, each of them being destroyed as it passes into one of the others, and each of them being created anew from the others. Lucretius might have presented fire in a similar way. It is created from fuel, which has been formed from earth, air, and water, and it passes into air and into earth-like ash. Instead he takes a particular manifestation of fire, light, which has heavenly bodies and earthly fires as its sources; but he does not explain the origin of fire or of the fiery particles from which the sun is formed, and he has nothing to say of what happens to light when it ceases to be. The atoms in motion that we have recognized as light must continue to exist, but nothing is said of the new form that they assume.

310 boundary set by fate nor struggle against the laws of Nature? Do we not see that the fallen monuments of men continue to ask whether you believe that they are becoming infirm with years? Do we not see that flints torn from high mountains are broken and do not withstand or endure the great force even of limited time? For stones that had already endured without destruction all the attacks of the ages from infinite time would not now be torn apart and quickly come to nothing.[33]

Then consider this aether that holds all the earth in its em-
320 brace about and above. If it creates everything from itself, as some say, and receives all things back when they are destroyed, it is clear that the aether as a whole is of mortal substance and had a beginning. For whatever increases and nourishes other things from itself must be diminished thereby, and it must be re-created when it receives these things in return.[b]

Moreover, if there has been no beginning of life for earth and the sky, if they have existed for ever, why have not other poets sung of other exploits before the Theban War and the fall of Troy? Why has it happened so many times that so many deeds of men have perished, and nowhere flourish, inscribed within
330 the eternal memorials of fame? But, I think, this whole system of ours is new, and the world itself is recent and had its beginning not long ago.[34] For this reason certain arts are even now being perfected or are still being developed; of late many devices have been added to the art of navigation, and the musician has but now produced resounding melody from his instrument. Finally, the character and the governing principle of the natural world have only recently been discovered, and I myself am now the very first man able to turn this doctrine into the language

[33] This paragraph, like the next, seems an afterthought. Lucretius has already shown that the earth is worn away and perishes. Here he points out that the same is true of the hardest stones and metals. The last sentence does make a new point: they cannot already have existed for an infinite time if they are now wasting so quickly; therefore they must have had a beginning.

[34] But compare II. 1144–74, where Lucretius tells us that the earth is worn out with long life.

of my native land. But if by chance you believe that all these same things existed before this, but that generations of men have perished in burning fire, that their cities have been destroyed in a great upheaval of the world, or that, after continued rains, greedy floods spread forth upon the earth and destroyed the towns—so much the more must you yield and confess that there will also be an end for the earth and the sky. For if, at the time when they were subjected to such ills and dangers, a mishap a little more severe had occurred, they would have fallen in great ruin and wide destruction. In this same way we recognize that we are mortal because one after another we fall ill with the same diseases as did those whom nature has removed from life. 340 350

Finally, that which remains forever must either turn aside blows by virtue of its solid body, not permitting itself to be penetrated by anything that could separate the tightly packed parts within, as is the case with the atoms, whose nature we considered above; or second, it must be capable of enduring through all eternity for the reason that it is immune to blows, as is the void, which remains intangible and is not at all affected by any impact; or third, it must be eternal, as is the universe, because there is no void about it into which its matter can, as it were, recede and be dissolved, and no space into which its parts may escape, nor are there any external bodies that can fall upon it and break it up with a mighty blow.[35] But as I have shown, the world is not a solid body, since void is mixed with its matter; nor yet is it like the void. Moreover, there is no lack of bodies which, coming at random from infinite space, can rush with violent twisting upon this world or introduce some other dangerous catastrophe; nor is there lack of a vast void into which the walls of the world might be scattered; or else these walls can perish struck by any other violence you please. Thus the gate to destruction is closed neither for the sky, nor for the sun and the earth, nor for the deep waters of the sea; but it is wide open and waits for them with a vast, widely gaping mouth. 360 370

[35] Lines 351–63 are repeated with slight changes from III. 806–18. They seem more appropriate here than in the earlier passage, where they are presented among the arguments for the mortality of the soul.

Therefore you must admit that these same things had a beginning; for things that are subject to destruction cannot hitherto have existed through infinite time in defiance of the mighty forces of unmeasured ages.[36]

380 Finally, since the great elements of the universe are fighting so mightily among themselves, roused in a war that is by no means sacred, do you not see that it is possible that some end of the long conflict will be given them?[37] Perhaps the sun and heat will drink up all the moisture and prevail. Indeed, they are trying to do this, but as yet have not accomplished their undertaking. The rivers supply water equal to the loss; and going beyond this, the waters threaten to rise from the deep abyss of the sea and inundate all; but in vain, inasmuch as winds sweeping over the seas and the sun of heaven unraveling 390 them with its rays make them grow less, and winds and sun are confident that they will be able to dry up all things before the waters can accomplish what they plan. Breathing out such war in equal combat, sun, wind, and water still are struggling to reach a decision among themselves about great matters, although once ere this, fire was superior, and once—so the report goes—water ruled the plains. For fire gained control and, spreading, burned many things when the runaway violence of the horses of the Sun carried Phaëthon from his course and dragged him through the whole heaven and across all lands. 400 But then the all-powerful father, roused by keen wrath, with the sudden blow of his thunderbolt hurled bold Phaëthon from his chariot to the earth; and the sun-god, meeting him as he fell, caught the eternal lamp of the world, controlled the struggling horses, and yoked them as they trembled; then, directing them along their proper course, he restored all things. This, at least, is the song sung by the ancient poets of Greece,[38] but it is very

[36] See lines 315–16 above.

[37] For the strife of the elements, see the section on Empedocles in the Introduction (pp. xii–xiv). The Stoics believed that our world would be destroyed by fire.

[38] Ovid (*Metamorphoses* II. 1–400) later told the story in detail; but we do not know the Greek poet or poets whom he followed or those to whom Lucretius here refers.

far from the truth. Yet in very fact it is possible for fire to gain the upper hand if too many of its atoms come together from infinite space; then, either its violence will somehow be overcome and controlled, or all things will perish, burned by the scorching air. Likewise, as the story goes, water once came together and began to win mastery at the time when its waves destroyed the crops by which men live.[39] Then, when all the violence that had gathered itself from infinite space was turned aside by some cause and withdrew, the rains halted and the rivers lost their strength. 410

But I shall set forth, in orderly fashion, how this gathering of matter laid the foundations of the land, the sky, and the deep sea, and established the courses of the sun and the moon.[40] For surely the individual atoms did not put themselves in their proper places as a result of deliberation with conscious intent, nor, we may be sure, have they agreed what motions they shall produce; but since from infinite time many atoms in many ways, kept in motion by blows and being stirred by their own weight, were always being carried along and coming together in every possible fashion and trying all the combinations that could be created as they joined each other, it naturally resulted that the atoms, having been tossed through great ages, trying every manner of combination and motion, at length came together into those combinations from which, once they are formed, there often arise the beginnings of mighty things, of the earth, the sea, and the sky, and of the race of living creatures.[41] 420 430

At that time one could see neither the sun's orb, flying high with its generous light, nor the stars of the great heaven, nor the sea, nor the sky, nor even the earth and the air; nor was

[39] Reading *vitas . . . undis*; or, reading *multas . . . urbis*, "when it destroyed many cities of men."

[40] See Epicurus, *Letter to Herodotus* 73b; *Letter to Pythocles* 88b–90a. See also Diodorus of Sicily, I. 7, quoted in Appendix note *i* below.

[41] See lines 187–94 above; also II. 1063 and note. Except for lines 418 and 427, this whole paragraph is made up of lines that, in slightly different form, have been used earlier in the poem: I. 1021–26, II. 1061–63, V. 67–69, 187–91. This is the poet's way of reminding us of the earlier passages.

there anything to be seen that resembled the things of our world; but certain strange storms were visible and masses that had been composed from atoms of every sort, whose intervals, ways, unions, weights, blows, joinings, and motions were being
440 stirred and set in battle by Discord; for on account of the atoms' unlike shapes and various forms, not all the combinations thus made at hazard could endure and interchange harmonious motions with one another. Then the parts began to gather by themselves, and equal things, by joining with equals, began to separate the world from outer chaos and to divide its elements and arrange its great parts by themselves[42]—that is, to separate the high sky from the earth and form by itself the sea, which should receive the waters as they were set apart, and by themselves the pure and separate fires of the heaven.

450 First indeed the individual particles of earth, since they were heavy and interwoven, all came together in the middle and occupied the lowest places;[43] and the more they were interwoven and drew together, the more they forced out those particles proper to form the sea, the stars, the sun and the moon, and the walls of the great world.[c] For all these are composed of seeds that are lighter and more rounded, and of elements much smaller than those of which the earth is formed. First, therefore, the fiery aether, forcing its way through widely spaced passages, rose up from that region that the earth now occupies and, since
460 fire was light, carried many fires along with it. This is like what

[42] In the manuscripts the lines here numbered 443–45 follow line 436.

[43] See Epicurus, *Letter to Pythocles* 90b. What is meant by "middle" and "lowest places"? In the infinite universe these terms are meaningless; but Lucretius is dealing only with our world, and here he seems to be thinking of the portion visible from a given point. If we think of the visible circle of the earth surmounted by the hemisphere of the sky, we can say that the matter of which the earth has been formed has been gathered "at the middle" and "in the lowest places," while the matter for heavenly bodies and the "walls of the great world" (i.e., the visible hemisphere of the sky) has been pressed up and out. We shall find that Lucretius' real view of the world is much more complicated. Here he seems to have adopted a view of ridiculous simplicity in order to explain the creation of the system in the lowest possible terms.

we often see when, as soon as the golden morning rays of the bright sun grow red through the dew-studded grass, the ponds and ever-flowing streams send up a mist, while at times the earth itself seems to smoke. Then when all these mists, their substance solidified, come together on high as clouds, they veil the sky. So then at that time, after the substance of the light, expansive aether was solidified, it arched over the earth and surrounded it; and spreading widely in every direction, it hedged in all the rest with its eager embrace. 470

The formation of the aether was followed by that of the sun and moon, whose spheres follow their orbits in the air between earth and heaven. These bodies neither earth nor the great aether claimed for itself, for they were not so heavy that they were forced down and came to rest, nor so light that they could glide through the highest regions; but they so exist in the space between that they whirl along their living bodies and are parts of the whole world, as in our own case some of our members may remain in place, while yet there are some that are in motion.[44]

When these had withdrawn, suddenly the surface of the earth sank where now the great blue expanse of the sea extends, and the earth sent forth salty floods into the depressions. And each day the tide of aether and the rays of the sun round about, striking repeated blows from all sides upon the outer surface of the earth, forced it into narrower bounds so that it was driven in and condensed in the center.[45] The more this happened, the more the salty sweat was pressed from the earth's body and flowed into the sea and its liquid plains, increasing them, and the more the many seeds of heat and air, escaping outside and flying upwards, strengthened the high, gleaming regions of sky 480 490

[44] In the two paragraphs ending here, Lucretius stresses the idea of the common origin of the earth and the heavenly bodies regarded as belonging to it. This contrasts with the theories of some of the early atomists, who explained these bodies as independently created and later drawn into the system of which the earth is the center. See Epicurus, *Letter to Pythocles* 90b.

[45] Probably not the center of the earth, but the center of the earth's surface as Lucretius knew it. In other words, the Mediterranean sea was formed.

far above the earth. As the plains sank, the elevation of the high hills increased; for the rocky places could not subside, nor could all parts settle equally.

Thus with its mass solidified, the heavy earth stood firm; and as mud sinks to the bottom from water, or the dregs from wine, so the heavier parts of the world gathered together and settled down. Thereby the sea, the air, and the fiery aether itself have all of them been left pure with their liquid bodies, each of them 500 lighter than the one before; and the aether, lightest and most liquid of all, flows above the winds of our atmosphere, and does not mingle its liquid body with the stormy gusts of air. Although all these are turned in violent eddies, although they toss in changeable gusts, the aether itself, gliding with unalterable motion, carries on its own fires.[46] That the heavenly currents can flow steadily and in one direction is shown by the Pontus, a sea that flows with an unchanging tide, still keeping the single tenor of its gliding.[47]

II. The Heavenly Bodies

509–771[1]

The motion of the stars may have any of a number of causes. The earth rests in the middle of the world by virtue of the support of its airy underside. Both sun and moon are about the size they appear to be; the sun's heat may be caused by any one of several factors. There may be one sun and moon, or new ones formed each day and night; the moon's phases may be the result of its movement or of an unseen body obscuring it. Solar and lunar eclipses have many possible causes.

[46] Probably the fixed stars, but possibly all the heavenly bodies.

[47] Since the rate of evaporation in the Mediterranean is high and since the Black Sea receives the chief rivers of central and eastern Europe (the Danube, the Dneiper, and the Don), there is a constant flow from the Black Sea to the Mediterranean.

Let us now tell in our poem the reason for the motions of the stars.[48] As a first possibility, if the great sphere of the sky is turned, we may say that a current of air presses in upon its axis at each end, holding and blocking it on the outside from either direction, and that another current flows above and strains in the same direction as that in which the gleaming stars of the eternal heaven revolve; or else the second current may be below to move the heaven in a direction opposite to its own flow, just as we see that water wheels and their paddles are turned. Yet it is also possible that the sky as a whole may remain fixed while the bright constellations are moved, either because rapid tides of air are enclosed, which circle around as they seek an exit and roll the stars on throughout the nightly regions of the sky, or because an external current of air flowing from some source turns and drives the starry fires; or they themselves may make their way, going where the fuel of each summons and invites, and nourishing their fiery bodies throughout the whole sky.[49] It is difficult, indeed, to say which of these is true in this world, but I am teaching what is possible and what may happen in various worlds throughout the whole universe, each created in its own way; thus I set forth, in proper order, many causes that may account for the motions of stars in the whole. One of

510

520

530

[48] See Epicurus, *Letter to Pythocles* 92 and first sentence of 93. Our present section deals with the apparent daily motion of the fixed stars, which are the most distant from the earth and so are most subject to the force of the currents on the outside. These stars form the background against which the sun, moon, and planets follow their special courses, which will be considered at lines 614–750 below.

[49] The first two of the three explanations in this sentence are subject to two interpretations. It is possible that the rapid tides of air are shut up in each of the heavenly bodies and as they seek their way out cause the stars to rotate and so to roll through the heavens; or the tides of air may be exterior to the individual stars but pent up within the world and as they seek to leave this system they drive the stars. If we accept the first as the meaning in the first theory, the external current of air in the second is external to the individual stars but from a source within the world; if the second, it is from some source external to the world itself. For the third explanation, see I. 231, and Epicurus, *Letter to Pythocles* 93.

these must be the cause that here, too, puts our stars in motion; but it is by no means within the power of one who is making progress step by step to set forth which of these various causes it is.[d]

Men agree that the earth, in order that it may remain at rest in the middle of the world, gradually becomes thin and decreases in density, and that it has a different character on its lower side, joined and closely fitted from the beginning of time to the airy parts of the world, resting on which it holds its position.[e] For this reason the earth is not a burden upon the air and
540 does not press it down, as each man's own limbs are of no weight to him, nor is his head a burden to his neck; nor are we conscious of the weight of the body resting upon the feet. But any weight, even though it be much smaller, that comes from without and is placed upon us is felt as a burden. So much depends on the power native to each thing. Thus, then, the earth is not a foreign body suddenly brought in from somewhere and placed upon air foreign to itself; rather, it has been conceived from the first beginning of the world along with the air, and is a regular
550 part of the world, as our limbs are of us. Moreover, when the earth is struck by a great thunderbolt, as it shudders it shakes everything that is above it; in no way could it do this if it were not closely allied to the airy parts of the world and to the sky. Truly, they cling closely together with common roots, joined and intimately united from the beginning of time. Do you not see how great is the weight of the body, which the soul with its slender strength sustains, for the reason that it is so closely joined and fitted to it? Finally, what can raise the body in a sud-
560 den leap, except the soul that governs the members?[50] Do you now see how strong a slender nature may be when it is joined with a heavy body, as air is joined to earth or our mind is joined to us?

Neither the sun's orb nor its heat can be much greater or much less than they appear to our senses.[f] [51] For from whatever

[50] See IV. 877–906.

[51] Or possibly: "The circle of the sun cannot be much larger than it ap-

distance fires can throw their lights and breathe warmth upon our limbs, these distances by the intervening spaces take nothing from the bulk of the flames, and the fire is no less in apparent size. Then, since the heat and light poured out from the sun do come to our senses and shed light upon our surroundings, the form and size of the sun ought likewise to be seen from here as they are, so that in truth you may neither add nor subtract anything at all.[52] 570

Whether the moon moves along illuminating places with borrowed light, or sheds her own light from her own body,[53] whichever it may be, she moves on with a form no greater than it seems to be as we see it with our eyes.[54] For all things that we see through much air when they are far removed seem blurred in appearance[55] before their size is diminished. Therefore, since the moon shows a clear appearance and an unblurred outline, she must appear to us, as from the earth we gaze on her above, of just the size and shape that she is, with her outline clearly marked. Finally, as to whatever stars of heaven you may see from earth: since the fires we see on the earth, as long as their twinkling light and clear blaze are visible, are seen to increase 580

---

pears to our senses, nor can its heat be much less." For this whole section, see *Letter to Pythocles* 91; although nowhere in the extant remains does Epicurus mention heat in this connection, he does refer to color in the Scholium. Is it possible that Lucretius, in his notes or in his memory, has confused the Latin words *calor* (heat) and *color* (color)? The Greek words concerned are quite dissimilar.

[52] The absolute certainty of this sentence is less in keeping with Epicurean theory than the qualified statement of lines 564–65. The argument of the last two sentences, not very clearly expressed or logically applied, appears to rest on the fact that the apparent size of a light from a source so small or so distant that it can be regarded as a point depends on the intensity of the light, not on the size of the source. This argument, which is in place below, in connection with the stars (lines 586–91), does not apply to the sun, the disk of which can be seen.

Line 574 of the manuscripts is identical with line 571 and is omitted by all editors; line 573 is placed before line 570.

[53] See lines 705–50.

[54] See Epicurus, *Letter to Herodotus* 91.

[55] See IV. 353–63.

590 or diminish but little as their distance becomes greater, truly we may know that the stars are but a trifle smaller than they seem, or else greater by a very small degree.[56]

Likewise, one need not wonder how so small a sun is able to emit that great light which, spreading over all the seas and lands and heavens, fills them and floods everything with warming heat. It is possible that a single, free-flowing fountain of the whole world has opened here, and that it gushes up and pours 600 forth light because seeds of heat from the whole world have come together in such a way, and accumulated in such a manner, that heat flows forth here from a single wellspring. Do you not see how widely a small spring of water irrigates the pasture and at times overflows the fields? It is also possible that heat from the fire of the sun is small, but ignites the air with feverish burnings if the air happens to be in such condition and of such sort that it can be set on fire when struck by a small amount of heat. Thus we sometimes see a fire from a single spark spread 610 far and wide through standing grain and stubble. Perhaps, too, the sun, shining on high with its rosy lamp, may hold about itself much heat of unseen fire, which is marked by no gleam but brings heat only, so that it increases the effect of the sun's rays.

There appears to be no single straightforward explanation telling us how the sun goes from his summer position to his winter turning in Capricorn, and then, retracing his course from that point, pauses and turns at his goal in Cancer; and how the moon every month is seen to pass through the course 620 in which the sun spends the period of a year.[g] No single cause, I repeat, has been given for these things.[57] Perhaps the following explanation, proposed by the sacred wisdom of Democritus, may seem the most probable. The nearer each heavenly body is to the earth, the less swiftly can it be carried on by the rotation of the sky. The keen and rapid force of this rotation be-

[56] See note 52 above. With most editors, line 596, which repeats line 584, is omitted, and the two lines that precede it are placed after line 589.

[57] See Epicurus, *Letter to Pythocles* 93, 112b–114a.

comes less on the lower side; for that reason the sun, because it is much lower than the fiery signs of the zodiac, drops slowly back to the signs that are behind it. This is even truer for the moon. In the degree that its course is lower—more distant from the sky and closer to the earth—to that degree it is less able to keep pace with the signs. Because the moon, which is lower than the sun, is carried on by an even weaker current, all the signs catch up with it more rapidly and are swept beyond it. As a result we see the moon return rapidly to each sign, for the reason that the signs overtake it. It may also happen that, in a fixed sequence, winds blow alternately from the two regions of the world at right angles to the sun's course, one of these winds thrusting the sun from the summer signs clear to the winter turning and the stiff cold, and the other throwing it back again from the cold gloom into the heat-producing regions and the fiery signs. And in the same way we may think that the moon and those stars that roll their great years in great orbits[58] can move with winds from opposite directions. Do you not see how with different winds the lower clouds are driven in directions opposed to the upper? Why is it less possible that these stars be carried through their great orbits in the skies by winds that differ from each other? 630 640

But night covers the lands with great darkness, either when the sun after his long course has reached the most distant regions of the sky and wearily gives up his fiery breath, that has been shaken by the journey and weakened by the mighty wind,[59] or when the sun turns his course beneath the earth, im- 650

[58] The reference may be to all the celestial bodies, but it is probably to the five planets recognized by the ancient astronomers. These appear to move with somewhat erratic motion through the zodiac, Mercury and Venus accompanying the sun, now preceding it and now following it, while the planets exterior to the earth appear to move more slowly and regularly through the signs, although reversing their direction at times. Mars completes its orbit in less than two years, Jupiter in about twelve, and Saturn in about thirty.

[59] This was the view of Heraclitus and Xenophanes. For this whole section, see Epicurus, *Letter to Pythocles* 92.

pelled by the same force that carried his orb above it. Likewise, at a fixed time Matuta scatters the rosy dawn along the shores of the aether and unfolds the light, either because the same sun, himself returning beneath the earth, first masters the
660 sky with his rays as he attempts to rekindle it, or because fires are coming together and many seeds of heat have been accustomed to gather at a fixed time, and these cause the birth of new sunlight each day.[60] This theory would explain the report that from high Mount Ida scattered fires are seen at break of day, which then come together as if into a single globe and form a sphere.[61] In this matter there is no cause for wonder that at so definite a time these seeds of fire can flow together and form anew the splendor of the sun; for throughout Nature we see
670 many things occurring at a fixed time: at a certain time the trees flower and at a certain time they lose their bloom; at times no less certain does increasing age bid the teeth to fall, and the beardless youth to send out a soft down of hair and to grow a soft beard equally on each cheek; and finally, thunder, snow, rain clouds, and winds occur in not too uncertain seasons of the year. And since from the very origin of the world the first beginnings of causes have been like this and things have happened in this way, they also now return in due sequence and in fixed order.[62]

680 Likewise it may be that the days increase and the nights wane, and that in turn the light becomes less while the nights assume greater length because, although there is but a single sun who passes beneath the earth and through the sky above,

[60] The two explanations of the dawn correspond to the two of the sunset, but in reverse order.

[61] This reputed phenomenon is described in about the same terms by Diodorus of Sicily, XVII. 7. 5–7. It is impossible to guess what gave rise to the story.

[62] Almost incidentally and in passing, Lucretius makes an important statement of the rule of law in Nature. Once a world has been formed by the particular motions of a particular group of atoms, the phenomena of that world tend to repeat themselves in a fixed pattern. See Epicurus, *Letter to Pythocles* 92.

yet he divides his journey through space into unequal lengths and cuts his circuit into parts that are not even, adding what he takes from one portion of his journey to the opposite portion in equal measure as he completes his daily round, until he comes to that sign[63] where the "knot of the year" makes of equal length the shades of night and the daylight. For, in the mid-course of the north wind and the mid-course of the south, the sky holds the sun at equal distances from its own turning points, because of the position of the whole circle of the signs in which the sun in its course completes its annual period, shedding light obliquely upon the earth and heaven, as is shown in the charts of those who have plotted all the points of the sky, marking them with the signs of the zodiac in due order.[h] Or it may be that the days are of unequal length because the air is heavier in certain regions, and for that reason the glorious fire of the sun is delayed trembling beneath the earth, and cannot make its way through and come to its rising, and thus the nights of winter lag long before the escutcheon of the day with its radiant beams comes forth.[64] Or it may even be that the fires that cause the sun to rise in a certain position regularly come together more slowly or more rapidly in alternating portions of the year. Therefore they seem to speak truly . . .[65]

690

700

It is possible that the moon shines when she is struck by the rays of the sun,[66] from day to day returning more of this light for us to see as she recedes farther from the sun's orb until, opposite to him, she shines with full light and sees his setting as

[63] Aries for the spring equinox, Libra for that of autumn. For this section, see Epicurus, *Letter to Pythocles* 98a.

[64] Conversely, in summer, thick air above the earth would retard the sun during the day.

[65] There appears to be a lacuna of at least one line at this point. Munro suggests the following supplement: "who say that new suns are constantly formed"; Bailey proposes: "who believe that these things may happen for more than one reason."

[66] That the moon shines by reflected light was the opinion of Thales, the Pythagoreans, Parmenides, Empedocles, Anaxagoras, and Metrodorus (Diels, *Doxographi Graeci*, 358).

710 she rises and is clear of the horizon.[67] Then she must hide her light little by little on the side away from us, as she draws closer to the fire of the sun, passing through the circle of the zodiac from one side to the other—as they say who argue that the moon is like a sphere and follows a path beneath the sun.[68] But there is also a way in which she may roll along with her own light, and yet display her changing phases of brightness; for there may be another body that is carried and borne along with her, getting in front of her and obscuring her in all the various ways, 720 but which cannot be seen because it is without light.[69] Perhaps it is also possible that the moon, like a ball painted on one side with bright light, may rotate, and as she rotates her sphere may present changing forms until at one time it displays to our sight and to our observing eyes that part that is enriched with fire, and then little by little it turns away that bright portion of its curved surface and takes it from our sight. This the Babylonian doctrine of the Chaldaeans tries to prove, refuting the science of our astronomers, just as if that which each of them maintains 730 might not happen, or as if there were any reason to venture to accept this theory rather than that. Finally, why may not new moons be repeatedly created, according to a fixed order of forms and shapes, and the moon created on each separate day vanish and another be made in its role and place? It is difficult to disprove this by reasoning or to overcome it by argument, since so many things can be formed in a fixed sequence. Spring and Venus come; before them strides Zephyr, Venus' winged fore- 740 runner, and Mother Flora, closely following in his steps, be-

[67] It is hard to see how this would be possible if, as both Epicurus and Lucretius believed, the sun and moon were relatively small in comparison with the earth and their orbits quite close to it. Epicurus (*Letter to Pythocles* 94) omits this explanation, although a few sentences later he admits the possibility that the light of the moon is borrowed from the sun.

[68] See Epicurus, *Letter to Pythocles* 94–95a.

[69] This is fantastic when applied to the moon, since no such body could account for the changing shape of the bright portion of its face; but astronomers today recognize a large number of variable stars where the variation in the light that reaches us is caused by a dark companion that at regular intervals partly hides and dims the visible star.

strews and fills their path with wondrous flowers and perfumes.[70] Then dry Summer follows, with dusty Ceres as her companion, and the annual blasts of the Aquilones. Next comes Autumn, and beside her walks Bacchus, who is hailed with the cry "Euoe."[71] Then the other seasons and the other winds follow: high thundering Volturnus, and Auster mighty with lightning. At length Bruma brings snow and gives again the chilling frost; and Winter, her teeth chattering with cold, follows. Therefore it is less to be wondered at if the moon is born at a fixed time and again at a fixed time is destroyed, since many things can come 750 to pass at times so clearly fixed.

In the same way you must believe that the eclipses of the sun and the hidings of the moon may come to pass from different causes.[72] For why should we think that the moon is able to shut the earth from the light of the sun and to interpose her head high between him and the earth, putting her opaque orb in front of his bright rays, and at the same time refuse to admit that this can be done by some other body, which always moves about without light? Or why should it be impossible that the sun at some fixed time should grow weary and lose his light and then recover it when he has passed in his airy course beyond the 760 regions hostile to his flames, regions that cause his fires to be put out and to die? Or why should it be possible that the earth itself

70 The translation assumes that Venus is here the old Italian goddess who presided over gardens and their growth. Zephyr, the gentle west wind of springtime, would be appropriate as her forerunner. If, however, she is the Hellenized Venus (Aphrodite), her winged forerunner must be Cupid, not Zephyr. The translation then would run: "Spring and Venus come, and before her trips her winged forerunner; Mother Flora, following closely in the steps of Zephyr, bestrews. . . ." In this version Zephyr comes first, then Flora scattering flowers, next Cupid, and finally Spring and Venus. In the other, the order is the same but without Cupid. Of the winds named in the rest of the paragraph, the Aquilones are the northeast, Volturnus is the east-southeast, and Auster the south. Bruma is properly the winter solstice; but here it probably indicates one of the winter winds.

71 "Euoe" is the conventional way of representing in letters the wild cry with which Bacchus was hailed by his worshipers.

72 See Epicurus, *Letter to Pythocles* 96b. For both solar and lunar eclipses, the first explanations assume that sun and moon revolve about the earth.

in its turn rob the moon of light, hindering and restraining the sun, at the time when the monthly course of the moon carries it through the tangible blackness of the cone-shaped shadow,[73] and at the same time it be impossible that some other body pass below the moon or glide above the face of the sun,[74] and thus interrupt the rays of light that have been emitted? And finally, if the moon shines with her own light, why may she not grow
770 faint in a certain part of the sky, while she is passing through regions that are unfriendly to her proper light?[75]

III. The Earth

772–924

Life began on earth when grass and trees appeared, and the earth produced birds and animals out of eggs and wombs respectively. Mythical creatures have never existed; the monsters the earth produced could not survive, being unable either to protect themselves or to be useful to man. The plants that now spring from the earth maintain their species unchanged.

Now that I have given a rational explanation of each phenomenon in the blue expanse of the heavens, so that we may know what mighty cause sets in motion the changing courses of the sun and the wanderings of the moon, and in what way their light may be obstructed and they themselves fade away and shroud the unexpecting lands in darkness when they close their eyes, so to speak, and then again, with the eye of light opened, behold all places illumined with clear radiance—now
780 that I have made this evident, I shall return to the newly created world and the earth's tender fields, considering that

[73] With the earth larger than the sun, the shadow cast by the earth would be a truncated cone, but so wide-spreading that it would take the moon hours rather than minutes to pass through it.

[74] At the time of a lunar eclipse, the moon is above the earth and the sun below. To interrupt the light, therefore, a body must pass below the moon or above the sun.

[75] Line 771, which repeats line 764, is omitted by all editors.

which they first determined to lift up into the regions of light and entrust to the inconstant winds by a process of birth that was then new.[i]

First of all, around the hills and throughout the plains the earth produced glistening green grasses, the verdant flower-clad pastures shone, and trees of many kinds in rivalry unrestrained began to grow up through the air. As feathers, hair, and bristles at once begin to grow on the limbs and bodies of four-footed beasts and winged creatures, so the new earth at once sent forth grasses and shrubs,[j] and then created many races of mortal creatures, which arose in many ways and by no simple system; for living creatures cannot have fallen from the sky, nor can land animals have come forth from salty pools.[76] It follows that the earth justly gained the name of mother, since all things have been created from the earth.[77] Even now many living creatures spring from the earth, formed by the showers and the keen heat of the sun;[78] therefore it is less strange if then more and greater creatures arose, having grown when the earth and air were young. In the beginning the race of winged creatures and the swift birds of various kinds used to come forth from eggs,[79] hatched in the springtime, as now in the summer cicadas of their own accord leave their polished cells, seeking food and life. Next, for the first time the earth produced mortal generations.[k] Then warmth and moisture abounded in the fields, and because of this, whenever a suitable situation was presented,[80]

790

800

[76] The Stoics taught that animals fell from the sky; Anaximander, that they came from the sea.

[77] See II. 598–99, 991–98.

[78] See II. 871–73, and note.

[79] We must suppose the eggs themselves grew from the ground, as do the wombs of line 808.

[80] That is, when the proper atomic combinations and motions were present. The theory that the first men were formed in this way is ascribed to Epicurus by Censorinus: "It seemed to Democritus of Abdera that men were first created from water and mud. The opinion of Epicurus was not very different; for he believed that when the mud had become warm, wombs of a sort grew up holding to the ground by roots, and that when babies had been born from them, the wombs furnished to the infants by the aid of nature a milk-like liquid produced in themselves" (Usener, *Epicurus,* 333).

wombs grew up, holding to the earth by roots. When in due time
810 these were opened, as the developing young fled moisture and
sought the air, Nature turned toward the newly born the pores
of the earth, compelling it to open its veins and pour out liquid
similar to milk, just as each woman, when she has borne a child,
is filled with sweet milk because all that urgent flow of nourishment is directed to her breasts. The earth supplied the children
with food, warmth took the place of clothing, and the grass
provided a bed plentifully formed with much soft down. But the
world in its youth did not produce harsh cold, excessive heat, or
820 winds of great strength; for all things grew up and gained
strength side by side.

Therefore I say again and again that the earth won and retains the name of mother deservedly, since she herself created
mankind, and since, at the proper times, she produced every
kind of beast that revels here and there upon the great mountains, as well as the birds of the air with their varying forms.
But because some end of bearing was due her, she has ceased,
like a woman overcome by old age.[81] For time changes the nature of the whole world, and everything must pass from one
830 stage to another, nor does anything remain like to itself; everything moves about; Nature alters everything and forces everything to change. For one thing wastes away and becomes weak
by reason of age, and another grows up and rises from its former
place among objects that we scorn. Thus then the passage of
time alters the nature of the whole world and the earth enters
upon one state after another, so that it is not able to produce
what it once did, and can produce what it once could not.

At that time the earth tried many experiments in creation,
producing creatures with strange forms and strange members:
the hermaphrodite, between the sexes, neither the one nor the

[81] See II. 1150–53; and see also Diodorus of Sicily, I. 7. 6: "The earth, constantly being made firmer by the heat of the sun and by the winds, finally was no longer able to produce the larger creatures, but each kind of living creature was formed by mutual unions."

other and falling short of each; some creatures without feet, 840
others in turn bereft of hands, and some even that were dumb and without a mouth, or blind and without eyes; some that were so fettered by limbs adhering to their bodies that they could neither do anything nor move at all, neither avoid danger nor seek what was needed. The earth created other monsters and portents of this sort, but to no purpose since Nature refused them increase, nor could they attain to the desired prime of life, find food, or be united in the task of Venus. For we see that many points must meet favorably for creatures, if they are to 850
continue their race by propagating it. Their natures must be such that there is food for them, and such too that there are passages whereby the life-giving seed throughout the body may pass through the relaxed limbs, and means whereby both may share mutual delights in order that the female and the male may be joined together.[l]

Many kinds of living creatures must then have perished and been unable to reproduce and bring forth offspring. For whatever animals you see feeding upon the life-giving air, either craft or courage or, it may be, speed has saved and protected that breed since its first beginning; and there are also many 860
which, commended to us by their utility, survive because committed to our protection. In the first category, the fierce race of lions and their savage kind are protected by their courage, the foxes by their craftiness, and the stags by their speed. On the other hand, light-sleeping and faithful dogs, the whole race sprung from the seed of draft animals, and also the wool-bearing flocks and the breeds of cattle—all these have been entrusted to the protection of men, Memmius; for they have escaped from wild beasts and gained security, and with no effort of their own they have received the generous food that we provide as a reward because of their usefulness to us. But as for those to whom 870
Nature has granted none of these things, with the result that they may neither live their own lives as their own masters nor furnish us with any service in return for which we will permit their breed to feed and be safe in our protection—these in

truth fall as a prey and a booty to others, all of them entangled by their own fated bonds, until Nature brings the breed to destruction.

But neither have centaurs existed,[82] nor can creatures exist at 880 any time joined of a double nature and twofold body, with limbs of different breeds joined in such a way that the powers from this side and from that are in harmony. One with wit however dull may learn this from the following. In the first place, the active horse reaches full vigor when about three years have passed, but this is by no means true for the boy; for even at this age, he often searches in his dreams for breasts that flow with milk. Afterwards, when in old age the great strength and limbs of horses fail, weakening as life wanes—at that very age, when boyhood has finally reached its prime, youth begins 890 and the cheeks are clothed with the first beard. I say this lest by chance you believe possible the creation and survival of centaurs formed from mankind and from the burden-bearing race of horses, or Scyllas girding their semi-piscine bodies with mad dogs, or other creatures of this sort, whose members clearly are out of harmony with each other. Their parts do not reach maturity and gain bodily strength together, nor do they lose that strength in old age at the same time. They do not burn with a like love, nor are their habits harmonious, nor have they the same pleasures through their limbs. In fact, you may often 900 see bearded goats growing fat on hemlock, which is rank poison to men. Again, since flame always burns the tawny bodies of lions and consumes them just as it does the bodies of every other kind of beast on earth that consists of flesh and blood, how could it happen that a single beast with a threefold body—lion in front, dragon behind, and the Chimaera itself in the middle—could breathe hot flame out from its body through its mouth?[83]

As for the man who imagines that such creatures can have been created even then when the earth was new and the sky fresh,

[82] See II. 700–9, IV. 732–43.

[83] Lines 905 and 906 are based very closely on Homer, *Iliad* VI. 181–82.

depending on that empty name of newness, let him in the same way babble many tales from his mouth; let him say that then golden rivers commonly flowed through the lands and that orchards were wont to blossom with gems, or that a man was born with such mighty limbs that he could plant his steps firmly across the deep sea and revolve the whole heaven about him with his hands. For the fact that there were many seeds of things in the earth at the time when the land first brought forth living creatures is nevertheless no sign that it was able to create beasts intermixed among themselves with limbs of different animals joined together, especially since those things that now grow in abundance from the earth—the many herbs, fruits, and pleasant orchards—although abundant, nevertheless cannot be mixed; rather, each kind comes forth in its own way, and all maintain their differences by the fixed law of Nature. 910 920

IV. The Development of Society

925–1457

The first men lived on the bounty of unimproved nature, yet life was no more dangerous than now. Culture began when men formed family groups; man developed speech untaught. Some men dominated others by virtue of beauty and strength, and property rights were invented, entailing civil strife, anarchy, and ultimately the establishment of government. Men began to seek the favor of the gods through religious practice; metals made possible more lethal weapons, and the more peaceful discoveries included weaving, sowing, music, and later poetry.

That human race living in the fields was much hardier, as was natural for a race that the harsh earth had created; it was built upon greater and more solid bones within, and bound together with strong sinews through the flesh. Thus it was not easily afflicted by heat or cold, by strange food, or by the failure of any part of the body.[m] While the sun rolled through many a 930 great cycle in the sky, men dragged out life like forest-ranging beasts. Then no hardy farmer guided the curved plow or knew how to till the soil with the hoe, to set new cuttings in the earth, or to prune old branches from high trees with the hook. Whatever gifts the sun and rain had given and the earth created of its own will sufficiently pleased their hearts. For the most part they satisfied their bodily needs among the acorn-bearing 940 oaks. The fruits of the strawberry tree, which now in the winter season you see ripening with their purple color, the earth then produced in greater quantity and larger size. Then the earth's burgeoning youth produced much provender, harsh but ample for wretched men. The streams and springs invited them to quench their thirst, just as now the stream of water from the great mountain summons loud and clear the thirsty beasts from far afield.

They occupied the nymphs' woodland shrines, which they had come to know in their wanderings; they knew that streams of water, gliding from these holy spots with generous flow, 950 washed the damp rocks—the damp rocks whose green moss glistened with the drops from above—and in places these streams bubbled from the level ground and broke out on the plain. Not yet did they know how to make use of fire, or how to employ skins and to clothe their bodies with the spoils of wild beasts; they lived in groves and in mountain caves and forests, and they hid their unkempt bodies amid the bushes when driven to avoid the lashing winds and the rainstorms. They could not have regard for the common good, nor did they know 960 how to observe any customs or laws among themselves. Whatever booty Fortune offered to a man he carried off, taught by his own nature to seek strength and to live for himself alone. Venus joined the bodies of lovers in the forests; for one woman yielded to mutual love, another to the violent force and uncontrolled passion of the man, and another to a bribe such as nuts, the fruit of the strawberry tree, or choice pears.

Relying on the great strength of their hands and feet, they used to follow the wild beasts of the forest, with stones as missiles and with mighty clubs. Many they conquered, and a few they avoided by hiding. Like bristly pigs they threw their rustic limbs naked on the ground when overtaken by night, covering themselves round about with leaves and branches. They did not lament the day and the sun with great clamor, wandering in panic through the fields in the darkness of night; but silently and buried in sleep, they waited until the sun, with its rosy torch, brought the dawn back to the sky. For since they were accustomed from childhood to see darkness and light always produced in alternation, there was no reason that they should ever wonder at this or, losing their confidence, fear that eternal night would hold the lands and the light of the sun be forever withdrawn. But a greater source of anxiety was that the wild beasts often made sleep fatal for wretched men. Driven from home, they would flee their rocky dwellings at the coming of the foaming boar or the mighty lion and, quaking with fear, would yield their leaf-strewn beds in the dead of night to unwelcome guests. 970 980

But not much more often then than now did mortal men leave the sweet light of life amid lamentations. It more often happened then that some single one of them would be seized and would furnish living food for beasts, gulped down by their jaws, and would fill groves, mountains, and forests with his groans, seeing his own living flesh buried in a living tomb. And those who escaped by flight with their bodies partly eaten, thereafter holding quivering hands over their festering wounds, would call for death in dreadful tones until the griping pains took life away, since they lacked all aid and did not know what wounds require. But a single day did not hurl to destruction many thousands of men drawn up beneath military standards, nor did the troubled surface of the sea dash ships and men upon the rocks. In those times the ocean was often roused to no purpose and raged uselessly and in vain, then laid aside its empty threats, having accomplished nothing; nor could the deceptive charm of the placid sea entice anyone to his doom upon its smiling waves. Then the accursed art of navigation lay hidden in blind darkness. At that time lack of food gave men's 990 1000 weakened limbs to death; now, on the other hand, abundance overwhelms them. They, in their ignorance, often poured out 1010 poison for themselves; now, with greater guile, men give it to others.

Next, after they had prepared huts and skins and fire, after the woman joined to the man had come into a lasting ⟨union . . . and the laws of the family⟩[84] were known, and after they saw children sprung from themselves, then for the first time the human race began to become gentle.[85] Then the use of fire brought it about that shivering bodies could no longer endure the cold beneath the covering of the sky; then conjugal love lessened men's violence, and children with their charming ways 1020 easily tamed the haughty spirits of their parents. Then, too, neighbors, desiring neither to injure nor to be injured, began to join in bonds of friendship;[n] and they commended to each other their women and their children, while cries, gestures, and babbling showed it was right that all have pity on the weak.[86] Nevertheless harmony could not arise in every case, but the good part and the large part religiously preserved the agreement; otherwise the whole human race would at that time have been destroyed, and would not have been able to continue its generations down to the present.

Nature forced men to emit various sounds of the tongue, and

[84] There is a lacuna of at least a line here. Some such supplement as that given seems certain, but more than this may well be lost.

[85] See Diodorus of Sicily, I. 8. 2: "Being attacked by beasts they went to each other's aid, taught by mutual advantage; and when they were gathered together through fear, they slowly learned to know each other."

In this paragraph Lucretius assumes that fire has been discovered and probably that speech is already in use. In what follows, lines 1028–1104, he turns back and relates how these first appeared, and then in line 1105 he resumes his account of social development.

[86] The ambiguity of the translation is intentional. It is not clear whether the cries, gestures, and babbling are from the men or from the women and children; and it is also not clear whether we are to think that the cries are mere inarticulate sounds or articulate speech. It is probable that the men speak, and that the cries, gestures, and babbling are from the women and children.

utility molded the names of things[87] in about the same way as 1030
we see that the very lack of speech encourages infants to the use
of gestures, when it induces them to point with the finger at
things they see.[88] For each being feels its own powers and for
what purpose it can use them. Before the growing horns project
from the calf's forehead, it pushes and butts with these when it
is angry. The cubs of panthers and the whelps of lions already
fight with the claws on their paws and with their teeth, even
when teeth and claws have hardly been formed. We see birds
of every kind already trusting in their wings and seeking a shaky 1040
aid from their pinions. Next, it is foolish to think that some one
person assigned names to things, and that from him men learned
their first words.[89] For why should we suppose that he was able
to label all things with words and emit various sounds of speech,
while at the same time the others were unable to do this? Moreover, if others also had not made mutual use of their voices, how
was the concept[90] of the utility of this first implanted in him,
and whence was the original power given him so that he knew
and planned what he wished to accomplish? Likewise, one man 1050
could not force, overwhelm, and subdue many men, so that they
would consent to learn the names of things. And it is not easy
to persuade the deaf by any device and teach them what they
must do; for in no way would they suffer or permit strange vocal
sounds for a long time to thunder meaninglessly upon their ears.

87 On this passage Bailey writes: "There are clearly two stages represented here. . . . In the first, emotions and sensations produce involuntary cries, which tend to be the same on similar occasions. When this is noticed, men realize the advantage (*utilitas*) of this constant relation, and it suggests the application of definite sounds to definite things or actions."

88 See Epicurus, *Letter to Herodotus* 75b–76a.

89 This may be an answer to the argument of Plato (*Cratylus* 388e–390e) that the names of things were dictated to men by the "lawgiver"; or to the similar theory of Democritus, which we know of only through the commentary of Proclus on the *Cratylus*.

90 In the Epicurean system a concept of a thing can be formed in the mind only if the thing itself already exists. Men began to speak because it was their nature to do so, and they then recognized the utility of speech; but before speech existed anywhere, no man could have formed the concept of speech. See lines 181–84 above, and note.

Finally, what seems so wonderful in this, if the human race with well developed voice and tongue should denote things by sounds that vary in accord with the various feelings aroused by
1060 each? For dumb flocks and even the breeds of wild beasts, when they are in fear and pain, regularly send forth sounds that are different from and unlike those they utter when joy wells up. You may learn this at first hand. When Molossian hounds draw back their great soft lips in anger and, baring their cruel teeth, begin to snarl, the threat of their wrath has a sound far different from the baying with which they fill all the countryside. Again, when they are trying to lick their pups soothingly with their tongues or when they toss the pups with their paws and, attacking them with bites, pretend to swallow them, but do so gently
1070 and with teeth held back, as they play they give voice with a sound far other than that with which they howl when they have been left alone in a building, or when with cringing bodies they shrink yelping from the whip. Then does not the whinny likewise seem to differ when a young stallion in the prime of life, struck by the spurs of winged love, sports amid the mares and from beneath his expanded nostrils utters his challenge to war, and when he whinnies at some other time with his limbs all a-tremble? Lastly the flying creatures and the various birds—
1080 hawks and ospreys and the gulls that seek their food and life from the waves of the salt sea—utter cries that differ much from time to time when they are striving for food and fighting for the booty; and other birds change their harsh cries with the weather, as do the long-lived race of crows and the flocks of ravens when they are said to be calling for water and rain and at times to be summoning winds and breezes. Therefore, if their changing feelings impel animals, although they are dumb, to utter dif-
1090 ferent sounds, how much more is it natural that men have been able to indicate different things by different words!

If, by chance, you are at this point silently raising this question, it was the lightning that first brought fire to the earth for men, and from this has come all the heat of flames; for we still see many fires springing up when the blow of heaven, striking with celestial flames, has given heat. Or again, when one branching tree resting upon the branches of another is swayed and shaken by the wind, heat produced by the violent friction is pressed out,[91] and sometimes the fevered fiery flame bursts forth while limbs and branches are being rubbed together. In either of these ways fire may have been given to mortals. Then the sun taught them to cook food and to soften it with the heat of flames, since they used to see many things throughout the fields grow mellow when mastered by the hot blows of the sun's rays. 1100

From day to day those who were outstanding in talent and vigorous of mind showed men how to change their earlier manner of life by new discoveries and, in particular, by the use of fire. These men, becoming kings, began to found cities and to construct citadels as places of refuge for themselves; they divided herds and fields and distributed them to their followers according to the beauty of each and his strength and talent. For beauty then was of much value, and strength availed. Afterwards property rights were invented and gold was discovered, things that easily stole the honor from the strong and from the fair; for men, no matter how strong or fair of body, as a rule followed the party of the richer. But for any man who governs his life by the true code, to live on little with untroubled mind is great riches; for what is little is never lacking. But men wished to become famous and powerful in order that their fortune might rest on a firm foundation, and that they be able to pass a quiet life in opulence —in vain, since by their striving to rise to highest honor they have made the course of life's journey dangerous to themselves; and often, even if they reach the top, Envy strikes them like a thunderbolt and hurls them scornfully into the lowest Tartarus, since Envy, like the lightning, most often burns the heights and whatever is elevated above the rest. It is therefore better to obey in peace than to wish to rule the state with supreme power or to hold a kingdom. Then let men, having become weary for naught, sweat blood as they struggle up the narrow path of 1110 1120 1130

[91] To be taken quite literally. Fire is a material thing hidden in the wood and forced out by the friction and the pressure.

ambition, since their wisdom is from another's mouth and they base their search on what they hear rather than on their own feelings. And this was no truer in the past than it is in the present and will be in the future.[92]

Thus when kings had been slain the former haughty majesty of thrones and scepters lay in ruins, and the crown, once the ornament of the highest head but now covered with blood and trampled beneath the feet of the mob, mourned for the great
1140 honors it had lost; for men trample avidly upon what has been too much feared before. And so, when each man was seeking power and the highest place for himself, the control of the state would pass to the lowest dregs of the people. Then some of them taught how to elect magistrates, and they set up courts so that they might consent to abide by the laws. For the human race, weary of protecting its life by means of violence, was growing weak as a result of its hatreds. Therefore the more willingly did it submit to laws and to the strict administration of justice. Since each man in his wrath was prepared to take vengeance more
1150 severely than is now permitted by just law, men grew weary of protecting their lives by violence. Thereafter fear of punishment mars the prizes of life. Violence and injury spread their nets about each man, and most often they returned against that man from whom they had sprung. It is not easy for one to pass a peaceful and calm life if, by his deeds, he has violated the accepted covenants of peace. Even while he deceives both men and gods, he ought to have no confidence that his deed will be secret forever; for truly, many are said to have betrayed themselves by
1160 speaking in dreams or while raving in illness, and to have brought out into public their long-hidden sins.[93]

It is not difficult to explain with words the causes that have now made the divinities of the gods common through great

[92] See Epicurus, *Principal Doctrines* VII, XXXV.

[93] See Epicurus, *Principal Doctrines* XXXIII–XXXV. To the Epicurean there is nothing essentially good about justice, or evil about injustice. The one good is pleasure, and the ideal for the individual is to attain this in the highest degree without regard to others. In this imperfect world, however,

races, have filled the cities with their altars, have caused those festivals to be undertaken which today flourish in great cities and states, and have spread among mortals the deep-set dread that causes the erection of new shrines of gods throughout the whole earth and forces men to throng these shrines on festal days.[94] For already in those earlier times, mortal men in waking visions beheld great figures of the gods, and in sleep they saw them even more marvelously increased in size of body. To these figures they attributed consciousness, since they were seen to move their limbs and to utter haughty words in keeping with their beautiful faces and great strength. Men assigned to them eternal life because their appearance constantly presented itself with form unaltered, and because men thought, in general, that beings blessed with such strength could scarcely be overcome by any violence. They thought them far superior to men in fortune because not one of them was troubled by any fear of death, and because in men's dreams they appeared to accomplish many marvelous deeds and to suffer no weariness themselves as a result.[95] 1170 1180

Moreover, men saw that the systems of the sky and the seasons of the year were changed in a fixed order, and they could not understand by what causes this was done. Therefore they avoided the problem by turning everything over to the gods and assuming that all was moved at their nod. The homes and sacred

---

laws and the administration of justice are necessary if the individual is to have any freedom to seek and to enjoy pleasure. But these very laws are threats to the happiness of anyone who violates them. The laws are, therefore, to be obeyed, not because obedience to them or to any higher law is right in itself, but solely because obedience to them tends to secure happiness.

94 See II. 644–51, III. 18–24, V. 146–55; Epicurus, *Letter to Menoeceus* 123–24a.

95 If mental images are all caused by the impact of idols from without, and if these idols can come only from things having material existence, dreams and waking visions are valid evidence of the existence of the gods and also of their appearance and their activities. But when men ascribe to the gods control over the powers of Nature, and when they suppose that the gods can be reached by prayers and offerings, they go beyond the evidence and wander from the truth.

realms of the gods they placed in the sky, because they saw night and the moon revolving through the heavens—aye, the moon,
1190 day and night, night's august constellations together with its wandering celestial torches and its flying flames, the clouds and the sunshine, rainstorms and snow, winds, thunderbolts, and hail, the rushing turmoil and the great threatening murmurs.

O race of men, unhappy in attributing to the gods such deeds and, in addition, such bitter wrath! What great groaning did men prepare for themselves then; what wounds for us; what tears for our descendants! It is no piety often to be seen turning,
1200 veil-clad, to the stone and drawing near to all the altars,[96] falling prostrate upon the ground and extending the hands before the shrines of the gods, sprinkling the altars with much blood of beasts, and binding vow upon vow; but rather, it is piety to be able to behold all things with calm mind.[97] For when we gaze up at the celestial expanse of the great heaven, at the aether above us set with twinkling stars, and when we remember the courses of the sun and of the moon, then into our hearts, already weighed down by other evils, Anxiety also begins to thrust her reawakened head; and we fear lest these gods of ours possess the
1210 unmeasured power which turns the gleaming stars in their various courses. Lack of understanding vexes the mind, which questions whether there has been any life-giving origin of the world and whether there will be any end for it beyond which the walls of the world can no longer endure under this burden of troubled motion, or whether they have been divinely endowed with eternal safety and can scorn the mighty power of unending time as they pass down the eternal expanse of the ages.

Moreover, whose mind does not cower with dread of the gods,

[96] The Romans veiled their heads in prayer to avoid seeing unfavorable signs. The words "drawing near to all the altars" suggest the *supplicationes ad omnia pulvinaria,* of which Livy mentions twelve between 218 and 167 B.C. He records *supplicationes* of one sort or another in nearly every year from 218 to the end of the extant books.

[97] In other words, man should learn to imitate the eternal calm of the gods. The Epicurean, although not expecting the gods to heed his prayers, might look to them as perfect examples of happiness. With this whole section, compare VI. 43–78.

whose limbs do not shake in panic, when the scorched earth shakes at the awesome blow of the thunderbolt and murmurs run through the great heaven? Do not nations and races tremble, and mighty kings draw back their limbs, struck with fear of the gods, dreading that the grievious time has come to pay the penalties for evil deeds or proud words? When the great force of the wind, raging across the sea, sweeps the commander of the fleet over the waters with his mighty legions and his elephants, does he not court the favor of the gods with vows, and, in his fright, prayerfully seek for a calm in the winds and for favoring breezes? In vain, since nonetheless he is often caught up by the raging whirlwind and carried to the shoals of doom. To such an extent does a power that we cannot see[98] crush our human undertakings, and we behold it as it treads underfoot the fair fasces and cruel axes, and makes them a sport for itself. Finally, when the whole earth trembles beneath our feet and shaken cities fall or totter threateningly, what wonder that mortal men despise themselves and grant that there exist in the world gods, whose great strength and wonderful power govern all things! 1220 1230 1240

Next bronze,[99] gold, iron, silver, and lead were discovered when great forests on the mountaintops were set aflame by hot fire—fire that may have been started by a thunderbolt from the sky, or else by men waging sylvan war among themselves, directing fire against their enemies to frighten them; or perhaps, influenced by the fertility of the soil, men were eager to clear rich fields and turn the countryside into pasture; or else they wished

[98] Not, of course, the power of the gods, but the universal power of the unseen atoms moving subject to their own laws.

[99] The same word, *aes*, may be translated either "copper" or "bronze," the alloy of copper and tin that was far more useful than pure copper. In line 1270 below, bronze is certainly meant, for copper would be about as useless as gold for making tools. Since copper and tin are sometimes found closely associated in a natural state, and since the first bronze probably resulted from the reduction of such an accidental mixture (see Charles Singer and others, *History of Technology,* I. 590), the translation "bronze" presents no difficulty in lines 1256–57 below. As tin is nowhere mentioned, I have preferred the translation "bronze" here also.

1250 to kill wild beasts and be enriched by the booty, for men began to hunt with pits and fire before they surrounded the lairs with nets and drove the beasts with dogs. However this may have been, and whatever may have been the cause, when the heat of the flames with fearful noise had devoured the high forests from their very roots and thoroughly heated the earth with fire, streams of silver and of gold, of bronze and of lead,[100] flowing from the fevered veins of the earth, would collect in hollow places on the ground. Later, when men saw these hardened masses shining on the earth with clear gleam, they used to pick 1260 them up, drawn by the glitter and the smooth charm; and they observed that they were formed into shapes such as had been those of the depressions. The thought then came to them that these pieces could be made liquid by heat and cast into the form and shape of any thing, and then by hammering could be drawn out into the form of blades as sharp and thin as one pleased, so that they might equip themselves with tools and be able to cut the forests, shape wood, hew timbers smooth, and even fashion them with auger, chisel, and gouge. At first they were as ready to undertake these tasks with tools of silver and of gold as with the 1270 violent might of strong bronze; but to no purpose, since the tools were unavailing and inferior in strength, nor could they stand up as well to hard labor. Thereafter bronze had greater value, and gold, dulled and with edge turned back, was neglected because of its uselessness. Now bronze is cheap, and gold has risen to the highest place of honor. Thus time, as it passes, changes the fashions, and what was once valued is soon dishonored; another thing takes its place, rising from among the things held cheap, and when once brought to light is more sought for every 1280 day and blossoms forth with praises, being held in high esteem among mortal men.

Now it is easy for you, Memmius, to discover by yourself and

[100] These metals are found in nature in a sufficiently available form that their discovery in the way described is conceivable. Although Lucretius mentions iron in the first line of this paragraph, he advisedly omits it here (see next note). The other four were in use centuries before iron was refined.

for yourself in what way iron was discovered. The first weapons were hands, nails, and teeth, stones and branches broken from trees, and flames and fire after these had become known. Afterwards strong iron and bronze were discovered; and the use of bronze was known earlier than that of iron because it is easier to work and the supply is greater.[101] With bronze they used to plow the soil, with bronze they woke the waves of war, sowed great wounds, and harried herds and fields. For all that were naked and unarmed yielded easily to those who were armed. Then the sword of iron advanced into use little by little, and the glory of the brazen sickle was turned into dishonor. Men began to plow the soil with iron, and the conflicts of wavering war were made equal.[102] 1290

The armed man mounted on the back of a horse, drove it with reins, and fought with his right hand before he attempted the dangers of war in a two-horsed chariot. Two horses were yoked to a chariot before four, and before the warrior mounted upon a scythe-bearing chariot. Next elephants, their bodies capped by turrets, fear-inspiring and serpent-handed, were taught by the Carthaginians to withstand the wounds of war and to throw into confusion the great companies of Mars. Thus gloomy Discord produced one thing after another to be dreadful for the human race in arms, and from day to day she increased the terrors of war. 1300

Men even tried to use bulls in the work of war, and attempted to send savage boars against the enemy. Some sent before themselves strong lions, with armed trainers and stern masters to control these animals and hold them in chains; but in vain, since the savage beasts, heated in the confused slaughter, raged 1310

[101] The melting point of bronze is so low that bronze casting was common in remote antiquity; but iron, even in Lucretius' day, was wrought with difficulty, and the casting of iron was not practicable. Although iron is one of the commonest of the elements, it does not exist free in nature (except in the form of meteorites), and the ores that could be reduced by ancient methods are relatively scarce.

[102] In line 1292 and here, the poet mentions the first and last stages in the development (unequal contest of bronze against clubs, and equal contest of iron against iron), but he omits the intermediate stages.

against the lines with no distinction, shaking against both sides the terrifying crests upon their heads; and horsemen could not calm the hearts of horses terrified by the roars, nor could they rein them against the enemy. The lions furiously hurled their bodies through the air from every side, and attacked the faces
1320 of those who came against them; and, charging men behind their backs while they were off their guard, they dragged them wounded to the ground, fastening upon them and holding them firmly with mighty bite and hooked claws. The bulls tossed their own drivers and trod them under foot, while with their horns they gored the flanks and bellies of the horses from beneath and threateningly tore up the earth. The boars gnashed their brave companions with their tusks, in their madness staining with their own blood the weapons broken within their bodies,[103] and
1330 caused indiscriminate ruin of horsemen and footmen. The horses, shying, tried to evade the fierce thrusts of the tusks, or rearing beat the air with their hooves; but to no purpose, since you might see them falling with slashed muscles, and bestrewing the ground in their disastrous collapse. Although men thought that certain beasts had been sufficiently tamed at home, they saw them driven mad in action by wounds, clamor, flight, panic, and tumult; and they could not recover any part of them. The whole mixed force of beasts scattered, as often today elephants when
1340 badly mauled by the goad scatter after doing many wild deeds against their own army. However,[104] this was not done in the hope of conquering; rather, these men wished to give their foes something for which to groan and then to perish, since they themselves lacked confidence in numbers and had no arms—if indeed this sort of war was ever undertaken at all. But I am hardly persuaded that men, even before the common disaster and misfortune took place, were not able to anticipate and foresee the outcome; and you might better argue that this use of beasts in war took place somewhere in the whole universe on

[103] Line 1328 is omitted by most editors.

[104] I follow Martin in his rearrangement of the last nine lines of this paragraph. There is great uncertainty, and the only point on which all editors agree is that the order found in the manuscripts is impossible.

one of many worlds created in different ways, than that it took place in any one particular world.[105]

Knitted coverings were in use before woven garments;° for weaving came after iron, since the weaver's beam is made with iron tools, and without them such smooth heddles, spindles, shuttles, and noisy combs could not have been formed. Nature led men to work wool before the female sex (for the male sex as a whole is far superior in art, and much more skillful), until the hardy farmers made such scorn of spinning that men were willing to entrust it to women's hands and themselves to share in bearing heavy toil, in hard labor hardening their hands and limbs. 1350 1360

Nature herself, the creator, furnished the first pattern and beginning of sowing and grafting; for berries and nuts, fallen beneath trees at the proper season, sent numerous seedlings up from the ground. From this the desire came to men to graft scions into stocks and to set new trees in the ground through the fields. Then they tried one form of culture of the sweet fields after another, and discovered that the wild fruits were made more tasty by cultivation and by fostering care in the fields. From day to day they forced the forests to withdraw ever higher up the mountains, leaving the space below for cultivation, so that on the foothills and plains they might have pastures, pools, trenches, grain crops, and pleasing vineyards, and that the green bands of olive trees, clearly marked, might extend through the hills, valleys, and plains as now you see the whole landscape about clearly marked with beauty of two kinds: fields that the farmers have made beautiful with sweet fruit trees set out here and there, and fields that they have completely filled with fruitful orchards. 1370

[105] Throughout the whole account of the development of culture we find the poet interrupting his narrative with moralizing passages suggested by the context: e.g., lines 988–1010 (modern war, shipwreck, and crime), 1117–35 (ambition), 1151–60 (fear of punishment), 1194–1240 (religion and superstition), and 1275–80 (changing values). This description of war is another passage of this kind, but here the poet's fancy gets the better of his discretion.

1380 Men imitated the voices of birds with their own lips long before they were able to practice polished songs and give pleasure to the ear. The whispering of the breeze through the hollow reeds first taught farmers to blow upon the pipes of Pan.[p] Then little by little they learned the sweet laments that, when stopped by the fingers of the player, the pipe pours forth, an instrument developed among pathless groves and woods and pastures in the 1390 charming and solitary spots where shepherds rest.[106] They soothed and delighted their hearts with such music when they were filled with food, for then anything pleases. Thus as they lay in groups on the soft grass beside a stream of water beneath the branches of a tall tree, they often found comfort for their bodies in simple ways, especially when the weather was pleasant and the season of the year painted with flowers the grass as it grew green.[107] Then jokes, conversation, and pleasant laughter were the rule; then was the rustic Muse at her best; then happy 1400 Mirth taught them to bind heads and shoulders with wreaths woven of flowers and leaves. Then moving their limbs without rhythm they advanced in rude dance, rudely striking with their feet the earth, their mother. From this there arose jests and pleasant laughter, since all this, being new and therefore more worthy of wonder, was then in favor. For those forced to remain awake, these were the solaces for the lack of sleep: to sing in various ways as they followed the melody, and to run the hooked lip along the pipes. Hence even now watchmen accept these 1410 songs as traditional and learn to sing in rhythm; and they do not enjoy any greater sweetness than did the woodland race of the earth-born.

For what is at hand, unless we before have known something sweeter, is most pleasing and is seen to hold the field; but as a rule, when a newer, better thing is discovered, it displaces the earlier and changes our feelings toward each of the things of old.[108] So acorns began to be despised; so those cots built high

[106] Lines 1388 and 1389, which are repeated below as lines 1454 and 1455, are omitted below by all editors.

[107] Lines 1392–96 are repeated with changes from II. 29–33.

[108] See Epicurus, *Principal Doctrines* XXIX, XXX, XVIII.

with leaves and strewn with grasses were abandoned; so the garments of wild skins came into contempt. But I suppose that the coat of skins, when first devised, was the cause of such envy that he who first wore it met his death in ambush; and yet after all the pelt was torn in the struggle and completely ruined with much blood so that it could not be made of any use. Thus skins then, and now purple and gold, plague the lives of men with cares and weary them with war. Upon us, I believe, lies the greater blame. For unless they were provided with pelts, cold tortured the naked sons of earth; but it harms us not at all to be without a garment of purple or one embroidered with heavy golden figures, provided we have common garments to cover us.[a] So the race of man is always laboring in vain and to no purpose, and spending its days in empty cares, because indeed it has not learned what is the true limit of possessing and in general to what point true pleasure may increase. Because we have not learned this, we have brought our lives bit by bit to the highest luxury, and we have roused from their utmost depths the mighty tides of war. 1420 1430

But the watchmen, even the sun and the moon, shedding light round about us as they cross the mighty revolving regions of the sky, taught men that the seasons of the year are changed and that Nature is carried on by a fixed plan in a determined manner. Now men were living lives hedged in by strong walls, and the earth was being cultivated after having been divided and distributed; next, the sea began to bloom with sail-clad ships. On account of these things men developed governments[109] and had allies and auxiliaries held by sworn treaties. Then in their lays poets began to pass down men's deeds; and not long before this, letters had been invented. For this reason our age cannot look back at what happened before this except as reason shows the way. Navigation, fields under cultivation, walls, laws, arms, highways, dress and other things of this sort, prizes, every pleasure of life from its very foundation, songs, pictures, and the 1440 1450

[109] Following the suggestion of Mackay in *Classical Philology*, LVI (1961), 105, I read *florebat; propterea res* for the almost meaningless *florebat propter odores* of the manuscripts.

creation of wondrous works of sculpture—practice and, along with it, the experience of an active mind taught all these things slowly to men, who were making progress step by step. Thus time drew each single thing into view, and reason lifted it to the shores of light; for in their hearts men saw one thing after another come into bright light until they reached the topmost pinnacle of the arts.[110]

[110] Or "until by their arts they have reached the topmost pinnacle." In the text I have followed Bailey in taking *artibus* as a "Lucretian dative" used to avoid the metrically difficult genitive *artium*.

BOOK SIX

I. Atmospheric Phenomena

1–534

Following in the footsteps of Epicurus, the poet describes and explains natural phenomena, insisting that they are not signs of either divine wrath or divine favor. He discusses the causes and nature of lightning, thunder, and the thunderbolt, and then explains waterspouts, whirlwinds, clouds, rain, and the rainbow.

Glorious Athens, the city that was the first to distribute to poor mortals crops of grain, to reform their lives, and to pass laws, was also the first to provide the sweet blessings of life by producing that man of greatest mind—he who once poured forth from his truthful lips all wisdom, he whose fame, long established and widespread because of his divine discoveries, is even now after his death carried to the sky. He saw that almost everything that man's physical needs demand had been made 10 ready for mortals and had made human life secure as far as such things could, but that men, while prospering in the possession of wealth, honor, and praise, and proud in the reputation of their sons, nevertheless at home had troubled hearts, which despite their wills ceaselessly afflicted their lives with vexations and forced them to rage with tempestuous complaints.[1] Observing all this, he knew that the human vessel was flawed within and by its flaw corrupted whatever good thing had been gathered and collected from without; for he saw both that the vessel 20 was so leaky and broken that it could never in any way be filled, and that it defiled, as with an evil taste, whatever things it had

[1] The natural desires had been satisfied, but men were left with a limitless longing for praise and power, desires that, being unnatural, have no limit. See Epicurus, *Letter to Menoeceus* 127b–29a, and *Principal Doctrines* XV, XXV, XXIX, XXX.

received within itself. Therefore with his true teachings he purified men's hearts and established a limit for desire and for fear; he explained the nature of the highest good, for which all seek, and showed the way, the narrow path, by which we may press on directly toward this goal. He taught what evil there is here
30 and there in mortal matters, an evil which comes into being and flies about in various ways, through either natural chance or violence, because Nature has so prepared it; he showed from what gates we should sally forth to meet each ill; and he proved that men for the most part toss in their hearts a bitter sea of cares, all to no purpose. For like children who in the blinding darkness tremble and fear everything, so at times we, although in the light, fear things no more worthy of being feared than the phantoms at which children in the darkness shudder as they imagine that they are upon them. This terror, this darkness of
40 the soul, must be dispelled neither by the rays of the sun nor by the bright weapons of the day but by an understanding of the outer form and the inner law of Nature.[2] For this reason I shall hasten all the more to weave with my words the web I have begun.

Since I have shown that the world is destined to die and that the heavens had a birth, and have explained nearly all that takes place and must take place in them, hear now what remains: since once ⟨I have made bold⟩ to mount upon the glorious chariot ⟨of the Muses . . . I will tell how storms⟩[3] of winds arise and are calmed so that all that has raged is changed with
50 its fury soothed, and explain the other things that men see taking place on earth and in the sky. Often, at such times, their frightened minds are in suspense; they humble their hearts through fear of the gods, and throw themselves prone on the ground; for ignorance of the causes of things forces them to make Nature subject to the gods, and to grant to the gods do-

[2] Lines 35–41 were used before at II. 55–61 and III. 87–93; lines 39–41 were also used at I. 146–48.

[3] At least one line is lost between lines 47 and 48. The supplement translated is that suggested by Bailey in his notes.

minion.[4] For if men, even those who have rightly learned that the gods pass lives untouched by care, are nevertheless left to wonder from time to time in what way each thing in Nature can be brought to pass, especially in the case of the things they see above their heads in the region of the upper air, they are again carried back into the old superstitions and acknowledge cruel masters, whom they in their misery believe to be all-powerful since they do not understand what can come into existence and what cannot, and by what law there is for each thing a power that is limited and a boundary that is firmly fixed;[5] and so they stray the more, carried on by reasoning that is blind. Unless you cast these beliefs from your mind and put far away all thoughts unworthy of the gods and foreign to their peace, the sacred powers of the gods, harmed through you, will often act contrary to your interests; not that the supreme power of the gods can be so violated that they wrathfully determine to exact dire punishment, but that you yourself will suppose in your own mind that the gods, who are calm in their perfect peace, are breathing forth great storms of wrath. Hence you will not draw near the shrines of the gods with tranquil heart, nor will you be able with a calm and peaceful mind to receive the idols that are carried from their sacred forms to the minds of men, as heralds of their divine beauty. You may see what sort of life follows this. In order that the truest wisdom may drive this far from us, although I have already written much, much still remains to be made beautiful in polished verses: we must understand the system of the earth and the sky; we must sing of storms and bright thunderbolts, telling what they bring to pass and for what reason they are carried along. This we must do that you may not mark out the regions of the sky in fear and panic, asking

60

70

80

[4] Lines 56 and 57, "phenomena whose causes they can in no wise understand, and they believe that these occur by divine power," which are found again below as lines 90–91, are omitted in both places. They are repeated from I. 153–54, where they seem more in place. It is probable that some early commentator, noting the similarity between the argument in Book I and in this section, quoted the lines here in the margin, and that then some copyist incorporated them in the text here and below.

[5] Lines 58–66 are repeated from V. 82–90.

whence the flying bolt has come and into which region of the sky it thereafter took its course,[a] in what way it has penetrated the enclosed rooms and how, after acting as master here, it has departed.[6] Wise muse, Calliopê, refreshment of mankind and delight of the gods, do you point out the track for me as I run to the white line that marks my race's end, that under your leadership I may gain the crown with glorious praise.

First of all, the blue sky is shaken by thunder because[b] the scudding clouds of heaven collide high in the air when driven by opposing winds; for the sound does not come from a part
100 of the sky that is clear, but thunder with its mighty rumble more often comes from that quarter of the sky in which the clouds are in denser array.[7] (Clouds cannot be of such dense structure as are stones and wood, or as thin as flitting mist and smoke; for they would fall if brute weight pressed them down like stones, and if they were like smoke they would be unable to support and hold together snow and showers of hail.) The clouds also give forth a sound over the surface of the great spreading sky as sometimes the awning stretched over the great
110 theater gives out a cracking sound as it is tossed between masts and beams; and sometimes, whipping back and forth in the angry winds, it is torn and imitates the sound of tearing paper. For you might recognize a sound of this kind also among the thunders, or such a sound as when the winds beat with blows a hanging garment or flying papers and drive them through the air. It sometimes happens also that clouds do not thus rush together face to face, but scrape slowly along each other as they move in opposite directions; from this comes that dry sound
120 that grates upon our ears and is long drawn out until the clouds escape from the narrow space.

In the following way as well everything is shaken with heavy thunder and seems to tremble, and the great walls of the all-containing world are torn and seem to leap apart, when sud-

[6] Lines 90–91 are omitted; see note 4 above.

[7] See Epicurus, *Letter to Pythocles* 100b.

denly a gale of mighty wind collects together and twists its way into the clouds. When this whirling eddy has been shut up in a cloud, the cloud is forced to become more and more hollow while its outer portions become more dense; and finally the surrounding envelope, weakened by the force and keen violence of the wind, is rent and bursts with a terrifying crash; nor is this 130 strange, since a little bladder full of air in the same way often causes a small noise[8] if it suddenly explodes. It is also possible for clouds to make a sound when the wind blows through them; for we often see clouds that are branched and irregular in many ways being carried along, and in them the wind makes a noise, just as the leaves rustle and the branches crack when gusts of the northwest wind blow through a thick forest. It also happens sometimes that when the violence of a strong wind is aroused it tears a cloud, bursting directly through it. For our own experience suggests what a blast of wind can do in the air, since here 140 on earth, where its strength is less, it lifts and tears up tall trees from their lowest roots.

There are also waves throughout the clouds, and these give a sort of roar as they break heavily—the same thing that happens when a wave breaks on deep rivers or the great sea. There is also thunder, when the burning force of lightning falls from cloud to cloud. If by chance a cloud containing much moisture receives the fire, it quenches it at once with a great sound, just as when iron, white-hot from the fiery furnace, hisses as we plunge it into cold water. Again, if a drier cloud receives the fire, it is 150 suddenly kindled and burns with great noise, as if flame swept on by the great force of eddying winds were raging through laurel-covered mountains. (Nothing is burned by the crackling flame with a more dreadful sound than is the Delphic laurel of Apollo.) Finally, the great crackling of ice and the falling of hail cause a sound high in the great clouds; for when the wind drives them together, the mountains of clouds mixed

[8] Or, reading *saepe dat haud parvum,* a suggestion of Lachmann, for the *saepe ita dat parvum* of the manuscripts: "A little bladder full of air often causes no small sound."

with hail, which have been congealed and compressed, are broken.

160 When clouds collide, they likewise cause lightning[9] by striking out many seeds of fire, as when a stone strikes another stone or a piece of iron; for then too light leaps forth and the fire scatters bright sparks abroad.[10] But we receive the thunder in our ears after our eyes see the lightning, because things come more slowly to the ears than do the things that move the eyes. You may learn this also from the following: if you watch a man cutting down a full-grown tree with a double-bitted axe, you 170 see the blow struck before its sound reaches your ears; so also we see the flash before we hear the thunder that is sent forth at the same time and from the same cause as the fire, both created by the same collision.

In the following way as well the clouds with swift light scatter color, and the storm becomes bright with a quivering flash. When wind has entered a cloud and by whirling about there has made the hollow cloud more dense, as I have shown above,[11] the wind grows hot because of its own velocity, just as you see all things grow very hot and catch fire because of motion; for example, the leaden sling bullet is even melted as it whirls in its 180 long flight.[12] And so when the hot wind splits the black cloud, the seeds of fire that form the darting gleam of flame are scattered as if expelled by sudden violence; then follows the sound, which strikes our ears more slowly than the flash that comes through to the sight of our eyes. You must know that this happens in clouds that are dense and, at the same time, are piled up one over the other to a surprising height. Do not be deceived because from below we see the breadth of clouds rather than the

[9] See Epicurus, *Letter to Pythocles* 101–103a.

[10] Compare the first cause for thunder, lines 96–98 above.

[11] See lines 124–29 above.

[12] The same statement about the lead bullet melting in flight is found in Aristotle, *On the Heavens* II. 7, 289a19–26, and in Seneca, *Natural Questions* II. 57. 1–3, the latter using it to explain lightning. The atomic explanation of this is given below, lines 306–8.

height to which they are heaped up. Look when the winds are 190 carrying mountain-like clouds through the air from side to side, or when amid great mountains you see clouds piled one upon another and, arrayed in order, pressing down from above on every side and burying all the winds. Then you can recognize their great masses and see the caves, formed as if by overhanging ledges, which are filled by the winds as the tempest mounts. Confined in the clouds, these winds rage with a mighty roar, and threaten like wild beasts in their cages. Now on this side, now on that, they send a roaring through the clouds and whirl about 200 as they seek a road. They collect from the clouds the seeds of fire; and when they have gathered many together, they drive the flame round and round within the hollow furnace until the cloud is broken and they flash forth all ablaze.[13]

For the following reasons also the swift golden color of liquid fire flies down upon the earth. The clouds themselves must have many seeds of fire, for when they are without any moisture they often have the bright color of flame. Truly, they must also receive many seeds from the light of the sun; thus it is reasonable 210 that they be red, and pour forth fire. When the wind driving them squeezes them into a narrow space and forcibly presses them together, these seeds are expelled and poured out, and make the color of flame flash forth. There is also lightning when the clouds in the sky become thin; for when the wind separates and dissolves the clouds as they drift along, these seeds that make the flash must fall out driven by an impulse not their own. Then there is lightning without uproar, unaccompanied by noise or by hideous fear.

Next the nature of the thunderbolt[14] is made manifest in its 220 strokes, in the charring left by its heat, and in the scars that

[13] Compare the explanation of thunder in lines 121–31 above.

[14] The Greeks and Romans regularly distinguished between the lightning seen in the sky and the lightning that strikes the earth. We can use the term "thunderbolt" to designate the latter in English. They were regarded as having the same general nature, differing in force rather than in kind.

breathe out the heavy vapor of sulphur; for these are the marks of fire, not of wind or rain. Moreover, thunderbolts often set fire to the roofs of houses and with swift flames play the tyrant over the houses themselves. Nature has made this, the most subtle of fires, from minute and mobile particles, to which nothing can interpose a bar. Indeed, the mighty thunderbolt passes through the walls of houses like noise or voices,[15] goes through rocks and
230 through bronze, and melts bronze and gold in an instant. It also causes the wine in an unbroken jar to evaporate suddenly, since its heat drawing near makes the whole texture of the clay loose and open; and twisting its way in with rapid motion, it separates the atoms of the wine and scatters them. The heat of the sun could not do this in a man's lifetime, however mighty in its flashing fires; so much swifter and more overwhelming is the force of the thunderbolt.

I shall now set forth the way in which the thunderbolts are
240 made and acquire such violence that they can burst towers open with their blows, demolish houses, tear away the tiles and timbers of roofs, uproot and overthrow the monuments of heroes, deprive men of life, and lay cattle dead upon the ground. By what force they are able to do these things and all others like them I shall tell without keeping you waiting for what has been promised.

We must believe that thunderbolts are formed from heavy clouds piled high; for none ever strike from a clear sky, or from clouds of moderate density.[16] Obvious facts prove this without
250 a doubt, since at the time of a thunderbolt the clouds grow into such a mass through the whole sky that we might believe all the darkness has left the lower world and filled the great spaces of the sky, such faces of black fear hang over us on high where clouds have gathered in a noisome night[17] and the storm begins to set its thunderbolts in motion. Moreover, very often over the sea a black storm cloud filled with darkness from afar settles upon the waves like a river of pitch sent down from heaven,

[15] See I. 489–90.

[16] See Epicurus, *Letter to Pythocles* 103b–104a.

[17] With one slight change, lines 251–54 appeared at IV. 170–73.

and drags along a dark storm big with thunderbolts and winds, the cloud itself being filled to the utmost with fire and wind, so 260 that even on the shore men shudder and seek their homes. In this way, then, we must suppose that the storm rises high above our heads. Certainly clouds could not cover the earth with such darkness unless they were piled high, one cloud upon another, shutting out all the sunlight; nor could they as they come overwhelm us with such rains that they cause the rivers to flood and the fields to be covered with water were not the upper air filled with clouds heaped up on high. Then all things are full of wind and fire; from this arise crashings and lightnings on every side. 270 Nay, I have shown above that hollow clouds have very many seeds of fire, and they must receive many more from the rays of the sun and from their heat. When the very wind that has driven the clouds by chance into some one place has forced out the many seeds of heat and at the same time has mixed itself with the fire, then a whirling blast, which has made its way inside, turns about in the narrow space and sharpens the thunderbolt within at the hot furnaces. For the wind gains heat in two ways: it grows hot from its own motion and likewise from its contacts 280 with the fire. When the blast of wind has become hot and the mighty impetus of the fire has entered into it, then, as if ready for birth, the thunderbolt suddenly cuts through the cloud, and the burning flame in rapid motion makes its way, illuminating all places with its darting light. Such a heavy roll of thunder follows that the vaults of heaven above us seem suddenly to have been torn asunder and to overwhelm us. Then a trembling gravely tries the earth, and a rumbling runs through the high heaven; for then almost the whole storm cloud is shaken and trembles, and roarings are let loose. A rainstorm, violent and 290 dense, follows the shaking so that the whole sky seems to be turning into rain, and as the rain falls it seems to change the earth's surface back to mud; such is the storm caused by the shattering of the cloud and by the blast of wind as the fiery blow of the thunderbolt is released.

Sometimes also a blast of wind from without is set in rapid motion and strikes a great cloud whose top is already reared high.[18] When it cuts through the cloud, that fiery eddy—which our native tongue names the thunderbolt—at once falls out. This strikes in whatever direction the force of the wind has impelled it.

300 Again, it sometimes happens that, when a blast of wind containing no fire has been set in motion, in the course of its long passage it nevertheless becomes hot, losing as it moves in flight certain heavy particles that cannot maintain an equal velocity through the air, and gathering others that it sweeps from the very air and carries along—small particles that make fire when mixed with wind by the motion of the flight. In this same way a ball of lead often becomes hot in its course when it loses particles of cold and gathers fire in the air.[19]

It also happens that fire may be caused by the mere force of 310 the blow struck by a blast of wind, which at its start was cold and fireless;[20] the reason for this is surely that, when it delivers the violent thrust, seeds of heat can flow together both from the wind itself and also from that which is then receiving the blow. Just so fire flies out when we strike a stone with iron; and, when the blow is struck, the seeds of hot fire come together no more slowly because the iron is cold. So too, then, a thing ought to be set on fire by a thunderbolt if it is ready and fit for burning. 320 A blast of wind cannot easily be wholly cold when it has been put in motion with such force high in the sky, and even if it is not already set on fire in its flight, it comes to the end of its course at least warmed by the admixture of heat.

A thunderbolt gains mobility and great force, and commonly crosses the sky in rapid fall because, after its might has first of all bestirred itself and collected within the clouds, it builds up great energy for its escape; then at the point where the cloud is unable to withstand its growing force, the violent thunderbolt breaks its way through and for this reason flies with wondrous 330 force, as do missiles hurled from mighty siege engines. Moreover,

18 Reading *validam . . . culmine,* with the manuscripts.

19 See lines 177–79 above.

20 Quite certainly we should understand that the blow is struck against a cloud.

the thunderbolt is made of small, smooth particles, of a sort that nothing can easily resist. It slips through the porous passages and penetrates them, and is not checked or delayed by collisions; therefore it glides along in its flight with swift impulse. Next, by nature all weights tend downward; and when a blow has been added the speed is doubled, and the momentum itself grows so strong that the thunderbolt thrusts from its path rapidly and with violent blows whatever would oppose it; and thus it pursues its course. Finally, because the thunderbolt moves 340 with a long-continued impulse, it ought to gain greater and greater velocity, since velocity is increased by the very fact of motion, augmenting the mighty energy of the bolt and multiplying the power with which it strikes. For it causes all its seeds to be carried in one straight line as if toward a single spot, hurling them all in one direction as they fly. Perhaps too as it goes it drags from the air itself certain bodies that increase its speed by their blows.

The thunderbolt passes through many things and leaves them whole and unharmed, because its liquid fire penetrates their open pores. Many things it breaks because the particles of the 350 thunderbolt strike the bodies of these things where they are interwoven and held together. It easily dissolves bronze and melts gold quickly, because its might is intricately fashioned out of minute bodies and smooth particles, which easily enter the bronze or gold and, having entered it, free and release all the bonds that bind it.

It is in the autumn, and when the flowery season of spring spreads itself, that the expanse of heaven, set with shining stars, and the whole earth on every side are most violently shaken; for in winter fires are lacking, and in summer the winds fail 360 and the substance of the clouds is not sufficiently dense. But when the seasons of the sky stand between the two, then all the various causes of the thunderbolt come together; for the cloud needs both cold and heat for the fashioning of thunderbolts, and these two are then so mingled by the narrow passage of the year that there is discord in nature and the air seethes, tossed around in a great turmoil by fire and wind. The season of spring

370 is the beginning of the heat and the ending of the cold; therefore the unlike things, mixed together, must fight and rage. When the last of the heat rolls around mixed with the first of the cold, in the season called by the name of autumn, then too there is a conflict between the keen winter and the summer. For this reason these seasons are rightly called the narrows of the year, and it is not strange if at these times many thunderbolts are formed and blustering storms are roused in the sky, since the heaven is torn on either side in doubtful war, on this side by flame, on that by mingled wind and rain.

One may perceive the true nature of the fiery thunderbolt 380 and see the force by which it acts by such a study as this, not by reading over the rolls of Etruscan formulae to no purpose, or by seeking the hidden intention of the gods by signs, observing the quarter from which the flying bolt has come, the region into which it thereafter took its course, the way that it has penetrated the enclosed rooms, and how, after acting as master here, it has departed;[21] and questioning in what way the bolt from heaven can bring pollution. But if Jupiter and the other gods[22] shake the bright regions of the sky with terrifying crashes, and 390 hurl the fire wherever each of them wills, why do they not cause all men who have not been on guard against loathsome crime to be struck and to breathe the flame of lightning from transfixed breasts, a bitter lesson to mortals? Why rather is the man who is conscious of nothing shameful in himself rapt in flames and, although innocent, suddenly entangled and caught in the whirlwind of heavenly fire? Why do the gods seek out deserted places and waste their labor? Or are they then training their arms and making strong their muscles? Why do the gods permit the weapon of the Father to be dulled on the earth? Why does he himself allow this, and not save it for his foes? 400 Why does Jupiter never hurl his bolt and send forth his thunder upon the earth from a clear sky? Does he himself come down

21 Lines 383–85 are repeated from lines 87–89 above.

22 The Etruscans, from whom the Romans drew their augural science, assigned the lightning to nine of the gods. The rest of this paragraph is anticipated by II. 1101-4.

into the clouds as soon as they have gathered, in order to direct the blows of his weapon from that nearby point? For what reason, then, does he also send the bolt into the sea? What charge does he have against the waves, the watery masses, and the liquid plains? Moreover, if he wishes us to avoid the stroke of the lightning, why does he hesitate so to order things that we may see it cast? If, on the other hand, he wishes to overwhelm us with fire while we are off our guard, why does he thunder from that quarter, that we may avoid it? Why does he cause darkness, mutterings, and grumblings beforehand? Again, could you believe that he sends his thunder in many directions at the same time? Or would you dare contend that it never has happened that many blows were struck at the same time? But it has happened very often and must happen that, as it has rained and showers have fallen in many places, so at a single time many thunderbolts have been hurled. Finally, why does he strike the holy shrines of the gods and his own famous temples with his destructive bolt? Why does he break the well-made statues of the gods and take away the beauty of their likenesses with violent wounds? Why does he most often strike the high places, and why do we see most of the traces of his fire on the highest mountains? 410 420

Next, from this it is easy to learn in what way waterspouts, which the Greeks call by the descriptive term "presters,"[c] come into the sea, having been sent down from on high.[23] Often it happens that something like a column is let down and descends from the sky into the sea; around this the sea boils, severely stirred by the whirling blasts, and whatever ships are caught in this turbulence are shaken and come into extreme danger. A waterspout occurs when on occasion a blast of wind attempting to break from a cloud is not able to do so, but forces the cloud down, so that a sort of column is lowered little by little into the sea, as if something were being beaten from above by the blow of a fist or the thrusting out of an arm, and were being stretched down into the waves. When the force of the wind breaks this, it rushes from it into the sea and rouses a marvelous boiling 430

23 See Epicurus, *Letter to Pythocles* 104b–105a.

among the waves. In truth the spinning vortex comes down,
440 and it likewise draws down that cloud with its pliant body; and as soon as the vortex has brought the cloud, big with wind, to the surface of the sea, it suddenly hurls its whole self into the water and excites it, forcing the whole sea to boil with a great sound. It also happens sometimes that a vortex of wind itself wraps itself up in clouds, scraping the seeds of cloud from the air; when this is let down from the sky, it becomes something like a "prester," and when it comes down on land and breaks, it pours forth a huge force of wind, whirling about and in gusts. But because in any case this phenomenon is rare, and because mountains obstruct it[24] if it takes place on land, it is observed
450 more often in the wide expanse of the sea under the open sky.

Clouds are formed when many rather rough bodies, which when compressed can be held together although the bonds among them are slight, have in their flight quickly gathered in the higher region of the sky.[25] These at first cause small clouds to appear, which then grasp one another and gather together; and as they join each other they increase in size and are carried by the wind until finally severe storms spring up. It also
460 happens that the nearer the mountain peaks are to the sky, the more constantly do their lofty tops smoke with the thick darkness of dusky clouds, for the reason that when clouds are first being formed, even while they are only a thin mist that the eye cannot see, the winds that carry them drive them against the topmost peaks of the mountains. After these mists have come together here and are condensed in a greater mass, they become visible as clouds, which then appear to be rising to the sky from the very tops of the mountains. (When we climb high mountains our experience and our senses declare that the regions that are high are open to the winds.)

470 Moreover, when garments that are hung by the shore receive clinging moisture, they show us that Nature lifts out many seeds of water from the whole sea as well. Thus it is clear that

24 Or: "prevent its being seen."

25 See Epicurus, *Letter to Pythocles* 99b.

many bodies for producing clouds can rise up from the salty waves of the sea; for the moisture from the sky and that from the sea are akin in every way. Moreover, from all rivers and from the land itself we see clouds and mists arise; exhaled from their sources like breath, these are carried aloft, and as they slowly come together, they cover the sky with their darkness and form high clouds. The heat of the starry aether also checks the clouds on the upper side, and by holding them together it weaves, so to speak, a web of cloud beneath the blue. 480

It also happens that these bodies that form the cloud and the flying storm-cloud come into the world from outside. For I have taught that the atoms are without number and that space is infinite; and I have shown with what great velocity the bodies fly and how quickly they cross through a space beyond our computation. It is therefore not to be wondered at if often in a brief time tempests and darkness hanging above the seas and earth cover them with great storm-clouds,[26] inasmuch as from all sides all the pores of the aether and the breathing holes (if we may call them so) of the great world afford entrance and exit to the atoms. 490

Now listen and I shall tell how the moisture of rain gathers in the high clouds and how it is let loose and falls upon the earth in the form of showers.[27] First, now, I shall prove that many seeds of water rise up together with the clouds themselves from all things, and that clouds and whatever water is in the clouds both increase at the same rate, just as our bodies increase along with the blood and whatever sweat and moisture there are in our members. When clouds are carried by the winds high above the great sea, they frequently receive much moisture from it too, as does a hanging fleece of wool. In the same way moisture from all the streams is raised into the clouds. When in many ways very many seeds of water have come together and have been increased from every side, the well-filled clouds hasten to send down rain, for a twofold cause: the strong wind 500 510

26 Reading *tam magnis nimbis*.

27 See Epicurus, *Letter to Pythocles* 99c–100a.

forces the clouds together; and the very mass of the clouds, as they are driven together in greater confusion, exerts force and pressure from above and makes the driving rain pour out. (It is also true that when the clouds are made thin by the wind, and dissolved by the heat of the sun that strikes them from above, they send down rain in drops, just as the top of a candle is softened by the hot flame and melts freely.) The rain becomes violent if the clouds are violently pressed by both causes—their own heaping up, and the onset of the wind. But gentle showers 520 often continue and linger long when many seeds of water are gathered together as dripping mists and clouds piled one on another are carried back and forth from every side, and when the whole earth steams and breathes back moisture.

Under such conditions beneath a lowering sky, when the sun with its rays is striking full against the spray from the clouds, then on the black clouds the color of the rainbow becomes visible.[28]

As for all the other things that grow on high and are formed aloft, and those that take shape in the clouds—snow, winds, hail, 530 chill hoar frost, the great force of icy cold, the mighty hardening of the waters, the curb that sometimes bridles the impetuous rivers—in what way all these are formed and for what reason they are created is easy to discover and see in the mind, if once you have learned what powers have been granted to the atoms.[29]

II. Terrestrial Phenomena

535–702

Earthquakes may be caused by changes in underground rivers or caverns; similar hollows beneath mountains are responsible for volcanic eruptions. Although the sea is constantly receiving water, it is also constantly being diminished by the sun and wind; consequently it is always the same size.

[28] See Epicurus, *Letter to Pythocles* 109b–110a.

[29] See Epicurus, *Letter to Pythocles* 106c–109a.

Come now, and learn the cause of earthquakes.[30] In the first place, you must understand that the earth beneath, as well as above, is everywhere full of windy caves and carries in its bosom many lakes, hollows, rocks, and broken ledges; you must also 540 believe that the earth's surface hides many unseen rivers, in which submerged waves roll violently.[31] For Nature herself demands that the earth be everywhere like to itself.[32] Since all these are placed beneath the surface of the earth and are linked to it, the earth above them trembles and is shaken by great cataclysms when, down below, the passage of time makes huge caves collapse; indeed, whole mountains fall, and at the mighty impact tremors suddenly spread out far and wide. And this stands to reason: for wagons make roadside buildings tremble, whole buildings being shaken by a weight that is by no means great; and no less do the wagons themselves[33] rock when a stone 550 in the road jolts the iron rims of the wheels on one side or the other. It also happens that when a huge mass is freed from the earth by the long passage of time and rolls into the great waste pools of water, the earth too reels and is shaken by the moving of the water, as sometimes a jar cannot stand still as long as the water within tosses in unsteady motion.

Moreover, when the wind, collected throughout the hollow spaces of the earth, moves forward from one direction and, thrusting with great force, presses upon the high caverns, the 560 earth yields in the direction in which the on-pressing violence of the wind urges it. Then the houses built on the surface of the earth, in proportion as they reach up toward the sky, waver and sway, tipped in the same direction; and beams, moved from their places, hang ready to fall. And yet men are afraid to believe that catastrophe and a time of destruction await the great

[30] See Epicurus, *Letter to Pythocles* 105b.

[31] Reading *submersos caeca,* with Martin.

[32] The atoms acting everywhere subject to the same laws ought to produce everywhere the same results. If there are, for example, rivers on the surface of the earth, there ought to be rivers beneath its surface as well.

[33] Reading *ipsa ut lapi' cumque,* the text adopted by Bailey in his *Addenda.*

world, although they see such a mass of earth subside! For if the winds were to continue blowing, no force would check things or be able to hold them back from destruction as they 570 fall. But as it is, since the winds alternately pause and grow fresh and, so to speak, gather their forces and attack and then retire in defeat, the earth threatens collapse more often than she falls in ruins; for she leans over and sways back, and after tottering forward, she recovers her position in balance. In this way, then, all buildings are shaken—the tops more than the middle portions, the middle portions more than the lower parts, and these last only a very little.

The same great quaking is also caused when a certain mighty force of wind and air, either from without or rising in the very 580 earth, hurls itself into hollow places of the earth. There amid the great caves, it first rages in tumult and whirls itself around; then afterward, roused and awakened in its violence, it breaks out, cutting through the deep earth and leaving a great opening. This happened at Sidon in Syria and at Aegium in the Peloponnesus,[34] cities that were overthrown by such an outburst of wind and upthrust of the earth. And many other walled towns besides these have fallen in great earthquakes, and many 590 cities along the shore have sunk to the depths of the sea together with their people. But even if there is no bursting forth, yet the very violence of the air and the fierce force of the winds send a shudder and a trembling through the many passages of the earth, just as cold, when it settles in our members, makes them shiver and shake, forcing them against our wills. Therefore throughout the cities men are in panic with a double terror: they dread the buildings above them, and they fear lest the earth suddenly disclose the caverns beneath its surface, and, 600 rent apart, open wide a rift in itself and seek in utter confusion to fill this with its own torn fragments. Let men believe as much as they like that sky and earth will be inviolate, assigned to an eternal safety; yet at times the very present force of danger from

[34] Most of Sidon was destroyed and all Syria was shaken by a great earthquake late in the fifth century B.C. Early in the next century two towns near Aegium on the Achaean coast are said to have been engulfed by another earthquake.

some source applies the spur of fear that suddenly the earth, withdrawn from beneath their feet, will settle down into the abyss, and that all things will follow, overturned from their very foundations, and the utter destruction of the world will come to pass.

In the first place men wonder that Nature does not make the sea increase, since into it there is such a flow of waters and into 610 it come all the rivers from every side.[d] Add to this the passing showers and the flying storms that pour forth their rain and shed their water on all the seas and lands; add the ocean's own springs; yet in comparison with the whole of the sea all this forms an addition hardly equal to a single drop, and it is therefore less wonderful that the mighty sea does not increase. Moreover, the sun draws up a great amount of water by its heat. Indeed, we see that the sun with its hot rays completely dries clothes that are dripping with moisture; and we see that the oceans are many and widespread. Although from any one 620 place the part that the sun takes away may be as small as you please, yet throughout so great an expanse it drinks copiously from the waves. Then too the winds can carry off a great amount of moisture as they sweep over the seas, for we often see roads made dry by the winds in a single night and the soft surface of the mud made hard. Moreover, as I have shown, the clouds carry much water taken from the great surface of the sea and scatter it here and there over the whole earth when it rains 630 upon the lands and the winds are carrying the clouds. Finally, since the earth has a porous body and without any break surrounds the shores of the sea on every side, water must penetrate from the salt sea into the earth just as it goes from the earth into the sea; for the salt is filtered out, and the liquid parts seep back and all flow together to the sources of the rivers, from which the water returns over the earth in a sweet stream wherever the path marked by its liquid tread directs the waves.[35]

I shall now explain the reason why at times fires in such a whirlwind breathe through the jaws of mountains, for example 640

[35] Lines 635–38 are repeated with minor changes from V. 269–72.

those of Mount Aetna.[36] For the fiery storm that rose up and played the tyrant over the lands of Sicily with great destruction attracted to itself the attention of neighboring peoples. Then men, seeing all quarters of the sky smoking and flashing, filled their hearts with panic-stricken dread as to what new things Nature was undertaking.

In this matter you must look far and deep, and thoroughly examine in all directions so that you may not forget that the 650 sum of things is infinite, and may see what a little part, what a small fraction, of the whole sum is our heaven, not so large a portion as a single man is of our whole earth. If you keep your eyes fixed upon this obvious truth and if you see it clearly, there are many things about which you will cease to wonder. Does any person wonder if one of us has caught a disease that breaks out with a high fever, or has contracted some other painful illness in his members? For a foot swells up suddenly, a sharp, recurrent pain plagues the teeth or attacks the eyes themselves, 660 the cursed fire[37] breaks out and spreads over the body, burning whatever part it attacks and creeping over the limbs—all this because there are seeds of many things and this earth produces enough disease, this sky enough evil, that from them may develop a plague whose force is unlimited.[38] So for our whole sky and earth we must believe that all things are amply supplied from infinite space, whence of a sudden the earth may be struck and moved, a rapid whirlwind may sweep over the sea and land, the fires of Aetna may overflow, and flames may flash in the sky. 670 In addition to all this, the heavenly regions glow with heat; and there are rainstorms that gather more thickly when by chance the seeds of water have duly come together. "But," you say, "the eddying violence of the fire is too vast." So may one speak of a

36 For "jaws" meaning "craters," see line 702 below. Aetna was the active volcano best known to the Romans, for Vesuvius, although recognized as a volcano, was not active until its great eruption in A.D. 79. Lucretius in his description of volcanic activity may have drawn on reports of the eruption of Aetna in 122 B.C.

37 Or "the sacred fire." Probably erysipelas is meant.

38 This hint is fully developed in lines 1090–1286 below.

river that seems very great to a man who has never seen a greater one; in this way does a man or a tree seem tall. Each man regards as colossal the greatest thing of each kind that he has seen, although all these, together with our sky and land and sea, are nothing when compared to the whole sum of the sum total.

I shall now explain the way in which that flame is stirred up and suddenly pours forth to the air from the high furnaces of Aetna.[39] First, the whole mountain is hollow beneath, supported for the most part on basalt vaults. Next, in all the caves there are wind and air; for wind is formed when air is stirred and set in motion.[40] When this has become hot and in its rage has heated all the rock and earth about it in touching them, and has struck from them swift flames of hot fire, then it rises and shoots forth on high straight through the mountain's jaws. So it carries its heat afar, scatters abroad its ashes and the billowing smoke that spreads thick darkness, and at the same time hurls out rocks of wondrous weight. Have no doubt that this is caused by the wild violence of air. Moreover, the sea hurls its breaking waves against much of the base of this mountain,[41] and in turn draws them back. From the sea the caverns of the mountain extend beneath, all the way to the lofty jaws. One must admit that along this route goes ⟨wind mixed with waves,⟩ which Nature forces ⟨to rise⟩ and plunge in from the open sea,[42] and then to blow out and in this way carry flame, scatter

680

690

700

[39] See Epicurus, *Letter to Pythocles* 106b.

[40] Lucretius regularly (e.g., III. 231–36) differentiates between wind and air. We should note that here he does not say that wind is air in motion, although to us that seems so obvious that we may take that as his meaning. He rather states that when air is set in motion some atomic change takes place through which the air ceases to exist as air and becomes wind.

[41] Specifically, Aetna, but all the volcanoes known to the Romans were on the coast.

[42] The text here is very doubtful. The translation follows Diels' suggested supplement. The probable meaning is that the waves breaking in the caverns at the foot of the mountain drive in air, sand, and rock, and force these up the crater. It is possible that Epicurus, in *Letter to Pythocles* 106b, referred to something of this sort; but the text there too is doubtful.

rock, and raise clouds of sand. For at the very top are the "bowls," as the Sicilians call them; but we call them "jaws" and "mouths."[43]

III. Individual Wonders

702–1089

Such particular phenomena as the annual overflow of the Nile, the "Avernian" places fatal to living creatures, the thermal curiosities of springs and fountains, may all be explained by any one of a number of possible causes. After a brief review of atomic theory, the poet goes on to discuss the nature of the magnet.

There are also certain phenomena for each of which it is not enough to state a single cause; instead, you must give several causes, in order that the one true cause may be among them.[e] For example, if you should see from a distance the lifeless body of a man lying, it would be proper for you to mention all the causes of death in order that the true cause might be named. For you would not be able to prove that he had died either from 710 the sword, from cold, from disease, or from poison; but we know that, whatever happened to him, it was something of this sort. Likewise in the case of many phenomena we are in a position to speak only in this way.

The Nile, the river of all Egypt, is the only river on earth to rise and top its banks as summer begins.[44] One possible reason

[43] The Greeks call these openings *kratēres*, literally "bowls." *Fauces* and *ora*, literally "jaws" and "mouths," are the regular Latin terms, which Lucretius elsewhere uses.

[44] Although the season of the flooding of the Nile, in late July and early August, is not discussed in the extant works of Epicurus, it was one of the standard problems of ancient geographers and physicists. Aristotle wrote a work on the subject, and Diodorus of Sicily (I. 37. 1–41. 10) has a long discussion in which he presents not only the theories found here in Lucretius but several others, assigns each to its author, and rejects them all.

that this river regularly floods Egypt in the midsummer is that in the summer the north winds, which at this season are called "etesian,"[45] are against its mouths. By blowing against the river they delay it, and by driving the waves up the stream they raise its level and force its flow to halt. For without doubt these gales are borne against the current, since they are driven from the cold stars of the pole, and the river itself comes from the south from the lands of heat, rising far inland among the races of mankind that are black with a color caused by burning, and flowing from the mid-region of the day.[46] It is also possible that when the sea, stirred by the wind, drives the sand in, a great heap of sand is piled up against the river mouths opposing the current. As a result of this, the outlet of the river is made less free at the same time that its outward flow is slackened by the waves. It may also happen that rainstorms occur at the source of the river just when the blasts of the etesian winds drive all the clouds together into that region. Indeed, one would expect this since, when the clouds driven to the south have assembled there and are crowded together against the high mountains, they are violently compacted and compressed.[47] Perhaps the river rises far away in the high mountains of the Ethiopians where the

720

730

45 Literally, "annual." These winds blow with great regularity from the north against the shores of Egypt for some six weeks each summer. The belief that the etesian winds caused the summer flooding of the Nile goes back at least to Thales. See Aetius, IV. 1. 1 = Diels, *Fragmente,* 11 A 16: "Thales thought that the etesian winds by blowing directly against the Egyptian coast raised the level of the Nile since its outflow was hindered by the contrary swelling of the opposite sea." So, too, Diodorus, I. 38. 1–3.

46 In another context "the mid-region of the day" or "the region of the midday" would mean no more than "the south," and it is so translated where it occurs in line 732 below; but here it forms a climax to "the lands of heat" and "the color caused by burning."

47 Under these conditions the clouds would give up their rain (see lines 510–12 above). This theory in regard to the Nile is ascribed to Democritus. Compare Aetius, IV. 1. 4 = Diels, *Fragmente,* 68 A 99: "Democritus said that when the snows in the north melt and dissolve at midsummer, thick clouds are formed from the mist. These are driven to the south against Egypt by the Etesian winds causing violent rains, which fill the lakes and the Nile." There is a fuller statement in Diodorus, I. 39. 1–6.

sun, shining upon all things with its melting rays, forces the white snow to flood down into the plains.[48]

Come now, I shall explain to you the nature that has been 740 given to places and lakes that are called Avernian. In the first place, as to their being called by the name Avernus,[49] that name is descriptive, since they are hostile to all birds; for when birds in flight come directly over these places, they forget the oarage of their wings, slack their sails, and with languid necks outstretched fall headlong to the earth, if that chance to be the nature of the spot, or to the water if Lake Avernus extends below them. This lake is near Cumae, where the mountains smoke, choked with pungent sulphur and supplied with hot springs.[50] 750 In the town of Athens at the very top of the Citadel by the temple of Tritonian Pallas, giver of life, there is a place to which raucous crows never speed their bodies on their wings, not even when the altars are smoking with offerings. They are not still fleeing from the wrath of Pallas, who, as the Greek poets have sung,[51] is bitter because of their spying; instead, the very nature of the place itself performs this task. In Syria too there is said to be seen a spot whose very force compels even four-footed beasts, as soon as they have placed their feet within it, to fall heavily as if they had suddenly been sacrified to the spirits of 760 the dead.[52] All these things happen for natural reasons, and the causes from which they are produced are visible. Therefore let no one believe that it is possible that the gates of Orcus are in these places, and let us not suppose that from these places the

[48] The theory of Anaxagoras. See Hippolytus, *Refutation of all Heresies* I. 8. 5 = Diels, *Fragmente,* 59 A 42: "The Nile floods in summer since it receives the water from the snows of the Antarctic [mss. arctic] region." Diodorus (I. 38. 4–7) says that Euripides agreed with Anaxagoras in this belief. This is the correct explanation of the summer floods.

[49] Popular etymology derived *Avernus* from the Greek word *aornos,* "birdless."

[50] Described by Virgil, *Aeneid* VI. 237–41.

[51] See Ovid, *Metamorphoses* II. 552–65.

[52] For various similar tales, see Pliny, *Natural History* II. 207–8.

gods of the dead draw souls after death down to the shores of Acheron, just as swift deer are thought by their breath to draw writhing snakes from their hiding places.[53] Learn how far removed from the truth this is; for I shall now endeavor to speak about the facts themselves.

To begin with, I say this which I have said often before: in the earth there are particles with shapes of every kind, many life-giving ones that serve as food, and many that can induce disease and hasten death.[54] And we have shown above that some are more suited to the manner of life of some creatures, others to that of others, because of differences in their natures, their composition, and the shapes of their atoms. Many unfavorable particles enter through our ears, and many that are hostile and harsh to the touch make their way through our nostrils; and the number is not small that are to be shunned by the sense of touch or avoided by that of sight, or that are painful to the taste. Next one may see how many things cause a man a most disagreeable sensation and are repulsive and noxious. First, such an evil shade is cast by certain trees that they regularly cause pains in the head if one lies down in the grass beneath them.[55] There is even a tree on the great mountains of Helicon that often kills a man by the noisome perfume of its blossoms. Truly all these rise in different places from the earth, inasmuch as it contains many seeds of many things mixed in many ways, and gives them forth separately. When the night lamp recently extinguished offends our nostrils with its irritating smell, at that very moment it puts to sleep the man who is subject to the

770

780

790

[53] See Aelian, *On the Nature of Animals* II. 9: "The deer . . . pressing its nostrils against the hiding place of a snake breathes into it very powerfully and by its breath as if by a charm attracts and brings forth the snake." The tale may rest on a popular etymology, *elaphos,* the Greek word for "deer," being derived from *helkein* (stem *helk-*), meaning "to drag," and *ophis,* "snake." The same power was sometimes ascribed to the elephant (Greek, *elephas),* probably for the same reason (Pliny, *Natural History* XI. 278).

[54] See, for example, II. 398–477, 581–99.

[55] Examples of such trees are given by Pliny, *Natural History* XVI. 51, 70, XVII. 89, 91. The tree of Helicon has not been identified.

disease that makes him fall prone and froth at the mouth.[56] If the odor of sluggish castor[57] comes to a woman at the time of her monthly flow, she is lulled and falls asleep, and the gleaming handiwork slips from her gentle hands. Many other things relax the sleepy members throughout the body, and make the mind within unsteady in its place. Then if you linger in a hot 800 bath when you have overeaten, how easily you collapse on your bench amid the hot water! How readily the strong, heavy stench of charcoal makes its way into the brain, unless we have taken water beforehand! But when a burning fever has seized upon the limbs and overpowered them,[58] then the smell of wine is like a mortal blow. Do you not likewise see that in the earth itself sulphur is formed and natural pitch forms a hard crust with an offensive odor? Then when men follow the veins of silver and gold, exploring with iron tools the hidden places far 810 within the earth, do you not see what stenches Scaptensula[59] then breathes forth from below? What poisons gold mines sometimes exhale! What an appearance, what a complexion do they give to men! Do you not see or hear in how short a time men usually die and lose their vital power, when the great force of necessity binds them to a task of this kind? All these exhalations, then, the earth emits and breathes forth into the open spaces beneath the clear sky.

So likewise the Avernian places must send out a force fatal 820 to birds, which rises from the earth into the air in such a way that it poisons for a certain distance the expanse of the sky. As soon as ever a bird has flown on its wings into this space, caught there by the hidden poison it is so checked that it falls straight down where the fumes direct. When it has fallen there,

[56] Aristotle, *History of Animals* VIII. 24, 604b29, Pliny, *Natural History* VII. 43, and Aelian, *On the Nature of Animals* IX. 54, speak of the effect of this on horses and women, but they say nothing about epileptics.

[57] Not our castor oil, but a secretion of the beaver used as a drug and as a base for perfumes.

[58] Reading *membra domans percepit fervida febris.* The text is doubtful and the meaning uncertain. Pliny (*Natural History* XXVII. 129) warns against giving certain medicines in wine to patients who have fever.

[59] A mining town in Thrace.

this same exhalation takes from all its members what life remains. For first it causes a certain dizziness, so to speak; then when the birds have fallen into the very source of the poison, there they are forced to pour forth their lives because a great mass of the poison is about them. Or it may happen sometimes 830 that the mighty exhalation of Avernus forces apart what air lies between the birds and the earth, so that this space is left almost empty. When in their flight the birds have come right above this place, at once the lifting power of their wings is crippled into uselessness, and all the effort of their pinions on either side is of no avail. When they are unable to support themselves and to rest on their wings, truly their own weight carries them to the earth; and as they float down in the all-but-empty void, their spirit passes out through all the pores of their bodies.[60]

. . . Again,[61] the water in wells becomes cooler in summer be- 840 cause the pores of the earth are opened by the heat, and the earth sends forth into the air whatever seeds of heat it has in itself. And so the more the earth is exhausted by the heat,[62] the colder becomes the water hidden in the earth. On the other hand, when the whole earth, overwhelmed by cold, contracts and, so to speak, congeals, it naturally follows that by contracting it drives into the wells whatever heat it itself contains.

It is said that at the shrine of Ammon there is a spring that is cold by day and hot at night.[63] Men wonder excessively at 850 this spring, and some think it becomes hot because of the heat

[60] They die before they reach the ground. The living element, which is held in the body by the pressure of the surrounding air, escapes when that pressure is removed. This seems to be a new theory in regard to life and death.

[61] The beginning of this discussion is lost in a lacuna, probably of some length, between lines 839 and 840.

[62] Or possibly: "exhausted by giving birth to the heat." In summer the pores on the earth's surface are open and its heat escapes into the air. In winter these are closed and the heat passes into the water of the well.

[63] This spring and its peculiarities are mentioned by Herodotus, IV. 181, and after him by several other Greek and Latin writers.

of the sun below the earth when night has covered the earth with terrifying darkness; but this is very far from the true explanation. Indeed, if the sun touching the exposed surface of the water is unable to make it hot on its upper side although its light then is in the air above, and its heat is so great, how can this sun, when beneath the earth, warm the water through the earth's dense body and revive it with burning heat, especially since the sun can scarcely transmit its warmth through the walls of houses even when its rays are blazing? What then is the reason? Surely it is because the earth is more porous about the spring than elsewhere, and because there are many seeds of fire near the water. Therefore, when night covers the earth with its dewy waves, the earth at once grows cold to its depths and contracts. From this it follows that the earth, just as if squeezed in the hand, forces out into the spring whatever seeds of fire it contains; and these make both the water and the steam that rises from it hot to the touch. Then when the risen sun separates the earth with its rays and makes it porous as the warm heat mingles with it, the first beginnings of fire resume their former positions and all the heat of the water returns to the earth. For this reason the spring is rendered cold in the light of day. Moreover the fluid water is buffeted by the rays of the sun and, as the day advances, is rarefied by the quivering heat; as a result, it loses what seeds of fire it possessed, just as water often loses the cold which it contains, melting and loosening the ice that bound it.

If tow is placed above a certain cold spring,[64] it catches fire and bursts into flame; in the same way, a torch is lighted and gleams over the waves, floating wherever it is driven by the wind. Surely this is because there are many seeds of heat in the water and because many particles of fire from the earth itself far below—yet not so many that the spring becomes hot—must rise through the whole spring, issue forth, and go out into the air. Next, a force compels them, although they are scattered

[64] Pliny (*Natural History* II, 228) tells of a cold spring at Dodona that extinguished torches thrust into it, but then ignited the same torches if they were held close to it. In this same passage Pliny describes the spring at Ammon mentioned in the last section.

through the water, to burst out and to gather together above. In this way there is a spring in the sea at Aradus that sends forth 890 a stream of sweet water and drives apart the salt waves that surround it; and in many other places the sea offers a welcome resource to thirsty sailors because it pours forth fresh waters amid the salt.[65] So also the seeds of heat can burst through the spring and flow out. When they gather together in the tow or cling to the torch, they easily burst into flame of a sudden, for the tow and the torch, too, have and hold in themselves many seeds of fire. Do you not also see that when you move a recently 900 extinguished wick toward a lamp at night, the wick is kindled before it touches the flame, and that a torch is also kindled in the same way? Many things in addition, touched by heat alone, burst into flame at a distance before fire enters them from close at hand. This happens also in the case of that spring.

Finally, I shall undertake to explain by what law of Nature it is that iron can be attracted by the stone that the Greeks call the magnet (taking that name from its place of origin since it comes from the lands of the Magnetes).[66] Men regard this stone 910 as a miracle. Indeed, it often makes a chain from rings hanging to it. One may see five rings, or sometimes more, swinging like a pendant in the gentle breeze, where one hangs down from another to which it clings, and each acknowledges the binding force of the stone transmitted to it through its neighbor; to such an extent does its force penetrate and prevail. But in a case of this sort many principles must be firmly grasped before you can

[65] Pliny (*Natural History* II. 227) mentions several such fresh springs rising in salt water. In the present section we do not have two alternative explanations but explanations of two successive steps, each with one illustration. The seeds of heat pass through the cold water without heating it as in certain places in the sea fresh water passes up through salt without there being any mixture. The tow catches fire readily because it contains seeds of fire as do recently extinguished torches, which burst into flame when held close to a source of heat.

[66] Some ancient authorities say that the magnetic stones were first found near Magnesia in Macedon, others that they came from another Magnesia in Lydia. It is also stated that the name came from the first man to discover the properties of the magnet, Magnes.

give an explanation of the particular phenomenon, and you must approach the problem by a path with many turnings;
920 therefore I demand attentive ears and mind.

First, from all visible objects bodies that strike our eyes and arouse the sense of sight must flow, be sent forth, and be scattered. From certain things odors ceaselessly flow; so too cold comes from rivers, heat from the sun, and from the waves of the sea comes the spray that eats away the dikes along the shores; without interruption various sounds flow through the air. When we wander by the sea, moisture of a salty taste comes to our
930 mouths; and on the other hand, when we watch as wormwood is diluted and mixed, its bitterness touches us. So from each thing its proper effluence arises in a flood, and these effluences are sent in every direction and from every side; nor is there any pause or rest in their flow, for we are continuously experiencing sensations and may see and smell all things and hear them sound.[67]

Now I shall tell again how porous all things are, a fact that is also made clear at the beginning of this poem.[68] Although this knowledge is pertinent to many things, in immediate con-
940 nection with the subject that I am about to discuss it is especially necessary for us to establish firmly that nothing exists in the visible world except body mixed with void. First, in caves the rocks above sweat with moisture, and are bedewed with trickling drops. Likewise, perspiration exudes from our whole bodies; beards and hair grow throughout all our members and limbs. Our food passes into all our veins, causes the growth of the most distant parts of our bodies even to the nails, and supplies them with nourishment. We feel cold and burning heat
950 pass through bronze; we feel them pass through gold and silver when we are holding full cups.[69] Then voices fly through the

[67] Lines 923–35 are repeated with minor changes from IV. 217–29.

[68] See I. 329–69.

[69] See I. 494–96. We must remember that to Lucretius cold and heat were corporeal. We feel the chill of the liquid poured into the cup because seeds of cold have passed from the liquid through the fabric of the cup into our hands.

stone walls of houses; smells,[70] cold, and the heat of fire find their way in; and fire is accustomed to penetrate even the hardness of iron. Finally, where the vault of heaven bounds ⟨our world, seeds of storm penetrate;⟩ so too ⟨does⟩ the might of disease when it comes from outer space;[71] and storms springing up in earth or sky are naturally carried off and make their way, respectively, into sky and earth. All this is possible because no thing exists that is not fashioned with an open-textured body.

Furthermore, the seeds that are given off from objects do not all produce the same effects and are not all equally fitted to all things. As the first example, the sun bakes the soil and makes it dry, but it changes ice to water and with its rays forces the melting of the deeply drifted snow on the high mountains. Wax too melts when placed in the heat of the sun. Likewise fire turns bronze into a liquid and melts gold, but it shrivels hides and flesh and draws them together. Finally, water hardens iron when it comes from the fire, but it softens hides and flesh when they have been made stiff by heat. The wild olive is as pleasing to bearded goats as if it gave forth the odor of ambrosia and were steeped in nectar, but, to a man, nothing that grows is more bitter than this leaf. Finally, the pig avoids marjoram and shuns every perfume; for that which seems almost to give us new life is a bitter poison to the bristly swine. On the other hand, the same mire that to us is the foulest filth is seen to be so pleasing to the pigs that they bury themselves entire in it again and again without being satisfied.[72] 960 970

This one thing remains that it seems must be said before I begin to speak about the subject in hand itself. Since many pores have been distributed to various things, these pores must 980

[70] In IV. 699 we are told that smells do not pass through solids, which is probably Lucretius' real opinion.

[71] Both text and meaning are very doubtful. I have translated the supplement suggested by Bailey in his note but not printed in his text. Other editors make changes in the words of the transmitted text without assuming a lacuna.

[72] See IV. 633–72. In this earlier passage Lucretius has nothing to say about inanimate things; and he gives fuller explanations, which here are postponed to lines 979–97 where they are given in a more general form.

be endowed with unlike characters, with each kind having its own nature and its own type of opening. For example, there are various senses in living creatures, each of which receives to itself that which is proper to it. We perceive that sound enters by one route, the taste of juices by another, and by another the
990 smell of a scent.[73] Moreover, we see that one emanation passes through rock and one through wood, another goes through gold, another makes its way through silver and still another through glass. Along this passage sight is seen to pass; along that passage, heat; and one effluence goes through one passage more readily than does another. As we have shown a little above, this is brought about since the nature of the passages differs in many ways, because of the unlike nature and structure of things.

Now that all these principles, previously settled, have been
1000 reaffirmed and brought to mind, it will be easy to set forth in full the theory of the magnet and the cause of the iron's being attracted. In the first place, from this lodestone very many seeds must flow, an effluence that by its blows thrusts aside whatever air lies between the stone and the iron. When this space is cleared and a large area between them has been made empty, at once the atoms of the iron, slipping forward together, fall into the vacant space, and naturally the ring itself follows and moves with its whole body. Nothing bound together by the in-
1010 terweaving of its atoms holds together more strongly than the iron with its chill, rough might. Since it is led on by its elements,[74] there is little wonder that, when many bodies together spring from the iron, they cannot be carried into the empty space without the ring itself following.[f] This it does, and it follows until it comes to the stone itself and adheres to it by hidden fastenings. This same thing happens in any direction. On whatever side space has been made empty, the bodies next to

[73] Lines 988 and 989, which are repeated by lines 995 and 996 below, are omitted, and the line that follows them in the manuscript is transferred to the end of the section, where it appears as line 997.

[74] The text is very uncertain. The manuscripts read *quod dicitur ex elementis.* I translate Bailey's *quod ducitur ex elementis.* Martin gives *quod dicitur esse alienum,* "which is said to be strange."

this void are carried into it, whether it be to the side or upward, 1020
driven by blows from the opposite side,[75] for surely they themselves cannot, by their own power, rise up together into the air. Moreover, this may take place all the more easily, since the motion is aided and assisted by the fact that, as soon as the air in front of the ring is made thinner and the space becomes more empty and vacant, at once whatever air lies behind the ring at the back carries it forward, so to speak, and thrusts it on. The air that surrounds a thing is always beating upon it; but in such a situation as this the air drives the iron forward because space 1030
lies open on one side only and receives the iron into itself. This air of which I am speaking to you, making its way through the many pores of the iron into its minute parts, pushes it and drives it as the wind drives a ship and its sails.[76] Finally, all things must contain air within their structure, for their bodies are porous and air surrounds and encloses everything. This air, then, which is buried far within the iron, is always tossed about in restless motion, and there is no doubt that for that reason it buffets the ring and keeps it in inner turmoil. Naturally the 1040
ring is carried in the direction in which it has already been set in motion and has made a start—that is, toward the empty space.[77]

It sometimes happens that iron withdraws from the stone, and is accustomed to be repelled and attracted alternately.[g] I have seen Samothracian iron[78] and iron filings dance about in

[75] The atoms of iron on the side toward the void created by the magnet are forced into that void by the pressure of the other atoms in the iron.

[76] The second explanation (lines 1022–30), in which the ring as a whole seems to be moving into the void, is now (lines 1031–33) restated in atomic terms. The air as a whole does not actually act on the ring as a whole, but the atoms of air penetrating the ring act on the atoms of iron in the ring.

[77] Lines 1034–41 probably mean nothing more than that the motion of the iron atoms and therefore the motion of the whole ring is made easier by the presence within the ring of moving atoms of air.

[78] Literally, "iron ⟨things⟩ of Samothrace." If Lucretius saw them acting like the iron filings of the next line, they must have been iron in some finely divided form, and hardly the "Samothracian iron rings" of the usual translation.

a bronze basin when a magnet was held beneath it, so clearly is the iron seen to avoid the lodestone.[h] Such great discord is created when the bronze is interposed for the reason that, without
1050 a doubt, when the effluences of the bronze have reached the iron first and occupied its opened passages, those of the lodestone coming later find all the spaces in the iron full, and have no way to penetrate as they could before. The stone must therefore beat upon the texture of the iron with its emanations and thrust it back. In this way, through the bronze, it repels and drives back that which, without the bronze, it normally attracts.[i] In this connection do not wonder that the effluences are not able to repel other things from the stone in the same way. Some things are unmoved because of their weight; an example of this is gold. Other things can never be repelled because they are of such
1060 porous structure that the emanations pass through them without making contact; we see that wood is of this class. When iron, which lies between these two, admits certain particles of bronze, the result is that the magnet stone repels the iron with its emanations.

Adhesion of this kind is not so foreign to other things that only a few parallel examples of substances adapted only to each other are available for me to cite. Stones are joined only by lime. Pieces of wood are held together so firmly by bull's glue[79]
1070 that the grain of a board often splits in a crack before the joints made with bull's glue can release their grip. The liquid wine dares to be mixed with water, but heavy pitch and light oil cannot be so mixed.[80] The purple dye of the shellfish is so joined with the substance of wool that it can never be separated from it, not even if you try to restore it with Neptune's stream; no, not if the whole sea tried to wash it out with all its waves. Does not one single material[81] join gold to gold? Is it not true that

[79] Glue is still made from scraps of hide, bones, and slaughterhouse waste in general.

[80] Alexander, just after the passage quoted in appendix note *i* (p. 285), says that Empedocles made this same statement about water, wine and oil (Diels, *Fragmente*, 31 B 91).

[81] This substance, called by the Greeks *chrysocolla*, "gold glue," has not been certainly identified.

bronze is joined to bronze by white lead?[82] How many other examples can be found! But to what purpose? You have no need of such long involved illustrations, and it is not fitting for me to spend so much labor on this point; it is better to encompass many things briefly in a few words. It is clear that those things are best joined whose contours fit together, each to each, in such a fashion that hollows and projections of their respective surfaces fit together. For it is even possible that certain things can be held joined to one another and intertwined as if with rings and hooks. We see that this is what happens in the joining of the magnet and the iron. 1080

IV. Pestilence

1090–1286

The poet explains the causes and nature of pestilence, such as the great plague that came to Athens from Egypt, and the poem concludes with a detailed description of the miseries and terror of the Athenian plague.

I shall now explain what is the cause of plague and from what source an unwholesome power may suddenly accumulate, producing a death-dealing disaster for the human race and the herds of domesticated beasts. First, I have shown above that there are seeds of many things that give us life; and, on the other hand, many seeds must fly about that are sources of disease and death. When by some chance the latter are gathered together and disturb the sky, the air below becomes diseased. All that force of disease and pestilence either comes from outside this world like clouds and mist through the sky from above, or else it gathers together and rises from the earth itself when the earth, damp from excessive rains and heated by too much sun, has become corrupt. Do you not see that those who travel far from their homes and native lands are attacked by disease on account of the changes in the climate and the water, merely because conditions are far different? For what difference do we 1090 1100

[82] That is, tin.

think there is between the climate of the Britons and that found in Egypt, where the axis of the world is crippled and aslant?[83] Or in what way do we think that that which is in Pontus differs from that at Gades and far away among the races of mankind 1110 that are black with a color caused by burning?[84] Not only do we see that these four lands in the four directions beneath the four quarters of the sky are different from each other, but also the complexions and features of their inhabitants are very different, and diseases attack each of the various races after its own kind.[85] There is elephantiasis, which occurs beside the Nile in the middle of Egypt, and never elsewhere. Gout is common in Athens, and ophthalmia among the Achaeans.[86] So one place is unfavorable to one part or member, another to another. The differing climate brings this about. Then when a sky that is foreign to 1120 us moves in and when an unfriendly air begins to drift about us, it creeps slowly like clouds and mist, confusing everything where it passes and forcing everything to change. When it finally comes into our sky, it corrupts that, making it like to itself, and alien to us.[87] Thus suddenly this strange disaster and pestilence either falls into the sources of water, or enters into the grain itself or the other kinds of food and fodder for men and beasts; or else this power remains suspended in the air itself, and when the breath we inhale in breathing has this air 1130 mixed in with it, we must at the same time also draw these ma-

[83] Anaxagoras, Leucippus, and Democritus had all taught that the earth tips up at the north and down at the south (see Diels, *Fragmente*, 59 A 67, 67 A 27, 68 A 96).

[84] Since in the fourfold division Gades represents the west, Lucretius seems here to be thinking of the colored races as living beyond Gades, that is, down the African coast. In line 722 above, he places them far to the south of Egypt on the headwaters of the Nile.

[85] This belief was quite generally held, and was one point on which Stoics and Epicureans were agreed (see, for example, Cicero, *On Divination* I. 79, II. 96).

[86] Although elephantiasis is found in other tropical countries, it is quite possible that the Romans knew it only in Egypt (see Pliny, *Natural History* XXVI. 8). There is no support for either of the other statements.

[87] In this passage Lucretius is probably thinking of the pestilence-causing air that comes into our world from outer space (see lines 1098–99 above).

lignant powers into our bodies. In the same way pestilence and distemper come also to the cattle and even to the lazy sheep. It makes no difference whether we go to the places that are unhealthful for us and change the sky that covers us, or whether Nature herself brings to us, of her own accord, a sky that is corrupt or something else to which we are not accustomed that can afflict us as soon as it arrives.

This kind of disease and deadly emanation in the territory of Cecrops once filled the fields with dead, made the roads desolate, and drained the city of its people.[88] Coming from far away, having risen in the lands of Egypt and made a long passage through the air and over the expanse of the sea, it finally settled upon the whole folk of Pandion. The people in crowds were given over to the pestilence and to death. First, each felt his head burning with fever, and his two eyes inflamed with burning heat. The throat sweated blood and turned black on the inside, and the passageway of the voice was blocked, choked up with ulcers. The tongue, the spokesman of the mind, becoming weakened by pain, sluggish in motion, and rough to the touch, dripped blood. Next, when the violence of the disease, passing through the throat, had filled the breast and gathered in the wretched heart of the victim, the very fastnesses of life were shaken. The breath sent forth through the mouth a foul odor like that which comes from bodies that decay where they lie unburied. Next, the vital power of the whole mind and the entire body collapsed at the very door of death.

1140

1150

Bitter anguish was the constant companion of unbearable pain, and lamentations were mingled with the groans. Often through night and day repeated retching, constantly forcing the tendons and limbs to contract, would break men down, exhaust-

1160

[88] Cecrops and Pandion were mythical kings of Athens. The pestilence here described is that which descended upon Athens in the second year of the Peloponnesian War. In describing it Lucretius has drawn heavily and constantly (although sometimes inaccurately) upon the famous account in Thucydides, II. 47–52. In spite of Thucydides' factual account, the pestilence has not been identified. Identification is even less possible in Lucretius' more emotional and rhetorical description.

ing those who were already wasted. You could perceive that on the surface of the body the skin was not heated with excessive fever but rather felt warm to the hands, and at the same time the whole body was red as if with scars of ulcers, as happens when erysipelas is spread over the limbs. But the inner parts of a man, clear to the bones, were on fire; fire burned in his stomach as
1170 if within a furnace. No one of them could endure anything, however thin and light, covering his body; they always sought for the cool air.[89] Some of them threw their limbs burning with the pestilence into chilly streams, hurling their naked bodies into the waves. Many cast themselves headlong, deep into the water of wells,[90] falling with their very mouths agape. A parching thirst that could not be quenched, pervading their bodies, made a great draught seem like a few drops.

There was no relief from pain; their bodies lay exhausted. In
1180 silent fear the healing art had naught to say, while men rolled back and forth so many times their staring eyes, burning with fever and bereft of sleep. Then, moreover, many signs of death were given: the mind tormented with grief and fear, the brow gloomy, the face frenzied and pinched, the ears tortured and ringing with noise, the breath rapid or drawn in deep, infrequent gasps, the neck wet with glistening sweat, and small bits of salty, yellow phlegm painfully raised through the throat with
1190 a harsh cough. The sinews of the hands contracted without ceasing, the limbs shivered, and a chill ascended slowly but surely from the feet. Then finally at the last moment, the nostrils were pinched together; the top of the nose became sharp and thin, the eyes sunken, the temples depressed, the skin cold and hard, the mouth open with lips drawn back, the forehead drawn and puffy. Soon their limbs lay there in cold death. For the most part they gave up their lives on the eighth day, or sometimes on the ninth. If one of them, as did sometimes hap-
1200 pen, avoided the destruction of death at this point, yet death

89 A free paraphrase. Literally: "Nothing however thin and light could you turn to the advantage of any one for his limbs, but only wind and coldness."

90 With most editors, line 1178 of the manuscripts is placed after line 1173.

still awaited him as he wasted away with foul ulcers and a black discharge from the belly, or even repeated pains in the head and a copious flow of impure blood from his choked nostrils; in this all the strength and flesh of the body flowed away together. If a man survived the violent discharge of foul blood, the disease nevertheless passed into his sinews and members, and into the private parts of his body. In deadly fear at the gates of death, some survived with their genitals cut off by the knife, some remained alive without hands and feet, and some 1210 lost their eyes[91]—so sharply had fear of death come upon them. Forgetfulness of all things laid hold of some of them, and they could not even recognize themselves.

Although many unburied bodies lay heaped upon one another on the ground, yet birds and beasts of every kind either darted away to escape the vile stench or, when they had tasted, collapsed in swiftly approaching death. But yet hardly any bird appeared on those days, nor did the cruel breeds of wild 1220 beasts come out of the forests. Many of them too were weak with the pestilence, and were dying. In particular, the faithful dogs lying about in all the streets gave up their lives after a struggle; for the violence of the disease tore the life from their limbs.

Unattended and deserted, funerals contended with each other in speed.[92]

No one method of cure was found that was certain and beneficial to all alike; for that which had made it possible for one to draw into his mouth the life-giving air and to gaze upon the regions of the sky, was fatal for others and hastened their death. Under these conditions this thing, beyond all others, was ex- 1230 ceedingly pitiable and full of anguish: when a man saw that he was afflicted by the pestilence, losing courage just as if he had been condemned to death, he dropped down with despair-

91 In Thucydides the loss of parts of the body is usually interpreted as the direct result of the disease, but may possibly be due to surgery. In Lucretius it may be the result of surgery, but the context certainly suggests that it is mutilation self-inflicted in fear of death. For the thought, see III. 79–81.

92 Some editors place this line, which seems out of place here, in the lacuna that follows line 1246.

ing heart and, foreseeing his own end, gave up life on the spot. For at no time did the contagion of greedy death cease to seize upon them one after another, like woolly sheep or herds of cattle. And this in particular heaped death upon death: for if 1240 any, too greedy for life and fearful of dying, shunned visiting their friends who were sick, lack of care from others soon punished them, destroying them, deserted and without help, by a shameful and evil death. But those who attended others died from contagion and from the labor they were forced to undergo by shame and by the pleading voices of the weary and their words of lamentation. Thus all the most noble met ends of this kind.

. . . one upon another, striving to bury the host of their own kin.[93] Worn out with tears and grief they returned, and many 1250 of them threw themselves on their beds in sorrow; no one could be found at a time like this unassailed by pestilence, death, or grief.

Moreover every shepherd, herdsman, and stalwart guide of the curved plow fell sick, and their bodies, surrendered to death by poverty and disease, lay thrust into their huts. You might see corpses of parents heaped on dead children, or children breathing out their lives on the bodies of fathers and mothers. To no small extent it was from the fields that this affliction took 1260 its course into the city, brought there by the throng of farmers who assembled, weak and diseased, from every side.[94] They filled every place and every building; and all the more for this reason, packed together in the heat, death piled them in heaps. Scattered about were many bodies of those who had been cut down by thirst upon the streets and beside the fountains of water, their breath shut off by their too great eagerness for the drink; and here and there, through the public places of the

[93] This section begins with a lacuna. It is probable that line 1225 belongs here somewhere, but more than that is needed to explain the words with which line 1247 opens. Martin follows Bockenmüller in transferring the five lines to the end of the poem.

[94] In Athens the overcrowding of the city by the country people was not the result of the pestilence, but of Spartan raids.

people and through the streets, you might see many fallen with weakened limbs and half-dead bodies, rough with dirt and covered with rags, perishing in their own filth, mere skin stretched over bones, already all but buried under ulcerous sores and dirt. Death filled all the sacred shrines of the gods with lifeless bodies, and every temple of the celestial ones was crowded with random corpses—the very places that the wardens used to fill with guests. For now there was no reverence for the worship of the gods or for the gods themselves; the present sorrow overwhelmed all this. The funeral customs of the city, according to which before that day men had always been buried, no longer prevailed; for the whole people was confused and panic-stricken, and each in his grief buried his own dead as best he could. Press of time and poverty persuaded to many dreadful deeds; for with much lamentation they placed their dead kindred upon the pyres heaped up for others and applied the torch beneath, often rioting with much bloodshed rather than abandoning the bodies.

1270

1280

APPENDIX NOTES

APPENDIX NOTES

Introduction

Note *a,* p. ix. Except for Thales, all of these philosophers wrote books. None of these survive, and we are dependent for our knowledge of them upon citations made from their writings by later writers whose works we have and the more voluminous comments (usually hostile) upon their theories made by these same authors. The standard collection of the "fragments" (quotations preserving more or less exactly the actual words) and *testimonia* (less direct citations and discussions) is Hermann Diels, *Die Fragmente der Vorsokratiker,* 10th edition by Walter Kranz. (For this and the other books mentioned in this note, see the Bibliography, pages xxxvi–xl.) The fragments have been translated by Kathleen Freeman in her *Ancilla to the Pre-Socratic Philosophers.* Standard works in English on the pre-Socratic philosophers are Kirk and Raven, *The Presocratic Philosophers;* J. Burnet, *Early Greek Philosophy;* and Cyril Bailey, *The Greek Atomists and Epicurus.*

Note *b,* p. xxii. See note *c* below. Accounts of the life and teachings of Epicurus will be found in any of the standard histories of Greek philosophy. The most important recent work on Epicurus has been done by Italian scholars. The most important works in English are Cyril Bailey, *The Greek Atomists and Epicurus;* Norman W. DeWitt, *Epicurus and His Philosophy;* and B. Farrington, *Science and Politics in the Ancient World.* For more about these, see the Bibliography, pp. xxxvi–xxxix.

Note *c,* p. xxii. The only complete edition, including the papyrus fragments from Herculaneum as well as the fragments preserved through literary sources, is that of Graziano Arrighetti; this contains the Greek text, an Italian translation, and a commentary, also in Italian. Bailey, *Epicurus: the Extant Remains,* contains only a few of the chief fragments together with the *Letters* and the *Principal Doctrines.* This edition includes a commentary and an English translation. The Greek text and an English translation of the *Letters* and the *Principal Doctrines* will also be found in R. D. Hicks's edition of Diogenes Laertius, *Lives of Eminent Philosophers,* Vol. II, in the Loeb Classical Library. My own translation (Liberal Arts Press) contains the three *Letters,* the *Principal Doctrines,* and the *Vatican Sayings,* and is accompanied by an introduction and commentary intended for readers with no knowledge of either Greek or Latin. In the notes of the present work I have sometimes referred to the notes of that translation.

Note *d,* p. xxxi. For many years the standard edition of Lucretius, at least for the English-speaking world, was that by H. A. J. Munro, first published in 1864; the fourth and last edition, in three volumes, appeared in 1886 and was reprinted several times. This has been superseded by the three-volume edition by Cyril Bailey (Oxford, 1947). Less pretentious is the edition by Leonard and Smith (Madison, Wis., 1942). The editions by Munro and by Bailey have translations in English prose, and all three have commentaries in English. For brief comments on these see the Bibliography, pp. xl.

Book One

Note *a,* p. 22. Two explanations of this paragraph seem possible. Later Lucretius will explain that every object is constantly receiving atoms from without and also losing them. In the case of living creatures growth continues as long as more atoms are received than are lost. Here he may be arguing that if matter is infinitely divisible and if destruction is more rapid than growth, the smallest particles will become constantly smaller, and over the years will have become so minute that growth either will require a very long time or will become impossible. Or he may be referring to the successive births and growth of individuals of a species. If a rose takes six months to grow from atoms of a given size and six weeks to decay into atoms of the same size, and if at that point disintegration stops, atoms of the given size will always be at hand for producing new roses. But if the division goes on without end, the particles available for the growth of roses will become smaller and smaller and the time required for growth will become longer and longer.

Note *b*, p. 23. The earlier atomic philosophers had differed on the size of the atom. Leucippus seems to have argued that the atom was indestructible because it had no parts (Diels, *Fragmente,* 67 A 13), which was open to the objection that what has no parts has no extension and therefore no material existence. Democritus did not stress the smallness of the atoms, which, he said, were unlimited in size as well as in number (Diels, *Fragmente,* 68 A 1.44; Laertius, *Lives of Eminent Philosophers* IX. 44); but in that case some atoms would be visible. Epicurus held that the atoms differed from each other in size and form but were all so small as to be invisible. According to him, the differences in size and shape are caused by differences in the number and arrangement of the least parts; but these least parts do not exist separately and the atom is the smallest individual unit (*Letter to Herodotus* 56b–59). Munro assumed that in the present paragraph Lucretius followed Epicurus' argument for the existence of the least parts (57b–58) and that at least two lines have been lost after line 599. He suggested a supplement with which the text could be translated as follows: "Next, since there is an extreme point ⟨in sensible bodies which is the least that can be seen by us, there must also be an extreme point⟩ of that atom which our senses cannot discern; this surely is without parts. . . ." Compare lines 749–52 below, where Lucretius states the argument in somewhat fuller form.

Note *c,* p. 23. Lucretius here is appealing to common sense and at the same time tacitly relying on the Euclidean axiom that the whole is greater than any of its parts; but in Book Two he will argue that although the number of different atomic shapes is finite (II. 478–521) the number of atoms of each shape is infinite (II. 522–68). If infinities are equal, the number of atoms of each shape is equal to the number of atoms of all the shapes, and the part is equal to the whole, which here he calls absurd. Actually, the statement that the whole is greater than any of its parts is true of finite but not of infinite values. For example, the series 1, 2, 3, 4, 5, 6, . . . and the series 2, 4, 6, . . . each contain an infinite and therefore equal number of terms, but the second series is clearly a part of the first. See addendum, p. 285.

Note *d,* p. 29. We do not know of any school holding this exact theory. Heraclitus believed that fire was basic and that there was a constant, evenly balanced change from fire to water to earth, and back from earth to water to fire (see Introduction, pp. x–xi, and Kirk and Raven, pp. 196–201); but air does not form part of his series. When Lucretius uses the indefinite third person plural, as he does here, he often means the Stoics; and it is possible that some of them, accepting fire as the basic substance as did Heraclitus, tried to combine this with the four elements of Empedocles. This is made more probable by a passage in Cicero, *On the Nature of the Gods* II. 84, where a Stoic is represented as saying:

> Since there are four kinds of bodies, the world is maintained by their interchanges. For water is formed from earth, air from water, and the aether from the air; then backward in turn, air from aether, then water, and from water the earth below. So, as these elements from which all things are formed go up and down and to and fro, the earth is held by the joining of the parts.

Note *e,* p. 32. Following Lambinus and many later editors I omit line 873: "Moreover whatever bodies the earth nourishes and increases." This interrupts the construction and is certainly out of place here. It may be an alternate version of line 867, which has in some way gained a position here; or it may belong after 874. In that case it must have been followed by lines now lost, and the paragraph may have ended in some such way as this: "Moreover whatever bodies the earth nourishes and increases must themselves be made up of parts unlike themselves, that is, of earth; and the earth too will be made up of alien parts."

Note *f*, p. 32. If we place a period at this point, that which precedes would remain as it is, but we would continue: "In the same way when we rub green vegetables on a stone with a stone, blood ought to ooze forth; and pools of water ought to give forth drops, sweet and of a savor like that of the rich milk of sheep. When clods. . . ." The text of the words describing the milk is doubtful, but the general meaning is clear.

Note *g*, p. 33. Here after the criticism of former theories and before the new theme of the infinity of the universe is introduced, Lucretius pauses for what is really a second proem. Lines 926–50 will be found again at the beginning of Book Four. This is the longest of many repetitions in the poem, and has been the occasion of much discussion. The statement of Lucretius' purpose in writing is certainly more suitable for an early position in the work. It might well have been incorporated in the proem of this book, had that not already been long. It seems probable that Lucretius wrote these lines for their present position in Book One. They were then added at the beginning of Book Four either by Lucretius himself as a stopgap pending the composition of an introduction for that book, or by someone else if Lucretius died leaving Book Four with no proem. The lines seem to have been known in both places in antiquity.

Note *h*, p. 35. It has been objected that the spearman and his spear show that the universe is boundless as the surface of a sphere is boundless, but not that it is infinite. It it true that Lucretius' example is expressed in terms of two dimensions, but, *mutatis mutandis*, the argument could be applied in three dimensions as well. However if, as modern physics seems to teach, the universe has a fourth dimension—time—then the human spearman, capable of hurling his spear in only three dimensions, could prove only that the universe is boundless, not that it is infinite. See the articles by C. J. Keyser and E. Lasker in *Scripta Mathematica*, IV (1936), 232–34, and V (1938), 121–23.

Note *i*, p. 37. Instead of writing correctly the last half of this line, the scribe of the manuscript from which all the extant manuscripts descend repeated the last half of line 1022. The correction in this case is easy, since lines 1021–25 appear again at V. 419–23.

Note *j*, p. 37. While the view that our cosmos or world (i.e., the earth and the heavenly bodies that appear to revolve about it) was a spherical system set in empty space may go back in its simplest form to Parmenides, Lucretius here is certainly attacking it as the belief of the Stoics. Zeno, for example, said:

> All parts of the cosmos tend toward its center, this being particularly true of the heavier bodies. This is the reason that the cosmos retains its position in infinite space and the earth its place in the cosmos, since it is drawn to its place by a force operating in equal strength all about the center. But matter does not have weight under all conditions, air and fire lacking weight. But these too are drawn toward the center of the sphere of the cosmos and take their positions on its periphery, for they naturally rise to the surface [i.e., they are forced away from the center] due to their lack of weight [Stobaeus, *Eclogae* I. 19. 4].

Note *k*, p. 38. Lines 1068–75 are preserved in mutilated form in one of our chief manuscripts. Line 1068 lacks about the last half, while of each subsequent line a little more is preserved; line 1075 lacks only the final word. This same manuscript leaves space sufficient for eight lines where 1094–1101 should have been written. The other manuscript simply marks a lacuna at each of these places. Both the manuscripts are indirect copies of the same archetype, and it is clear that the upper corner of a leaf of this archetype had been torn off. When the scribe of the manuscript from which the first of the extant pair was copied came to this torn leaf he wrote down as much as remained of the lines on the first side of the leaf; but when he came to the other side where the beginnings of the lines were missing, he simply left a space. The scribe of the other manuscript or of the intermediate copy was content merely to mark a lacuna without indicating its length. From this and similar evidence Lachmann argued that the archetype had twenty-six lines to the page (see

Appendix note *d*, p. 268). Certain restoration of lines 1068–75 is impossible, but the supplements translated give the required sense. There is naturally much more doubt about lines 1094–1101.

Note *l*, p. 39. For the lacuna that follows, see Appendix note *k* above. There is some evidence that the Stoics connected fire with vegetable and animal growth, and there may have been reference to this in the first of the missing lines.

Note *m*, p. 39. The lacuna makes it impossible to establish any connection with what precedes. In the translation I am assuming that the criticism of Stoic teaching has ended, and that in a concluding paragraph the poem restates what has already been said at the beginning of this section (lines 1014–15). But it is also possible that he is here describing what would happen under the Stoic system (as he understands it) when air and fire, rising upward, reach the walls of the world (line 1102) and, being unopposed, burst through it.

Book Two

Note *a*, p. 43. It is possible that Democritus believed that the atoms lost some or all of their motion when they joined together to form a solid, or that in some way the motion of the atoms was converted into the motion of the solid as a whole. If the atoms did cease their motion in this way, it is uncertain how they recovered it. According to Epicurus and Lucretius the atoms never lose their motion, and this motion, even in what we call a solid body, is always through empty space. The physical philosophers following Parmenides had trouble in explaining the origin of motion. It is certain that Leucippus, followed by Democritus, made random motion one of the original attributes of the atoms along with shape, size, and mass, requiring explanation no more than did the very existence of the atoms. Epicurus certainly insisted that the atoms continued their motions with undiminished velocity, even in the hardest substances. For the earlier theories see Bailey, *Greek Atomists,* pp. 83–90, 129–37, and Kirk and Raven, *Presocratic Philosophers,* pp. 404–20.

Note *b,* p. 44. In the last part of this paragraph Lucretius describes three possible consequences of atomic collisions. Obviously there will be many gradations between the first and the second. In each case the colliding atoms rebound in new directions without loss of velocity (see note 5, p. 43). Sometimes, however, their shapes are such that the separation is not complete, and the atoms come together again and again, or in some way combine their motions into a single harmony, forming a solid. We might say that such atoms have an "affinity" for each other. Fluids and gases result when the affinity is not so strong and the atoms rebound to greater distances after colliding, but still return. Epicurus describes such fluids as contained within an invisible, self-formed membrane or envelope, which one is tempted to compare with "surface tension" (*Letter to Herodotus* 43). Finally, most atoms after colliding go off on completely independent courses, that is, they remain free atoms. We are told that for some reason these are not suitable to enter into any complex with other atoms.

That all matter, whether solid, liquid, or gas, consists of particles in motion is accepted today. Lucretius would agree with the essential points of the following:

> The evidence . . . leads us to believe that the molecules of all matter are in motion. This doctrine, known as the kinetic theory of matter, receives its support from the experimental confirmation of its predictions. The average distance which a molecule travels between successive collisions with its neighbors is called its *mean free path.* In solids, the mean free path is very short, the molecules resembling on a minute scale people in a very densely packed crowd. Each individual can move slightly, but his motion is restricted by contact with his fellows to the immediate neighborhood of a mean position. In liquids, the mean free path is longer than in solids; and, with many collisions, molecules may wander through the entire mass like dancers in a crowded ball room. In gasses, a mole-

cule's mean free path is relatively very large [Frank L. Robeson, *Physics,* Macmillan, 1943, p. 226, quoted by permission].

Note *c,* p. 44. The individual atom is too small to be seen and moves with a velocity beyond the reach of our senses. When it strikes a complex of atoms or attaches itself to such a complex, the larger body is moved, its velocity being less than that of the free atoms (see next section and Appendix note *d*). It in turn strikes or joins other larger bodies, which are moved with less velocity, until at last motion is imparted to particles (e.g., the motes in the sunbeam) that are large enough and move slowly enough to be perceived by our senses. Lucretius' argument is essentially the same as that by which evidence for the kinetic theory of matter is drawn from the behavior of fine particles in suspension in a liquid or a gas. If these are observed through a microscope, they are seen to be in continuous, irregular motion, and these "brownian movements" are explained as the result of the uneven bombardment of the particles by masses of moving molecules.

Note *d,* p. 45. The atom, according to Lucretius, always moves through empty space. This is true both of the atoms that are moving freely and of those that are parts of complexes which, in turn, may be parts of larger combinations. When an atom strikes another, either in free space or within a complex, it changes its direction without loss of velocity (see note 5, p. 43); until such a collision occurs the atom normally moves in a straight line. (For the atomic swerve, see lines 216–93, and notes.) Lucretius held the corpuscular theory of light (which was generally accepted as late as the time of Newton and is again gaining recognition as a necessary corollary of the wave theory). On this theory, light and heat consist of corpuscles or bodies that are emitted by the source and pass through space. The velocity of these is less than that of the atoms for two reasons: the corpuscles do not, as does the atom, pass through void space but through a region in which there are many atoms and complexes of atoms which retard their passage; moreover, each of these corpuscles is made up of many atoms moving in every direction within it. The motion of each corpuscle as a whole is the resultant of the movements of its atoms, and its velocity is therefore much less than that of the individual atoms of which it is composed.

A lacuna, probably of considerable length, occurs between lines 164 and 165. That there was originally more than the one illustration of the velocity of the atoms is strongly indicated by the words "in the first place" in line 144. Lines 165 and 166 are meaningless without a context.

Note *e,* p. 47. We have already been told that the atoms move because of their weight, and because they strike each other and are deflected. In this important section Lucretius undertakes to explain how the atoms swerve from their straight courses and thus can collide. Leucippus and Democritus appear to have supposed the atoms to be moving in all directions (Bailey, *Greek Atomists,* pp. 84–86, 129–34; Kirk and Raven, *Presocratic Philosophers,* pp. 414–18). Their atoms did not possess weight (that is, a tendency to accelerate downward) but only mass, which would keep them in motion once the motion had begun; and motion was regarded as co-existent with the atoms and not requiring explanation. With Epicurus weight is regarded as a characteristic of the atom; his atoms move downward, but with a uniform velocity (see note 10, p. 46). Since he is at pains to show that weight does not cause differences in the velocities of falling bodies and thus explain collisions (*Letter to Herodotus* 61), it seems certain that some unknown philosopher between Democritus and Epicurus is responsible for the addition of weight as a characteristic of the atom and an explanation of atomic collisions. In the extant writings of Epicurus there is no reference to the swerve, although there probably was such a reference in section 43 of the *Letter to Herodotus,* where most editors recognize a lacuna. It is certain in any case that the followers of Epicurus did explain the collisions in this way; and because of their almost slavish following of the master, we can safely assume that the explanation is his. The swerve was severely criticized in antiquity (e.g., Cicero, *De Finibus* I. 19; *On the Nature of the Gods* I. 69–70); and until recently modern scholars have seen little good in it (e.g., Kathleen Freeman, *Ancilla to the Pre-Socratic Philosophers,* p. 301: "The notorious swerve had to be introduced by Epicurus in order to bring the atoms together"). However, the idea is not entirely foreign to present physical theory. One of the laws of conventional physics is that a force applied to a moving body at right angles to the direction of motion causes a change of direction (a swerve in Lucretian terms) without expending any energy or doing any work. Moreover, modern physicists recognize at the atomic and sub-atomic levels motions and changes to which no causes can be assigned and which seem to follow the laws of probability rather than those of mechanics. Because the mass of these sub-atomic particles is so small in proportion to their energy (velocity) they, like Lucretius' atoms, are unaffected by gravity in their individual motions.

The difficulty with the swerve is not that it is contrary to any natural law but that, as limited by Lucretius (lines 243–45) and probably by Epicurus (see *Letter to Herodotus* 61, where, in discussing the motion of an atom after a collision, he says that it tends to be deflected by its own weight, that is, to return to a downward course), it will not bring about the random motions that Epicurus and Lucretius assume to be necessary for the formation of a cosmos occupying a fixed position in space. In combination with collisions, the swerve might cause such random motion relative to the absolute downward motion that is normal to all the matter of their universe, and these relative motions might create a world which as a whole is moving downward (as our solar system as a whole is moving in the direction of the constellation Hercules) with a velocity less than that of the atoms; but this seems foreign to their thinking. It is unfortunate that Epicurus or some predecessor, basing his reasoning on the evidence of the senses (e.g., the raindrops of line 222, which have reached a constant terminal velocity at which the friction of the air balances the acceleration of gravity), introduced into the system the idea of uniform downward motion as the normal motion of the atoms. The random motion of Leucippus and Democritus, combined with an uncaused swerve to make possible freedom of the will, would have avoided many difficulties.

In discussing the swerve it is hard to avoid speaking as if there had been an original downward motion of all the atoms to which the atom's power to swerve was later added. Both the motion downward and the power to swerve from the downward course are native properties of every atom, just as much as are its size and shape.

Note *f*, p. 49. This difficult paragraph sums up the discussion of the swerve, stating that it must exist together with weight and blows as a cause for motion. It may seem illogical to regard blows as a third cause co-ordinate with weight and swerve, since weight and swerve are the ultimate cause of the blows; but the swerve is apparently regarded as exceptional. Although it is an original power of the atom, it affects only a few at any given time, and at any given time the actual motion of most atoms results from weight and blows. Two reasons are given why the swerve is necessary. Without the swerve, free will would not be possible, "for no thing can result from nothing." The words quoted may seem an illogical reason to advance for believing in the uncaused swerve; but if we accept Lucretius' grounds, his argument is quite logical. The power of the atom to swerve at indeterminate times and places he regards as one of its original and natural properties, no more requiring a previous cause than does the mass, the motion, or the very existence of the atom. But the free will of the individual, which the reason instinctively refuses to deny, is a secondary effect and requires a cause. This cause is furnished by the swerve, which breaks the mechanical chain of cause and effect. Freedom of the will is thus linked to, and explained by, an original power of the atom. As suggested above (note 13, p. 48), Epicurus' chief purpose in introducing the swerve may have been just this: to avoid the determinism of the earlier physicists. The second point in the paragraph is simpler. We are told: "Weight makes it impossible that everything takes place as the result of blows." Democritus (see note *e*, on p. 258) had assumed random motion as an original property of the atom, and this motion and the resulting blows were enough to explain all physical phenomena. But if the atoms have weight and therefore move downward in parallel courses at equal velocities, there will be no blows. Weight therefore makes the swerve a necessary part of the system. In concluding this long note we refer once more (see note 12, p. 48) to the Epicurean *Canonicê*. The swerve is to be accepted because it explains perceptible phenomena (freedom of the will, and the complexes of matter that result from atomic collisions) and is not contradicted by any evidence of the senses.

Note *g*, p. 55. There is some difficulty with Lucretius' facts. He seems to be thinking of salt pans, the shallow pools into which sea water was led and permitted to evaporate. After this process was repeated many times a deposit of salt formed on the sides and bottom of the pool. Lucretius assumes that the walls of the pool served as filters which caught the salt while permitting the water, which would now be fresh, to flow into another pool. So too at V. 268–72 he assumes that the water of the sea makes its way inland through the earth and appears in springs with the salt filtered out. Lucretius was not alone in his belief that the salt in sea water could be removed by filtering. Aelian (*On the Nature of Animals* IX. 64) quotes Aristotle as saying, "There is fresh water in all the seas, and this is proved as follows: if one, making a wax vessel, lets it down empty into the sea . . . and draws it up again after a day and a night have passed, it is filled with sweet, fresh water."

Note *h*, p. 59. This long digression on the Great Mother gives Lucretius a chance to restate, in lines 644–60, his attitude toward the gods and to show how by allegorical interpretation valuable truth may be drawn from myth, but otherwise the passage has little relation to the poem. The worship of Cybelê, the Great Mother of the Gods, originated in Phrygia with an important center on Mount Ida, and was conducted by eunuch priests called Galli (line 614). The center of the worship of

Rhea, the Earth, was another Mount Ida in Crete, and her priests, called Curetes (line 629), were also eunuchs. The two cults, both of which included wild dancing and frenzied music, were more or less confused in popular thinking, and the names Cybelê and Rhea came to be almost interchangeable. In 204 B.C., toward the end of the Second Punic War, the Sibyline Books directed the introduction into Rome of the cult of Cybelê. The Romans seem to have been attracted and at the same time repelled by the strange orgiastic ritual. The cult was officially recognized; but no citizen might become a priest, at least at first. It is possible that by the time of Lucretius this restriction had been relaxed in practice, if not in law. Cybelê was pictured wearing a crown that suggested the wall of a city (see line 606), and she was popularly identified with Ceres, goddess of grain (see line 613).

Note *i*, p. 64. Some editors assume a lucuna before this line, some after it; Bailey believes that there are two. I have translated the supplements that he suggests in his notes but does not incorporate in his text. The one modern editor who retains the manuscript reading is Martin, but his text makes little sense.

Note *j*, p. 66. The argument is as follows. Neither the object nor the ray of light by itself gives the sensation of color. (This is true; we can see the color of a ray of light only if we look at its source or at some surface from which it is reflected. An opaque, or transparent, object has color only as it reflects, or transmits, light waves of a certain length and absorbs the others. The visible color is that of the reflected or transmitted rays.) When atoms of light strike the surface of an object, certain atomic motions are caused and those emanations are sent forth that we recognize as color. Differences in color are due to the different motions set up in the surface atoms, and these depend on the nature of the surface and of the light. Certain iridescent surfaces give off colors that change with changes in the angle of incidence. Such colors cannot be properties either of the surface or the light, but they must result from their interaction. (This also is true. The iridescence of, e.g., a soap film is due to the interference of light waves reflected from the inner and outer surfaces of the film. The colors are not present in the film, nor are they present as separate colors in the light, but they are due to the action of one on the other. The iridescence of feathers is caused in the same way by thin films on the surface of the feathers.)

Note *k*, p. 74. By the words "free projection of the mind" (*animi iactus liber*), Lucretius appears to be translating the Epicurean *epibolē tēs dianoias* (Diogenes Laertius, *Epicurus* 31a). The mind, being material, is normally set in motion by some other material thing. A succession of films given off from the surface of an object impinges on our eyes and causes the sensation of sight, as the spirit (*anima*) in the eyes and members carries the motion to the mind (*animus*) in the breast (see IV. 216–378). But the *animus* is more subtle than the *anima* and may be stirred directly by a single film, causing us to think of something that at the time our senses do not perceive although it has, or once had, material existence and emitted the film at some time, possibly in the remote past and at a distance (see IV. 722–822). It appears that in some way the *animus* can store up images created in it in either of these ways, and for this reason we are able to recall and visualize past experiences. But we can, as a matter of actual fact, also think of things that by their very nature can never have emitted films or effluences of any sort, e.g., the atoms themselves, the void, and space beyond the most distant star. In these cases the *animus*, comparing and studying images that have been created in the normal way and are still present in it, creates a new mental image. In the case at hand, the *animus* visualizes what is beyond the limits of our world, basing its new mental picture upon what it has learned of this world. This difficult Epicurean concept is discussed at length by Bailey, *Greek Atomists*, pp. 245–48, 557–76; and with quite different conclusions by DeWitt, *Epicurus*, 133–54.

Note *l*, p. 78. In the closing portion of this book, Lucretius presents the view usual in antiquity that the earth and all on it are in a state of decline. In mythology and literature, the Golden

Age is in the distant past. Elsewhere in the poem, however, particularly in the last part of Book Five, we are given a very different view, which is certainly that of the Epicureans and probably of Epicurus himself. If primitive man was stronger than are the men of today, his lot was harder. From the beginning mankind has been making slow but constant progress in his control of his environment. He has advanced in the arts and the sciences. In particular (and here we pass from Book Five to the eulogy of Epicurus at the beginning of Book Six) it is only recently that the true art of living has been discovered by the Master, and made known by him to men.

Book Three

Note *a,* p. 80. The difference in composition and function between the mind (*animus, mens*) and the spirit (*anima*) will be developed later. The spirit pervades the entire body; the mind, which is a special part of the spirit, is located in the breast. The spirit receives sensations and transmits information to the mind, which is composed of finer particles and directs the spirit, which in turn controls the body. Lucretius is not entirely consistent in his use of these terms; in particular, "spirit" sometimes includes and sometimes excludes the mind. In this translation, "soul" is often used where both spirit and mind are clearly intended. Strangely Epicurus in his *Letter to Herodotus* 63a–68a, where he discusses the soul, does not make a distinction between mind and spirit, but in a scholium on 66 we read:

> Elsewhere he says: "The soul is composed of the finest and roundest atoms, much surpassing those of fire. Part of it lacks reasoning power and is distributed through the whole body. The reason is in the breast, as is clear from our fears and joys."

Note *b,* p. 86. Lucretius has already said that at death particles of wind (or breath) and of warmth (or fire) leave the body (lines 121–29); to these is now added air, for the reason that air is always present in whatever, like fire, is of open texture. He does not feel it necessary to explain the difference between wind and air. At VI. 685 in a completely different connection he says:

"Wind is formed when air is stirred and set in motion." He does not say that wind is air in motion, but that when air is set in motion it ceases to be air and becomes wind, apparently through some change in its inner structure. Epicurus (*Letter to Herodotus* 63a) does not mention air but says that the soul "is a finely divided, material thing, scattered through the whole aggregation of atoms that make up the body, most similar to breath with a certain admixture of heat, in some ways resembling one, in some ways the other." Later Epicurean sources, however, add air as a third element (e.g., Plutarch, *Against Colotes* 1118d=Usener, 314). We must remember that the particles of air, fire, and wind are not atoms but complexes of atoms, since an atom cannot have the secondary qualities that are associated with those elements. This is also true of the nameless fourth element. We must not think of atoms having the qualities ascribed to that element, but rather of particles possessing those qualities, the particles themselves being made up of the finest, smoothest atoms.

Note *c*, p. 87. Of the particles of soul, those of the spirit are distributed throughout the body, those of the mind are concentrated in the breast, but all are contained in the body. The particles of the fourth element are contained within the other parts of the soul, just as the soul is contained within the body. Particles of this fourth essence near the surface of the body are set in motion by physical contacts from without, and this motion itself is sensation. The other three elements are then moved —first heat, which is thought of as next in mobility to the fourth essence, then wind, and finally air, the most sluggish of the elements. Now that whole particles of soul are in motion, the motion (i.e., sensation) is passed on to the body, going first to the more mobile parts, namely the blood and flesh, and then to the bones and marrow; but the motion becomes less violent as it is passed on from the surface, and severe pain rarely reaches the marrow, the seat of life. If, however, this does happen, the whole body is so disturbed that the particles of soul may be expelled from their places through the pores of the skin, and death may follow.

Note *d,* p. 91. In this paragraph Lucretius has confused two different problems. First he says that the seeds of the spirit are situated at considerable intervals on the surface of the skin, and that therefore small objects resting on the skin may chance to impinge only on seeds of body, and thus fail to arouse sensation. The first and last groups of examples are of this sort (dust, powder, minute insects, the feet of such creatures), but in between come examples of large, light bodies (spider webs, feathers, down), and the explanation with which the paragraph ends (that many body particles must be set in motion before any soul particles are stirred) applies to them. In either case the seeds of spirit when set in motion are pictured as vibrating in the open spaces of the body, and we can think of them (although Lucretius quite certainly did not) as transmitting their energy to the mind by compression waves, like those of sound.

Note *e,* p. 93. In the Latin, the paragraph up to this point consists of a single sentence, which has been rendered rather freely. A closer translation follows:

> First, since I have shown that it is thin and made of minute seeds and particles much smaller than is the liquid fluid of water or mist or smoke (for the soul is far superior to these in mobility and is more easily moved when struck by a small force, because indeed it is moved by idols of smoke or mist when, for example, while we are deep in sleep, we see the offerings on the altar breathe forth steam that rises high and send forth smoke, for without doubt these are brought to us as idols); and since, when a container is broken, you see water or milk pour out and scatter in all directions; and since mist and smoke are dissipated into the air—for all these reasons believe that the soul also is poured out and perishes more quickly than these, and is more rapidly separated into its original elements when once it has been taken out of the body of a man and has departed from it.

Lucretius here anticipates the explanation of sensation and of thought to be given in the next book (IV. 26–521 and 722–822). Sight is caused by a series of "idols" or "films" that are given off in rapid succession from the surface of an object, pass in constant series through the air, impinge on the eye, and cause in it the sensation of sight. Single idols, which have been given off in the past and are now moving at random through the air, are too thin to stir the eyes; but they may pass through the open atomic structure of the body and impinge directly on the mind, which is so mobile that it can be set in motion by a single such idol. In the waking individual thought results from such a contact; when one is asleep the result is a dream. Lucretius uses the most extreme example to illustrate the mobility of the mind. It may be set in motion by single idols coming from such tenuous substances as mist or smoke, and thought or a dream may result.

Book Four

Note *a,* p. 118. A lacuna of unknown length occurs here. The last sentence of the existing text must have ended in some such way as that indicated. Other illustrations and examples may have followed, but before the end of the lost passage Lucretius apparently returned to a discussion of the idols themselves, establishing some relation between the smallness of the atoms and the thinness of the idols, and ending with the statement of which we have the conclusion, that idols (i.e., single idols) cannot be perceived by the senses.

Note *b,* p. 118. A lucuna of at least one line occurs here. In lines 147 and 152 I read *vitrum* with most editors (see line 602 below), although the manuscript reading, *vestem,* "veil," is possible.

Note *c,* p. 120. All bodies contain void within themselves, here inaccurately described as *intervallum aeris,* "an interval of air," or "enclosed air." The idols themselves are of very open texture. Lucretius here seems to state that the atoms that make up the idols are so widely spaced that they can pass through the void spaces in any solid object without their velocity being diminished or their arrangement changed. Previously, however, he has stated that this is possible only in the case of objects of open texture such as glass (or veils). Possibly in our present passage he is thinking only of the isolated idols that cause thought. Since these reach the mind directly, they must be able to pass through the enclosing body. Epicurus (*Letter to Herodotus* 47b, and note) may give an additional reason for the velocity of the idols: the fact that their atoms are all moving in one direction.

Note *d*, p. 124. All the extant manuscripts of the poem go back directly or indirectly to a single archetype. One leaf of this archetype, which contained on one side lines 299–322 and on the other lines 323–47, was torn out and then replaced in a reversed position. All our manuscripts accordingly show lines 323–47 before lines 299–322.

Note *e*, p. 124. Lucretius imagines a soft mask forced against the end of a beam in such a way that it is turned inside out. We can more easily picture a plastic mask blown inside out by a jet of air. The inner surface, which was toward us, is still toward us but is now the outer surface, and the nose, which formerly projected away from us, now points toward us in the same degree. What was the right eye of the mask when it faced away from us is still on our right but has become the left eye of the mask in its new orientation. Since the idols have three dimensions, the parallel is quite exact. The idol of our own face goes to the mirror and then comes back to us turned inside out, just as was the mask.

Note *f*, p. 125. All editors seem to have assumed that Lucretius is speaking of a concave cylindrical mirror. Such a mirror will indeed form a reversed image such as he describes instead of the ordinary direct ("mirror") image, but the reversed image will be distorted and, at least if one is looking at himself as seems to be the case here, the distortion will be so great that it is inconceivable that Lucretius should mention the reversal and say nothing of the distortion, especially when he could so easily have used the distortion to strengthen his case. (The vertical dimensions of the image are not changed but the horizontal dimensions are compressed, which is what one might expect to have happen in the case of an idol reflected from such a mirror.) It is much more likely that he is thinking of a pair of plane mirrors joined at right angles. Such a pair of mirrors will give back an undistorted reversed image of a person standing within the angle of the mirrors or their planes extended. In the case of the plane mirrors at right angles, the image is passed from one to the other, and Lucretius' first explanation is correct. In the case of the concave mirror there is no double reflection but the curve of the mirror "teaches the image to turn around."

Note *g*, p. 125. In this passage, if my translation is correct, Lucretius is remarking on the effect of the rule that the image formed by a plane mirror is behind the mirror, and the line joining object and image is always perpendicular to the mirror or its plane extended. Another interpretation is: "For Nature forces all images to depart and leap back, reflected at equal angles." In this case the "equal angles" are the angles of incidence and reflection, but the phrase *ad aequos flexus* seems regularly to mean "perpendicular"; and the first translation fits better the example of a person moving before a mirror and watching his image keep step with him. It might be noted in passing that Lucretius' example supposes the existence of mirrors much larger than our handbooks of antiquities lead us to expect.

Note *h*, p. 126. That a square tower when seen from a distance appears round may cast doubts on the validity of sensation as the source of knowledge; but (in spite of Bailey *ad loc.*) it is not a fatal objection to the idol theory of vision any more than it is to the wave theory of light. In each case the error has to be explained in terms of the theory held, and Lucretius' explanation is reasonable. The idols, when they reach our eyes, have had their shape altered, and our eyes record this altered shape. Lucretius seems to distinguish between this and the cases that follow (lines 387–469), where the idols that the eye receives and passes on to the mind correctly represent the object, and the error is due to the false addition of opinion. The shadow that appears to move (lines 364–86) forms a transition.

Note *i*, p. 137. The reasoning is similar to that of lines 649–72 above. The pores in the lion's eyes are of such size and shape that the rough particles given off by the body of the cock can enter them but tear the sides of the pores as they pass through. In the eyes of a man the pores are either so small that the particles cannot enter at all and are harmlessly repelled from the outer surface, or they are large enough that the particles pass straight through without causing any pain or injury. In this passage, which seems to be either an afterthought or a remnant of an earlier draft that escaped revision, Lucretius talks of vision in the terms that he has been using of sound, taste, and smell, neglecting the idols completely.

Lucretius' discussion of the relative subjectivity and objectivity of the different senses is confused by the fact that he describes smells and tastes only in terms that suggest the pleasure or pain caused to the recipient, and these feelings are subjective; but sight and hearing are discussed for the most part in terms of the information transmitted to the mind by the sense organs, and this is factual and objective. Even in the case of the lion and the cock, the lion's eyes receive the same information as do the man's, but the feeling in the eye is different.

Note *j*, p. 139. Just as in the smallest object that the senses can perceive, the mind can recognize the existence of many atoms and even of the many least parts of each atom, so in the shortest period of time that the senses can perceive, the mind can recognize the existence of many brief periods. Since in each of these briefer periods many idols can simultaneously present themselves to the mind, the number that can present themselves in the least perceptible time is inconceivably large. Of these idols the mind accepts only those for which it is ready. In this Lucretius finds the solution of both of the problems stated at the beginning of this section. If the sleeping mind has already accepted the image, let us say, of a person walking, it most readily accepts next the idols that show the natural continuation of that motion; and the images in our dreams therefore appear to carry out actions that we accept as normal. Again, in our waking hours, if we desire a thing, the mind selects an idol of that one thing from the many that are presented to it, ignoring the rest, and we think of that particular thing. Lucretius, however, ignores the basic problem of the origin and cause of the desire itself, unless it be one of the desires that arise from the natural material needs of the body (see lines 858–906). Line 808, which repeats line 804, is omitted.

Note *k,* p. 142. In lines 745–56 above, we have been told that a single idol can penetrate the mind and cause thought, and that thought is possible only when this happens. Here we find that physical motion has a similar cause and a similar limitation. The limitation, however, is not very serious, since, as pointed out in lines 777–817 above, countless idols of all kinds are constantly impinging upon the mind, and the mind has the power to select as it wills, this freedom of choice being in some way made possible by the uncaused swerve of the atoms (II. 251–93).

Note *l,* p. 143. The examples given represent two completely different situations. The sails and the pulleys are machines that receive energy in one form and deliver it (with some losses for friction) in another form more suitable for the task at hand. On the other hand the rudder, with a small expenditure of energy, directs the energy that the ship receives from other sources (the sails or oars). This last example seems to us more suitable for the control of the mind over the activities of the body; but the other two are closer to Lucretius' explanation in lines 886–97.

Note *m,* p. 143. Sensation from external stimuli originates in the particles of spirit *(anima)* near the surface of the body (III. 370–80) and is transmitted by them through other particles of spirit to the mind *(animus).* When these spirit particles leave the surface and cannot be touched by external stimuli, sleep follows. The mind, however, continues to function. In fact, being undisturbed by the spirit, it is more ready to receive isolated idols that come to it directly, and dreams result therefrom (see lines 757–76 above).

Note *n,* p. 147. Epicurus wrote a work *On Love,* of which no certain fragments remain. His attitude toward sexual gratification is not clear. Laertius (*Life of Epicurus* 6) says that Epicurus' detractors quoted a passage from his work, *On the Chief Good,* in which he names it along with the pleasures of taste, sound, and sight as essential to the good life; but the words as we have them are without context and may be quite misleading. In section 118 of the same *Life* we learn that the Epicureans believed that love is not sent by the gods, that sexual intercourse never did a man any good, and that a man is fortunate if it does him no harm. Epicurus would quite certainly have agreėd with Lucretius that passionate love is to be avoided since it destroys the calm that is necessary for true happiness; but there is nothing in the extant remains that approaches Lucretius' violent denunciation of love. A connection between our passage and Jerome's statement that Lucretius became insane as the result of drinking a love philter is probable. But are we to connect this passage and the philter with actual events in the poet's life; or did this passage suggest the philter to some literary historian (possibly Suetonius), who was trying to construct a biography out of scanty materials?

Book Five

Note *a,* p. 164. The destruction and creation of air, which is itself invisible, obviously cannot be seen. In describing the soul, Lucretius referred to the atoms or complexes of air that enter into its composition as being very small, very round, and very smooth (III. 203–5, 231–34). In our present passage the air seems to be made up of particles of all kinds given off from the earth and returning to it. It is probable that here he is speaking in loose terms of the atmosphere, the sea of air that surrounds the earth and through which must pass all the atoms of every sort that leave the earth or come to it from without. The air *per se* consists of smooth, round atoms or complexes of atoms; but through it in ceaseless succession pass atoms and complexes of all kinds, and these together with the air make up the atmosphere.

Note *b,* p. 166. Lucretius seems to be borrowing the language and to be answering the argument of the earlier Latin poet, Pacuvius:

> Behold this which holds the earth in its embrace about and above . . . which we call "heaven" and the Greeks term "aether." Whatever it is, it gives life to all things, forms them, nourishes them, increases them, creates them; it likewise buries all things and receives them back into itself. The same is the father of all things; the same things are created anew from this and likewise return to it [lines 86–92 Ribbeck].

The aether is perhaps to be identified with the Stoic *anima mundi,* the "spirit of the world." Its role as parent of all and tomb of all (see what Lucretius says of the earth in line 259 of this book), which some take as proving its immortality, is to Lucretius a sure indication of the opposite.

Note *c,* p. 170. With this we may compare the statement of the Epicurean theories in regard to creation as they are given by the late Greek writer, Aetius:

> The motion of the atoms, which was not the result of planning but was due to chance, was continuous and rapid. Many atoms gathered together in the same place, having a great variety of forms, sizes, and weights. When they had come together, those that were largest and heaviest for the most part sank down, but those that were small, round, smooth, and slippery were squeezed out by the concentration of matter and carried into the upper regions. Since the force that moved them became weaker in the upper air, its impulse no longer carried them upward, but the heavy particles prevented them from moving down. They therefore settled toward the regions that could receive them. These were on the outside; and here most of the lighter particles circled around. Because of their motion they became interwoven with each other and thus formed the sky. These atoms were of many kinds, as has been said. Those that were carried to the highest regions formed the stars. But most of the particles that rose like mist struck the air and squeezed it upward. The air moving like wind and surrounding the stars carried them about, maintaining the lofty orbits that we know. And thus from the particles that had settled down earth was created, and from those that were lifted up came sky, fire, and air. There was much matter

still left in the earth. As the earth was condensed by the blows of the wind and the rays from the stars, the matter that was in small particles was forced out and formed water. Since this was liquid, it flowed into the places that were hollow and able to receive and contain it; or else the water by its weight depressed the places over which it stood [Aetius, I. 4. 2–4= Usener, *Epicurus,* frag. 308. See also Diodorus of Sicily, quoted in note *i,* p. 277].

Note *d,* p. 174. For the view expressed in these lines, see Epicurus, *Letter to Pythocles* 85b–87a:

> First, do not think that knowledge about the things above the earth, whether treated as part of a philosophical system or by itself, has any purpose other than peace of mind and confidence. This is also true of the other studies. Do not attempt the impossible, and do not expect to conduct investigations in all fields in the way in which we have discussed ethics or found solutions for other physical problems (for instance, the composition of the universe from matter and void, or the indivisibility of the first elements), or of all problems that have single explanations in agreement with the visible evidence. For the case is different with the things above the earth. Each of these phenomena has more than one cause for its creation and more than one account of its nature, all of them in harmony with the evidence of the senses. We must not build up an explanation of Nature according to empty assumptions and dictates, but as phenomena invite; for our life does not have need for illogical and empty opinions, but for an existence free from disturbance. If one is satisfied, as he should be, with that which is shown to be probable, no difficulty arises in connection with those things that admit of more than one explanation in harmony with the evidence of the senses; but if one accepts one explanation and rejects another that is equally in agreement with the evidence, it is clear that he is altogether rejecting science and taking refuge in myth.

Note *e,* p. 174. Lucretius and Epicurus may have accepted the view of the earlier atomists on the shape of the earth. See Aristotle, *De caelo* II. 13, 294b13: "Anaximenes, Anaxagoras, and Democritus said that the earth remained in place because it was flat; for it does not cut through the air below it, but covers it like a lid. . . . Since the air has no place to go, it remains there in a mass." Elsewhere we learn that Leucippus said that the earth was shaped like a tambourine (a drumhead stretched over one end of a shallow cylinder), and that Democritus said it was a disk, flat on the surface and hollow in the center, probably meaning flat on the upper surface with the lower surface hollowed, essentially the same shape as that described by Leucippus (Diels, *Fragmente,* 67 A 26, 68 A 94).

Note *f,* p. 174. The causes and mechanism of celestial phenomena are concealed from our senses, and Epicurean theory neither seeks nor permits final knowledge about them; but we do have a view, even though distant and not very clear, of the disk of the sun, and therefore no such complete uncertainty is permitted. Our eyes tell us the size of the "idol" of the sun's disk that reaches them; and although this may have been somewhat distorted in transmission, it must be accepted as evidence. The sun therefore must appear to us about as large as would an object of its actual size and at its distance. The qualifying phrase "at its distance" is not found in Lucretius or in the remains of Epicurus, but it must have been implied since otherwise the statement is meaningless. Unfortunately its absence made it possible for Cicero (*De finibus* I. 20) to imply that Epicurus believed that the sun was but a foot in diameter. The only situation in which we have any standard for comparison is at sunrise or sunset, and no one could think the sun smaller than objects on the horizon subtending the same angle. (For the distance of the sun beyond the horizon, see IV. 410.) Since to the Epicureans the heavenly bodies were all parts of an earth-centered system and at no very great distance from the earth, their opinions as to the sizes of these bodies were altogether wrong, but they were not illogical (although some of Lucretius' reasoning may be) nor inconsistent with their other teachings.

Note *g,* p. 176. Much of the difficulty of this section arises from the poet's failure to distinguish the different elements in the celestial motions he is describing. Various reasons have already been given for the apparent daily movement of the fixed stars, or of the heavens in general (lines 509–33). Lucretius now undertakes to explain why the sun (and the moon as well, although he is less interested in this) does not act in the same way as do the stars. He takes it for granted here that the heavenly bodies revolve around the earth (although he will question it below), and that, although we cannot see them, the stars are moving across the sky in the day as well as the night. Thus he can speak (as do we) of the sun being in one of the signs of the zodiac, although the sign in which the sun is, is not visible. On March twenty-first or twenty-second the sun is in the sign Aries. If we think of the stars and the signs as setting the pace, the sun drops behind at the rate of about four minutes a day. By September it has lost twelve hours and is in the sign Libra, directly opposite Aries, and after six months more it has lost another twelve hours and is in Aries again. But in the sun's motion there is another component at right angles to the motion of the stars. In March the sun is on the celestial equator, that is, it is 90° from the celestial pole (near the North Star). For the next three months it moves slowly north, and in June it is 23.5° north of the equator. Here in the sign Cancer it pauses at the summer solstice (*solstitium,* "a pausing of the sun"), and then moves south, crossing the celestial equator at the autumnal equinox in September, and on December twenty-first or twenty-second reaching its winter solstice in Capricorn, 23.5° south of the equator. After its pause here it moves north once more. Looked at from the earth, the sun seems to follow a great spiral with its axis pointed at the pole star, winding northward for six months and then following a reversed spiral toward the south (see Epicurus, *Letter to Pythocles* 93). If we think of its motion in relation to the stars, in that same period it traces through them a complete circle (the ecliptic) inclined at an angle of 23.5° to the celestial equator, which it crosses at the equinoxes in March and September. The orbit of the moon also lies in the zodiac, but the moon drops back fifty minutes a day and thus passes through all the signs in a little less than thirty days. The apparent motions of the planets, which all lie in this same path through the stars, are somewhat similar although much more complicated.

In our passage Lucretius first speaks (lines 614–17) of the winter and summer turnings of the sun (the solstices), which are significant for the motion of the sun north and south of the celestial equator but not for its motion through the signs; but instead of explaining this he raises the question (lines 618–20) why the sun passes through the zodiac in twelve months and the moon in one. He then (lines 621–36) gives one answer to this question (the different distances of the sun and moon from the stellar whirl); and immediately (lines 637–42), beginning with a phrase that he commonly employs to introduce a possible alternate explanation of the same phenomenon, he presents a reason for the sun's motion north and south of the celestial equator (winds in different directions at different seasons). Next (lines 643–49) he generalizes this explanation so that it can apply to any of the celestial motions (winds in different directions at different altitudes). In the following section (lines 650–79) he gives several explanations of the daily motions of the sun, but in terms of its rising and setting rather than of its motion through the sky, and finally (lines 680–705) he returns to the problem of summer and winter, but without any reference to the explanation already given (lines 637–42).

Note *h,* p. 179. With some hesitation I follow Bailey's interpretation of this difficult sentence. The opening phrases refer back to the theory of lines 637–48, where winds from north and south cause the shifting of the sun's course between its summer and winter positions. An expanded version might run as follows:

> When the north wind has been blowing for half its time ⟨and the fall equinox is at hand⟩, and again half through the south wind's blowing ⟨at the time of the spring equinox⟩, the sun in the sky is equidistant from its two turning points, ⟨that is, from its positions in midwinter and in midsummer,⟩ because of the position of the whole circle of the zodiac in which the sun completes its annual period. . . .

Note *i,* p. 183. Compare the account of the origin of living creatures given by Diodorus of Sicily, I. 7. 1–7, which appears to be based on Epicurean sources:

> [1] They say that at the formation of the world, the sky and the earth had the same form, their substance being mixed.

Then, as their bodies separated, the world took on a form in general like that now seen in it. The air was in continuous motion; and the fiery portion gathered together in the highest places since the elements of this nature tend to move upward because of their lightness. For this reason the sun and the rest of the stars were caught up by the whirl, and that which was muddy and turbid and moist settled down into one place because of its weight. [2] As this was pressed in upon itself without interruption and became congealed, from the moist elements the sea was formed, from those that were firmer, the land, still soft and muddy. [3] As the fires of the sun beat upon it, the earth solidified; then, with its surface in a ferment because of the heat, in many places some of the moist parts swelled up and from these there arose putrid blisters covered with membranes. It is possible even now to see such things formed in swamps and marshes whenever the sun suddenly and without any gradual change heats places that had been cold. [4] While life was thus developing from what was wet, in the way described, the mist that fell from the surrounding air furnished food by night to the growing things, and by day the sun solidified them by its heat. Finally, when the embryos were fully grown and the membranes had been heated to excess and ruptured, every manner of living creature was born. [5] Of them, those that had the greatest share of heat, becoming birds, went off into the regions above the earth; those that held to an earthy nurture were counted among the creeping things and other terrestrial creatures; and those that partook most of the watery nature moved together to the places of the same character, being called fish. . . . [7] It is probable that Euripides did not have an opinion about the origin of all things differing from what has been said, since he was a pupil of Anaxagoras, the physicist. In the *Melanippê* he speaks thus: "Heaven and earth were a single nature. When they were separated apart from each other, they gave birth to all things and brought them to light: trees, birds, beasts, creatures of the sea, the race of mortals."

Note *j*, p. 183. Compare the belief of Empedocles as given by Aetius (V. 26. 4 = Diels, *Fragmente*, 31 A 70):

Empedocles says that trees were the first living creatures to grow from the earth . . . raised up by the warmth from the ground so that they were members of the earth as the embryo in the womb is a member of the mother.

The belief that the different animals grew from the earth was held in various forms by Anaximander, Anaxagoras, and Democritus.

Note *k,* p. 183. It is impossible to tell whether the next fifteen lines apply to all animals that walk the earth or only to men. In what follows, the phrase *mortalia saecla,* here translated "mortal generations," is used frequently of men, not of beasts (e.g., lines 988, 1169, 1238). In line 791 above, however, where it has been translated "races of living creatures," it certainly includes not only four-footed beasts and men, but also birds. In our passage it is equally certain that birds are excluded. Although most of the section would apply to animals as well as to men, the references to children (*pueri,* literally "boys") and to clothing in line 816, appear to point to mankind. Moreover, the opening sentence of the next paragraph seems to indicate that the birth of the human race has just been described. However, if our paragraph is given this limited interpretation, there is no explanation of the creation of beasts, only the statement in line 823 that the earth produced them at the proper time.

Note *l,* p. 185. This surprisingly modern doctrine of the survival of those organisms that are fitted for their environments is ascribed by Aristotle (*Physics* II. 8, 198b29) to Empedocles:

> Those survived whose parts had come together as if according to some design and which were of themselves organized in a suitable way. Those of which this was not true perished; and they continue to perish, as Empedocles stated in regard to the man-faced calf.

For the surviving fragments of Empedocles dealing with this, see Diels, *Fragmente,* 31 B 57–62. It should be pointed out, however, that Lucretius and his predecessors, as far as is known, thought of the law of the survival of the fit as securing the preservation of species that had been formed spontaneously, not as explaining the origin or development of species. The survival of the fit merely maintained a static world. This is made very clear by V. 923–24.

Note *m,* p. 187. See Diodorus of Sicily, I. 8. 1, 5–9:

> [1] This is what we learn about the first beginnings of all things. They say that the men who were first born, living each by himself in a disorganized and beast-like manner, went out for food and gathered the tenderest of the herbs and the wild fruits of the trees. . . . [5] The first men lived with difficulty, none of the things useful for living having been discovered, being without clothing, unused to houses and fire, with no knowledge whatever of gentle nurture. [6] Since they knew nothing of the harvesting of foods, they made no collection of fruits for times of need. Therefore many of them were destroyed in winter by the cold and the lack of food. [7] Gradually learning by experience, they took refuge in caves in the winter and stored up fruits that could be preserved. [8] Learning about fire and other useful things, they slowly discovered the arts and whatever else is of advantage for the common life. [9] In general, need itself was the teacher for men, supplying the appropriate instruction in each matter for a creature who was naturally clever and who had to aid him in all things hands, speech, and cleverness of mind.

Note *n,* p. 190. For Epicurus' view of justice as resting on a compact entered into by men for their mutual advantage, see his *Principal Doctrines* XXXI–XL, particularly XXXI and XXXIII. The resemblance of this to the teachings of some of the political philosophers of the seventeenth century (e.g., Thomas Hobbes in the *Leviathan*) has often been remarked; but, as Bailey on this passage points out, Lucretius softens the harshness of Epicurus (which is shared by Hobbes) by his stress on family affection and on friendship. The resemblance between Hobbes and Epicurus is probably not a mere coincidence. Hobbes spent the years 1640–51 in France, where he was closely associated with Gassendi, the first great modern student of Epicureanism, whose *Syntagma philosophiae Epicuri* was published in 1649, two years before Hobbes' *Leviathan.*

Note *o,* p. 201. Before this, men had worn skins (lines 954, 1011, 1418, 1423). *Nexiles,* here translated "knitted," comes from a verb meaning "to tie," and is used elsewhere of fishnets.

The poet may not have had any very clear picture in his mind, but he evidently means that before men wove on the loom they made textiles of some sort by tying or interweaving fibers together by hand. These might be natural vegetable fibers of some sort, but were probably woolen threads, since spinning with distaff, spindle, and whorl is relatively simple and requires the simplest of equipment. There is some doubt about the identification of the parts of the loom in the lines that follow.

Note *p,* p. 202. Literally, "upon the hollow hemlocks." The poisonous hemlock *(Conium maculatum),* a plant of the carrot family, has a hollow stem, which was used in making the Panpipes, a musical instrument made of reeds of varying lengths closed at one end, each reed having its own pitch. It was played by blowing across the open ends of the reeds (see line 1407 below). In the next sentence Lucretius contrasts this with the *tibia,* an instrument whose single tube had holes that were stopped by the fingers. It is often described as flute-like, but it probably more nearly resembled a clarinet or an oboe than a modern flute. It is not clear how the breezes "whispered through the hollow reeds" in a way to suggest pipes of either sort.

Note *q,* p. 203. The desire for the coat of skins is both natural and necessary, such a garment furnishing a bare minimum of warmth. The woven garment will answer the purpose better, and the desire for it is natural but not necessary. The purple robe decked with gold is no more useful than the simple cloak, and the desire for it is therefore neither natural nor necessary. Since pleasure is the absence of pain, it can be increased only to the point where pain is removed, as the pain of cold is removed by the woven garment; beyond this point it may be varied but not increased, and the efforts to increase it (e.g., by dressing in purple) will bring no increase in pleasure, and they may rather bring pleasure to an end since they naturally lead to envy and hostility (see Epicurus, *Letter to Menoeceus, passim*).

Book Six

Note *a*, p. 208. Roman augural science professed to interpret the will of the gods as expressed in flashes of lightning. The sky was divided into sixteen parts, and the regions in which the flash began and ended were regarded as significant (Cicero, *On Divination* II. 42, 45). The strength of this officially recognized "science" explains the disproportionate length of Lucretius' accounts of thunder, lightning, and the thunderbolt. It is possible that the *religio* which he attacks throughout the poem is this politically controlled machinery of the Roman state rather than popular superstitions in general. For a somewhat one-sided presentation of this interpretation of Epicureanism as a whole and of the poem of Lucretius in particular, see B. Farrington, *Science and Politics in the Ancient World,* Oxford, 1940.

Note *b,* p. 208. In Book Five, while treating the things of the heavens, Lucretius usually gives several explanations of each phenomenon, one or more of which may be true of this world and all of which are assumed to be true, or at least to be possible, somewhere in the universe if not here. In the first half of Book Six, in discussing the phenomena of the atmosphere and the earth, the various explanations are, as a rule, not alternate explanations of the same phenomenon but explanations of the various forms that a particular phenomenon may take. In this first section, for example, we have some half dozen causes of thunder given and we are told what sort of thunder is produced by each.

Note *c,* p. 217. The Greek word is from a root signifying "fire," and the traditional explanation, found for example in Aristotle, *Meteorology* III. 1, 371a17, connected the waterspout with both fire and wind. It was regarded as closely akin to the thunderbolt, but less violent. Neither Lucretius nor Epicurus in the *Letter to Pythocles* names fire as one of the causes; but Lucretius preserves a trace of that theory in his opening sentence: "From this [i.e., from the theories about the thunderbolt] it is easy . . ."

In the explanation that follows, Lucretius seems to repeat himself, but probably lines 426–30 are to be regarded as a general description of the waterspout, most of which is repeated in the first explanation of its formation.

Note *d,* p. 223. The question why the sea does not increase in size is not discussed in the extant works of Epicurus, but it seems to have been one of the standard problems of the physicists. Compare, for example, Seneca, *Natural Questions* III. 5:

> Certain men claim that the earth receives again whatever water it sends forth, and that the seas do not increase for the following reason. They do not retain as their own what flows into them but at once return it; for it goes beneath the earth by a hidden course, and what flows to the sea openly returns in secret, the salt being filtered out in transit.

Because of its abrupt introduction and because it separates what might seem kindred topics, earthquakes and volcanoes, many believe that this section is out of place. Bockenmüller, for example, placed it after line 711, making it the first of the individual wonders. Other editors keep it in its present place and believe that some lines have been lost before it. It is probably better to regard this simply as one of the many indications that Book Six had never received its final form.

Note *e,* p. 226. See Epicurus, *Letter to Pythocles* 85b–88a. The phenomena hitherto described have been general and may have different causes at different times and places, and different forms of each may be produced by different causes. On the other hand, according to the poet, it is probable that each of the individual wonders that follow has its single cause; but we must be content if we can show that there are various natural causes any one of which might cause the phenomenon, even though we cannot tell which of them is the actual cause. This is the case, for example, with the corpse in lines 705–11. We can only be sure that the cause of death was one of those mentioned or something similar to them, that is, that the cause was a natural one. If this all seems very unsatisfactory to the modern reader, we should remember that Lucretius' purpose was to show that there was no need to evoke the powers of the gods to explain anything in the natural world. He therefore wished to show that natural explanations could be given for each of these phenomena, and he seems to have regarded two explanations as better than one.

Note *f*, p. 236. The motion of the whole ring is explained in terms of the motion of its atoms. These are always in constant motion within the ring but as long as there is equal pressure from the air on all sides the sum of their motions is zero and the ring does not move. When the magnet drives the air from the space between it and the ring, some of the atoms on that side of the ring, no longer subject to external pressure, move into the empty space. This permits atoms further back in the ring also to extend their motions in that direction. The sum of the atomic motions is no longer zero but has a positive value in the direction of the magnet, and the whole ring is in motion.

Note *g*, p. 237. If by "alternately" we can understand "as the iron is reversed," these two lines state a fact, which is only confused by what follows. A piece of magnetite, Lucretius' lodestone, has two poles as does any other magnet. If the end of a bar of iron is held against the positive pole of the lodestone, the bar itself becomes a magnet by induction, the end toward the lodestone being its negative pole and the other end its positive pole. When removed, the bar will retain its magnetism for a time, and as long as it does, its positive pole will be repelled and its negative pole attracted by the positive pole of the lodestone.

Note *h*, p. 238. Lucretius errs in saying that the iron filings are repelled by the lodestone because they are separated from it by bronze. The bronze itself is of no significance, since any non-magnetic substance such as paper, papyrus, or any of the common metals except iron and nickel would serve as well. If iron filings are shaken over a paper laid on top of a bar magnet or a piece of magnetite, they tend to arrange themselves along lines of magnetic force, which pass outside the magnet from one pole to the other. If only one pole is presented to the lower surface of the paper, the filings in trying to arrange themselves along these lines will form a small heap above the end of the magnet. Lucretius may have observed this and explained it as repulsion. The filings in the bronze bowl or on the paper will dance if the magnet or the bowl or paper is moved, but otherwise, once they have taken their positions, they will remain at rest.

Note *i,* p. 238. This whole explanation of repulsion implies a new theory to explain the action of the magnet on the iron, namely that the bodies emitted by the magnet fit the pores of the iron; and this is the theory for which the preliminary discussion of lines 906–97 has prepared the way. With this new theory we may compare the somewhat confused account of Empedocles' explanation, as given by Alexander Aphrodisiensis, *Quaestiones* II. 23 (Diels, *Fragmente,* 31 A 89):

> Empedocles said that the iron was drawn to the stone by the effluences from both because the pores in the stone are of proper size for the effluences from the iron. The effluences from the stone brush away the air that is in the pores of the iron and set in motion the air that blocks them. He says that when this is cleared away the iron follows the effluences that flow out in a body. When the effluences from the iron have been carried into the pores of the stone, the iron also follows and is carried along because the effluences of the iron are of the proper size for the pores of the stone and fit them.

Addendum. An article, "Infinity in Epicurean Philosophy" by Marshall E. Blume, *Classical Journal,* LX (1964/65), 174–76, which reached me after final proof was approved, discusses Lucretius' ideas of infinity. One with more understanding of the "new mathematics" than is possessed by the translator may find this discussion of interest.

INDEX